The Guide To Digital Television

Third Edition

*DTV in the Real World • Understanding Digital •
Pre-Production • Production • Audio
• Graphics & Compositing • Post Production •
Duplication & Delivery • Engineering & Transmission*

Edited By Michael Silbergleid and Mark J. Pescatore

www.DigitalTelevision.com

Miller Freeman
A United News & Media company

$19.95 US   ISBN 0-9670700-1-5 $27.95 CAN

TABLE OF CONTENTS

GUIDE TO DIGITAL TELEVISION
PUBLISHER'S PREFACE

With more than 100 stations on the air, digital television is a reality in the United States, but it hasn't been easy for broadcasters and manufacturers. The government-mandated transition from analog to digital television has been complicated with dozens of competing DTV transmission formats, as well as equipment and programming issues.

To viewers, DTV means better pictures and sound, plus the potential for interactivity, increased channels, personalized programming, and pay-per-view services. To broadcasters, advertisers, and manufacturers, DTV means an unprecedented opportunity for business growth and technological advancement.

Broadcast DTV is, however, just one facet of digital television, which has long been central to high-end commercial post production and—more recently—motion picture effects. The advent of compressed digital video has helped established non-linear editing and QuickTime for desktop computers. And while broadcasters and cable industries work toward delivering DTV to the home, digitally encoded programming is already there via direct broadcast satellite receivers, DVD players, computer CD-ROMS, and the Internet.

In an effort to sort out these dramatic changes in the broadcast industry, Michael Silbergleid, former Editor-in-Chief of *Television Broadcast* and now President of The SilverKnight Group and Editor of *Digital Television: The Site*, produced the first edition of this book in 1998. Continued developments in the DTV industry, however, have prompted two updates of this text. Since the second edition, Michael has been joined by one of *Television Broadcast's* contributing editors and the ETV Field Editor for *Government Video*, Mark J. Pescatore. Together, they have assembled an impressive group of writing talents from different areas of the broadcast, video, and audio industries, including professionals from the Miller Freeman PSN family (including contributors to *Television Broadcast*, *Pro Sound News*, *Videography*, *Government Video*, and *Digital Television: The Site*). The result is another timely, important book that the broadcast and teleproduction industries can use as a resource in the often confusing world of DTV.

As we enter the new millennium, digital technology promises enormous potential for commerce and communication. I hope this book improves your understanding of the technology in ways that will be beneficial to your business.

—Paul G. Gallo,
President and Publisher, Miller Freeman PSN Inc.

PREFACE TO THE THIRD EDITION

Welcome to the future of broadcasting. We hope you're enjoying the ride. Digital television is a reality, and it has brought exciting twists and turns to the broadcast industry. Dozens of channels are on the air, but hundreds more are still preparing to make the move to DTV. With so many technical options (most with very high price tags), broadcasters are being cautious. After all, how does DTV affect your job in broadcasting and video production?

We created this book to help answer that question. Consider this your textbook for DTV 101. *The Guide To Digital Television* is not a "how to" book as much as it is a "what to do" book. Our goal is to provide a practical guide for the digital transition that helps you make the right decisions for your particular circumstances.

As in previous editions, *The Guide To Digital Television* follows the typical production cycle from pre-production to delivery and transmission, and has been updated to include the latest DTV developments. We've also added a new chapter, "DTV in the Real World," that puts the DTV transition in perspective for the broadcast industry and non-technical readers. We think this addition will help clarify your goals during this historic time in the broadcast and teleproduction industries.

Finally, we realize that DTV issues will continue to change after you read this book. We invite you to stay current through Digital Television: The Site at www.DigitalTelevision.com. You'll find timely discussions on business and legal issues, technology and more.

ACKNOWLEDGEMENTS

We'd like to acknowledge the efforts of all the individuals who contributed to the third edition of *The Guide To Digital Television*. Our contributing writers share in the success of this book, as do the staffs of *Television Broadcast*, *Government Video*, and *Videography* magazines, as well as *Digital Television: The Site* at www.DigitalTelevision.com. Specifically, we would like to thank Brian McKernan, editorial director, video division of Miller Freeman PSN, who originally suggested a book on digital television, Jessica Webb, senior editor of *Television Broadcast*, Teba Cespon, web administrator for Miller Freeman PSN, and Mark's wife, Adriana, for putting up with long distance editorial phone calls at all hours of the day and night. We would also like to thank our families and friends for supporting us in this venture.

Michael Silbergleid
New York, NY

Mark J. Pescatore
Chapel Hill, NC
March 2000

INTRODUCTION TO
THE THIRD EDITION

Broadcast stations have several digital television broadcast options, including multicasting several channels of programming at once, upconverting standard definition images, or providing high-speed data services. When many people think of digital television, though, they think high definition television, and some industry experts predict HDTV sports coverage will really help sell the idea of DTV to the public. For the 1999-2000 season, ABC broadcast its entire season of Monday Night Football *and the Super Bowl in HDTV for the first time. Norm Samet served as director for the broadcasts and reflected on a successful season of HDTV...*

IT'S BETTER THAN LIVING COLOR!
NORM SAMET

What looked great in NTSC before I began directing the ABC *Monday Night Football* HDTV feed in August 1999 pales in comparison to the pictures I get from HDTV cameras today. After 17 *Monday Night* games, one playoff game, and Super Bowl XXXIV, I still feel like a kid with a new toy—a very expensive new toy.

You almost get into a trance looking at HDTV pictures because you really see more. The wider 16:9 aspect ratio makes a big difference in covering football. With the old 4:3 aspect ratio screens it was often tricky to cover the defense. In HDTV they are already in your picture, so you can see more of the play develop.

The HDTV picture is so superior with brilliant colors and so sharp you can pick out numbers on players easily. I remember having a wide shot all the way down the field and there was a lady in a Jets t-shirt—and I could read the number on her shirt! I would have needed to walk all the way down to the other end of the field to see that detail in person.

And then there were the black spots all over the field in Dallas. "What's that!" I yelled, thinking something had gone wrong with a camera. A Dallas native calmly turned to me and said, "Those are crickets." My jaw dropped. The 525-line analog pictures have never picked out the kind of detail that the 720 progressive cameras capture. The point is, the amount of detail and clarity in HDTV pictures is unsurpassed by anything we have seen until now.

HDTV brings more than just better pictures. There are 5.1 channels of audio versus two in an analog feed. I now hear the referee's microphone on one channel, the announcer's on another, the crowd in another, and the sideline reporters have their own. As if I can't keep all of that straight, one channel plays music. With two channels of audio, the crowd, the referees and the announcers share the same channel and a lot of audio information is muffled.

There are a few negatives in covering NFL football with HDTV cameras. The first thing our crew had to overcome was working with fewer cameras. The standard *Monday Night Football* production had 24 cameras, but the HDTV production only had seven. This meant our camera crews had to work harder and cover more of the field that they would with the old cameras. In some stadiums, the analog and HDTV cameras can't be placed side by side because there is no room. Our HDTV cameras had to go higher and at a steeper angle.

Since we didn't have our own announcers, we had to follow the plays Al Michaels and Boomer Esiason called, even though we didn't always know what to anticipate. We always had the option to go to the standard feed, but that was rarely necessary. It was the extraordinary situation that sent us to the standard feed.

People will be blown away when they see and hear HDTV. The game really comes alive. You gotta see it to believe it.

Norm Samet started in the mail room at ABC, then moved to ABC News as a copy boy. He moved up the ranks to associate director at ABC News, covering special events, elections, conventions, and NASA, among other assignments. Later, he became an associate director and a director for ABC Sports, covering almost every type of athletic event, including football, basketball, boxing, figure skating, auto racing, bowling, triathlons, the Tour de France, and the Olympics.

THE ^{New} ROUTE TO DTV

CAUTION DTV AHEAD

DPS 465

DPS 470

DPS 475

What's So Special About This DPS Synchronizer?

- 12-Bit Component Digital Video Processing
- Proprietary Multi-Mode Adaptive Comb Filter Decoder
- Built-in Animated AV Logo Inserter
- Digi-Duplex Mode Provides Bi-Directional Analog/Digital Interface

  DIGI-DUPLEX ↑↓ **TWO-WAY TRAFFIC**

- Adjustable Spatial and Temporal Digital Noise Reduction
- Integrated Video Framestore with Linear Keyer
- Adjustable Digital Bandwidth Filtering
- Enhanced Digital Test Pattern Generator with Zone Plate
- DV (1394) I/O Option

Multi-Format AV Synchronizer & More

From the beginning, DPS has defined the way networks, broadcasters and mobile operators interface analog sources to their DTV facilities. Our DPS-465 was the world's first multi-format 10-bit serial digital synchronizer. The DPS-470, with integrated four-channel digital audio, refined the concept and quickly became the industry benchmark. Thousands are in daily use throughout the world.

Our new DPS-475, with 12-bit component video processing and proprietary adaptive comb filter decoder technology, packs such an incredible array of features into its compact 1U chassis, that we hesitate to even call it a synchronizer. We'd like to call it the "DPS-475 AV Synchronizer, Animated Logo Inserter, Linear Keyer, Time Base Corrector, Framestore, Bi-Directional Transcoder, DV Interfacer, AV Test Signal Generator, VITS Inserter, MPEG Pre-Processor and Digital Audio Embedder/De-Embedder". For now, we'll just settle for "DPS-475". It's more than a synchronizer.

DPS®

dps.com
800-775-3314

DPS.COM/403
more ? info

Running digital and analog can be tough.
Good thing there's geeks like us.

Sure, some broadcasters call us industry geeks. Others call us industry experts. But it's all the same to us. Because when it comes to the chaos of adding digital while maintaining a profitable analog operation, we're the geeks you need. Harris is the most experienced, most reliable choice for analog and digital operation. We've delivered more DTV transmitters, encoders and support equipment than any of our competitors, with expertise that has built a reputation for reliability. A reputation that carries over to our systems integration work, whether you're adding DTV capabilities or building from the ground up. So when analog and digital collide, call us. Because whether we're experts or geeks, we're still Harris. And we can help.

next level solutions

WIRELESS

BROADCAST

GOVERNMENT

NETWORK SUPPORT

1-800-4-HARRIS ext.3035 ■ www.harris.com

DTV IN THE REAL WORLD 1

Mandated by the FCC, television stations have started to make the transition to digital television. But how did we get here? And how well is the industry responding to this revolutionary time? While the rest of this book will discuss technical issues associated with digital television, this chapter provides an historical context for DTV development and implementation, as well as observations about these early days of commercial DTV broadcasting. We begin our journey with the introduction from the first edition of this book, which provides a roadmap to DTV from the early days of broadcast.

FROM YESTERDAY TO TODAY:
A PERSPECTIVE ON THE DIGITAL REVOLUTION
RENVILLE H. MCMANN, JR.

I was born a little too late to see mechanical television over the air, but my family was lucky enough to have a 441-line, RCA-built, Westinghouse 12-inch mirror-viewed receiver in time for the opening of the 1939 World's Fair. This switch from mechanical disks to all electronic vacuum tube pickup and display was probably the first revolution in television history. Since then, revolutions have happened so fast and so often in TV broadcasting that there is a widespread belief, especially among non-engineering management, that the upcoming digital ATV transition is just another ho-hum change in the way of doing things. Those holding this belief are very, very wrong as a little history will show.

The first real revolution in broadcasting was the change from radio to television in 1939. Engineers, used to thinking of base bandwidths measured in kilohertz not TV's megahertz, generally had no knowledge of phase linearity, transient response, cathode ray tubes, gray scale, gamma, photo cathodes, etc. In fact, for the most part, they did not even have high frequency oscilloscopes to look at the TV waveforms they were trying to generate. Luckily for the industry, World War II trained thousands of engineers and technicians in the art of radar, the first cousin of television. Also, the total number of television stations was very small in 1945, building slowly over the next 10 years so there was time to learn the new art of television. Even so, lots of mistakes were made, and on some occasions some pretty terrible pictures were transmitted, but every year, little by little, the pictures got better. The Iconoscope gave way to the Image Orthicon, the Image Orthicon to the Vidicon, and the Vidicon to the Plumbicon, with these improvements occurring roughly over two decades.

Although each of these improvements was a revolution in its own way, each could easily be understood by engineers and technicians trained on the previous generation of technology. Ham radio was a good background and many a chief engineer got his start that way. For the most part, a few days' training by the manufacturer of the equipment was all that was necessary, along with a basic understanding of a circuit design, a little mathematics, and Ohm's law. We tend to forget that in those days equipment broke frequently, and the broadcast engineer was expected to quickly fix it himself and know how to work with a soldering iron and how to climb a tower to check out the antenna. Only in major breakdowns could he (there were very few shes in those days) get help from the manufacturer. At some stations, the chief engineer could not only fix the equipment, but he had actually built it in the first place.

The next two revolutions took place more or less simultaneously in the late 1950s, color and video tape recording. Color cameras could be considered as three black and white cameras operating in parallel and hence easily understood; the encoder and decoder did require going back to the books for a refresher on modulation theory, but the same skills honed over the previous 10 years were easily up to the task, and once again the engineers could easily fix it themselves. Video tape recording did require some new skills, mostly mechanical, and another refresher in modulation theory to understand the FM video. Tape recording, itself a revolution, spawned the TV production house, a new facet of our industry, and perhaps a revolution in its own right. However, for the first time the TV production house could not go it alone and build its own cameras and tape recorders, even if it wanted to, although some of the big networks did develop both on a limited basis. It was starting to be the age of specialists.

You will note that I haven't mentioned transistors as a revolution because, for the most part, transistors were just a new component, a small, low-voltage version of a valve, subject to the same design equations as the vacuum tubes before them. Transistors, while not a revolution themselves, did cause one: the

DTV IN THE REAL WORLD

UNDERSTANDING DIGITAL

PRE-PRODUCTION

PRODUCTION

AUDIO

GRAPHIC & COMPOSITING

POST PRODUCTION

DELIVERY & DUPLICATION

ENGINEERING & TRANSMISSION

APPENDIX

GLOSSARY

advent of small, portable equipment which revolutionized station operations, especially ENG. Although small, this new equipment was very complex, and it caused a large-scale start of servicing by replacing boards, not individual components. TV engineers began to rely more and more on the manufacturer to fix things at the board level, and, as a result, had less understanding of the subtle intricacies of the equipment's design. Collections of transistors and integrated circuits came on the scene in the 1970s, and made possible high-speed analog-to-digital conversion, introducing the industry to digital picture manipulation, time-based correction, digital tape recording, electronic editing, etc.

Note that over 20 years later, this digital conversion of our plants is still not finished, and the equipment has grown so complex that sometimes the manufacturers themselves cannot understand or fix the designs they delivered only a few years previously. Just try and get a 1980 vintage frame synchronizer or noise reducer repaired if anything more involved than a power supply has failed. Thus in 20 years, we have passed from a completely analog plant to a partially digital one. The myriad problems encountered along the way were solved one by one as new pieces of equipment were introduced without jeopardizing the picture quality or interrupting the program flow. There was time for the manufacturers and users to experiment with the new gear in a non-crisis atmosphere, because the older versions were still around and could always be used as a backup.

Now comes digital television and ATV with its subsets of HDTV, SDTV, data transmission, program guides, etc. Not to mention video compression of 50:1 or more.

The FCC wants a complete conversion in nine years. This time, there is no time for an evolutionary approach. The job can be done, but it will require a massive effort on the part of manufacturers and users, both stations and production houses. Much of the needed equipment hasn't been designed, and in some critical areas, it hasn't even been invented. The old-time engineer is going to need lots of help from the new breed of software maven. Circuit design, while still important, needs to be supplemented by strong logic design and de-bugging skills. A mathematical background will be very handy when trying to decipher the discrete cosine transform or Trellis Coding. At first there will be problems, but none that can't be solved by the same type of person that can keep an Ethernet LAN up and running.

DTV: A BRIEF HISTORY

MARK J. PESCATORE

DTV has been in development for more than a decade. The FCC began its first inquiry into advanced television (ATV) services in 1987 at the request of 58 broadcast organizations, which jointly petitioned the Commission to explore the possible impact of ATV technologies on existing broadcast service. Later that year, the FCC established the Advisory Committee on Advanced Television Service (ACATS) to provide recommendations about ATV technical and economic issues. As discussion continued, all-digital ATV systems were developed, and ATV became DTV. In 1988, broadcasters and manufacturers funded the Advanced Television Test Center (ATTC) as a private, non-profit organization to test new DTV technologies. Also that year, a group of cable television system operators established Cable Television Laboratories, Inc. (CableLabs) to work with the ATTC on the cable portions of DTV standards tests.

One important consideration throughout the evolution of DTV was that there would be no disruption of service to the public during the transition period. As a result, it was determined that broadcasters would be assigned a *separate* channel for their DTV signals. Once the DTV transition was complete, broadcasters would be required to surrender their NTSC frequencies. In fact, the spectrum containing NTSC frequencies is already set to be auctioned in 2002.

By February 1993, four competing digital systems were under consideration for (1996), the group developed a DTV system that would "...dramatically increase the tech adoption by the FCC, but none were recommended by the ACATS. A few months later, seven companies and institutions from the four DTV systems organized a cooperative effort called the "Grand Alliance." As detailed in the FCC Fourth Report and Order(1996), the group developed a DTV system that would "...dramatically increase the technical quality of broadcast television, helping to preserve for consumers and for our democratic society the benefits of a vibrant and healthy free over-the-air television service in the future... [and] give consumers access to a host of potential information services..."

The Advanced Television Systems Committee (ATSC), formed by the Joint Committee on Inter-Society Coordination (JCIC) to create voluntary technical standards for DTV, considered which elements of the Grand Alliance's system would be voluntary and which would require FCC action. They also detailed five specific areas of the complete system: video, audio, transport, transmission, and receivers. The Advisory Committee recommended the standard to the FCC on November 28, 1995.

DTV IMPLEMENTATION

The FCC adopted a modified version of this standard as the DTV standard in the Fourth Report and Order on December 27, 1996. The FCC remarked that the ATSC DTV standard exceeded their expectations, and it would "provide a measure of certainty and confidence to manufacturers, broadcasters and consumers, thus helping assure a smooth implementation of digital broadcast television..."

On April 21, 1997, the FCC released the Fifth Report and Order, which outlined a number of service policies and rules for DTV. It included an aggressive eight-year strategy for the DTV transition (it was originally going to be phased in over a 15-year period), because the FCC felt that if DTV is not "available quickly, other digital services may achieve levels of penetration that could preclude the success of over-the-air, digital television." On November 1, 1998, 26 volunteer stations were scheduled to begin digital transmissions. By May 1, 1999, all stations in the top 10 markets affiliated with the major networks (ABC, CBS, Fox, and NBC) were required to be broadcasting a digital signal. Six months later, on November 1, all ABC, CBS, Fox, and NBC affiliates in the top 30 markets were required to have their digital signals on the air, though dozen of stations failed to meet their deadline and had to file for a six-month extension, with some filing for a second six-month extension.

All other commercial stations, including independent stations and UPN, WB, and Paxnet affiliates, have until May 1, 2002, to begin digital transmissions. All noncommercial stations will be required to have their digital signal on the air by May 1, 2003. The FCC has set a target date of 2006 for broadcasters to complete their transition to digital transmission and surrender their NTSC frequencies. This market-staggered approach was favored by most manufacturers and broadcasters according to comments received by the FCC.

In an effort to make sure the viewing habits of NTSC viewers are not disrupted during the transition, the FCC will begin a phased-in simulcast several years before NTSC is eliminated in 2006. By April 1, 2003, DTV stations will be required to simulcast at least 50 percent of the video programming from their NTSC analog channel. A 75 percent simulcast requirement will take effect on April 1, 2004. All analog programming will be required to be simulcast on April 1, 2005, a policy which will remain in effect until broadcasters surrender their NTSC analog channels. Note, the FCC can modify this schedule at any time and will review it in April 2001 and April 2003.

FCC REACTIONS

A few weeks before the November 1, 1998, volunteer start-up date, FCC Chairman William Kennard announced that 15 additional stations would join the original 26 volunteer stations in digitally broadcasting the October 29 space shuttle launch with astronaut John Glenn. Kennard said, "The fact that so many stations have committed to accelerating their DTV start-up...will be remembered as one of the most significant developments in the DTV transition process."

One year later, Kennard remained enthusiastic concerning DTV. "I am excited about the potential benefits digital television will provide to consumers," he said. "The build-out of digital television stations is proceeding at a fast pace, and is indicative that broadcasters understand the importance of getting up and running to compete in this digital era.

"It is heartening to see the increase of network broadcasts, including news, entertainment, and sports, that are being sent in digital format. This trend will only increase as more stations begin their DTV transmissions. As I have emphasized many times, additional content will be crucial to the immediate success of DTV."

FCC Commissioner Susan Ness was optimistic and realistic in her evaluation of DTV's commercial debut. "At the first year anniversary of digital television in the United States," she commented, "there is much to celebrate and much still to be done." Growing pains include tower construction (in some areas), copyright protection, cable carriage and compatibility, and receiver quality. Ness added, however, that consumer response to DTV has been positive.

NOVEMBER 1999: MOMENTUM IS BUILDING

MIKE KELLER AND ROSS KAUFFMAN

WCVB, the ABC affiliate in Boston, is the largest station owned by Hearst-Argyle Television Group and has served as a test site for all others in our group. Since we went on the air with a digital signal in October 1998, there have been many issues that we've had to deal with regarding equipment interfaces and specific gear that simply was not available in the beginning.

Basically, we've made all the mistakes here and paid the high prices for first-generation equipment so that the other stations in our group can benefit from our experience. We chose to be an early adopter station, even though our Harris transmitter was on the air before we had a single receiver in the market. In retrospect, we feel it was a good idea because our group had a number of stations that had to be up in May 1999. We didn't want to reinvent the wheel at every station. By getting a head start, we were able to recognize recurring DTV issues.

Including LMA agreements, we'll eventually install 29 digital transmitters within our group. As of November of 1999, the Hearst-Argyle group has five stations broadcasting in digital—WCVB, WTAE, in Pittsburgh; KCRA, in Sacramento, CA; KITV, in Hawaii; and WLWT, in Cincinnati, OH. Our goal as a station group is to have every station on the air and be capable of upconverting their NTSC programming to digital and passing through their respective network HD signals (when available) by the FCC's timetable. That's as far as we're going to go at this point.

The atmosphere in the early days of DTV was excellent, because stations were all trying to get a signal up and everyone seemed willing to lend their moral support. We were able to discuss different issues with other stations across the country that were doing exactly what we were. There were a lot of interface issues that caused us trouble initially, particularly the encoders.

One year later, the atmosphere surrounding DTV has become more competitive. At the station, we can easily view three stations with "rabbit ears" on our digital set-top receiver. With an outside antenna, we can pick up five! From a transmission standpoint, DTV has progressed at lightning speed.

We're also proud to say that we now have paid HD commercial advertising on our digital channel in Boston. This, I believe, is a direct result of an HD segment we produced in May 1999 for a popular show we produce (five days a week in NTSC) called *Chronicle*.

Showing the beautiful countryside of Vermont in HD (1080i HDCAM converted to 720p) made all the difference for us in getting the attention we were looking for from our audience. They knew the show in NTSC, so showing the improved high definition images allowed them to recognize the difference.

The HD episode of *Chronicle* has also allowed us to get involved with the NATPE/HDTV consortium of stations that shares HD programming. We acquired enough material from the consortium to host an "HDTV Week" in January 2000. We also broadcast ABC's *Monday Night Football*, which is carried by local sports bars, and that's been equally successful with the public.

Everyone who sees HD in our market loves it. Retail stores regularly sell out of the small amount of product they stock. We get feedback from a dozen or so active viewers in retail stores, research labs, and consumer homes. To quote an e-mail from one of our viewers: "I'll never watch football in 'narrowscreen' again."

By early 2000, we'll be averaging about 10 hours of HD programming per week. It's enough to keep people watching, but we still hear complaints that there's nothing to watch. We're trying to get more programming, but it has been a challenge.

The last six months has seen everyone—marketing, our general manager, and the public—taking notice, and we see a real momentum growing. Now that we've got someone willing to spend money for commercials, DTV has taken on a whole different perspective in our sales department.

Editor's Note: This essay originally appeared in a special section of Television Broadcast *magazine commemorating the first year of commercial DTV service.*

TELEVISION NEWS IN THE DIGITAL ERA
Mark A. Thalhimer

Ask a broadcast engineer about the transition from analog to digital television and you're likely to hear about equipment upgrades, competing digital tape formats, disk-based video servers, television tower wind loads, digital signal dis-

DTV IN THE REAL WORLD

UNDERSTANDING DIGITAL

PRE-PRODUCTION

PRODUCTION

AUDIO

GRAPHIC & COMPOSITING

POST PRODUCTION

DELIVERY & DUPLICATION

ENGINEERING & TRANSMISSION

APPENDIX

GLOSSARY

tribution and the ongoing debate between 8-VSB and COFDM digital transmission technologies.

Ask a general manager about the same transition to digital and you'll hear about the unresolved digital must-carry question with local cable systems and the significant equipment expense in the switch to digital. He'll probably also bemoan audience fragmentation, the tense negotiations between corporate and the network about compensation and local avails, and the station's need to make the advertising budget next month.

Ask a news director about digital and you might hear about the need for a new news set because the old one shows too much wear in the crisp digital picture, or the need to frame the news anchors for both widescreen and standard format at the same time. You might hear some related talk about virtual sets and—if the news director is currently involved in talent negotiations—speculation about virtual anchors. The news director might also mention the need to upgrade the newsroom editorial systems—both the older script and wire editing system and the newer nonlinear video editing systems.

INTO THE FUTURE

If all goes smoothly, the engineer, GM and news director will each play their appropriate roles in the new world of digital television. According to the generally accepted scenario, this transition to digital should replicate the shift decades ago from black and white to color television. It is supposed to follow a pre-approved course: Set a standard. Buy equipment. Begin broadcasting. And the audience, mesmerized by those beautiful pictures, rushes out to pick up a new DTV set. "Game highlights at eleven," is even more glorious and engaging in widescreen hi-def than it is today.

But something funny has happened on the way to the future. Namely, the Internet.

Some will ask what the Net has to do with a local television newscast. The answer is lots, and the answer can be summed up in one word: broadband. Fat, fast pipes into the American home. Those fat pipes are coming via cable modems, DSL telephone services and possibly the DTV signal itself. And those pipes won't just be going to a personal computer in the home office. They will also go to the digital television set and to the personal digital video recorder.

INTEGRATED DIGITAL STRATEGY

Stations should view their transition to digital television as a part of their overall broadband strategy, with the local newsroom playing a central role in this new digital world. The newsroom is the only way that a station can create and distribute high value content. News is the only content a station actually owns and that can carry a long-term brand. Local news often provides a significant amount of revenue for the station and is a significant editorial voice in local communities. Without the newsroom the station is just an antenna.

In this future scenario, the newsroom serves as the central information gathering space in the community. From that nexus the station is a "publisher" of information. In the morning, it publishes on television and perhaps also on radio, for those viewers who have left home and are driving to work. During the day, it publishes on the Web because busy people at work have access to PCs, not TVs. In the evening, it publishes on cable, over the air and even via satellite. And now the industry is starting to buzz again about "interactive television," which may provide yet another platform for the station: continuously updated local news and information available on-demand for the audience.

ANALOG EXAMPLES OF THE DIGITAL FUTURE

Much of this on-demand future is already beginning to happen. In almost 30, mostly major markets around the country, local 24-hour cable news channels have been set up to produce hyper-local news. These local news channels are priming the audience to expect news-on-demand, with an emphasis on local issues.

In New York, NY1 has a full-time subway reporter. In Washington, D.C., Newschannel 8 produces and broadcasts three separate newscasts (and associated regional advertising) for the three zones that comprise the nation's capital: the District of Columbia, Northern Virginia and suburban Maryland. This type of time-shifting or geographic zoning becomes very appealing if a local broadcaster decides to multicast the digital television signal.

Many broadcasters are already forming partnerships with other local media, like radio and newspapers, to share resources and increase the amount, availability and depth of local news. In Chicago, for example, CLTV "debriefs" numerous *Chicago Tribune* reporters each day to extend the reach of its local cable newscasts.

EXTENDING THE BROADCAST

In Seattle, meanwhile, Microsoft's Web-TV is developing "Web enhanced" television newscasts with local television partners, as well as with NBC News and the *News Hour with Jim Lehrer* on PBS. In Silicon Valley, Internet start-up companies like Yahoo Broadcast.com, FasTV, Zatso and a number of others are approaching local stations to begin streaming their newscasts onto the Net in anticipation of the broadband future. Today, it may be jerky, postage-stamp-sized video. In the future, it will be an on-demand newscast. Imagine the day when the audience can stack their own newscast. Or perhaps the technology will deliver something more like a personalized video clipping service. We just don't know.

Intel, the other west coast technology heavyweight, recently opened its Center for Datacasting Innovation, which will work with broadcasters to develop applications for data broadcasting on digital television. While just beginning, Intel describes its effort as focusing on the "tremendous opportunities

DTV IN THE REAL WORLD

UNDERSTANDING DIGITAL

PRE-PRODUCTION

PRODUCTION

AUDIO

GRAPHIC & COMPOSITING

POST PRODUCTION

DELIVERY & DUPLICATION

ENGINEERING & TRANSMISSION

APPENDIX

GLOSSARY

that the convergence of Internet and broadcast technologies brings to the television industry."

On a more focused level, Silicon Valley start-up Geocast will soon unveil its turnkey system for local stations to datacast news, information, programming, advertising and e-commerce applications to personal computers. Geocast has announced partnerships with several major station group owners.

Not to be outdone, America Online is soon to unveil its entry into the interactive television marketplace. Calling it—what else—AOL-TV, the service is supposed to begin to bring together the best elements of the Web with the ease of television. AOL, don't forget, has a track record of simplifying technology for wide consumer acceptance where others have struggled.

DIGITAL REFOCUSES THE PICTURE

Where does all this lead? Is it high definition or standard definition? Is it widescreen? Is it multi-channel? Is it active or passive? Is it video or data? Does it need to complement my station's Internet strategy? What exactly does this "interactive television" thing that's being talked about include, anyway? Will we do a 24-hour local or regional channel? Will we time-shift local news programming? Will we try to geographically zone our newscast for different parts of our community?

These are just some of the questions local stations must answer in the next few years. Because, it's not just television anymore. It's digital television.

THE FUTURE OF NEWSGATHERING IS NOW

MARK BELL

Digital newsgathering is 100 percent here.

Successful wireless communication is a miracle. However, once invented and used, making it more efficient is the challenge.

You can't speed up realtime acquisition of events. If the event is not carried live, however, it needs to be archived (at least temporarily), transmitted to an accessible point of storage, and processed for broadcast transmission or longer-term archive. Usually the last archive process includes compression of the material, as press conferences, long speeches, and a great amount of field material is not suited for archive or broadcast. Some call the process editing.

There may actually be a time in the future where it will be cost effective to have entire conferences and other long time events permanently archived, as digitized storage will be cost effective but intensive editing will not.

Today, we don't have to have any perception of information while it's in storage, unlike past days when film archives were kept in cans on special shelves. We have faith, perhaps more than ever before, that information will be just fine when it's retrieved, as it has been up to now in so many cases (and we're getting better at it). Many people are so absolutely sure information will be in their computers that they may become complacent and not so good at backing up their data as needed. Overconfidence? Yes. That's how dependable digital storage has become.

And that's what the future of news is about now. Acquisition of realtime events, multi-access storage, meta-tagged archiving so even the smallest visual gesture or single word can be retrieved. No degradation as with film and tape, and no cryptic scribbling on a label to try and decipher what's in the box or on the tape. It's just a matter of capacity, and capacity seems to be a product of time.

Storage capacity of systems has increased almost endlessly based on applications and operating speed, which have been built based on the availability of storage space. This phenomenon seems to be a perpetually upward-moving spiral. In the data storage intensive video industry, that's just fine, as hardware meets or exceeds what is needed, and is staying ahead of the ability of companies to keep up with technological changes and training.

At the time of the first edition of this book a few years ago, hard drives, as in the Avid CamCutter, were considered cutting-edge at a 1-1.5 gigabyte (Gb) capacity. Two of them fastened together in the CamCutter's disk pack would allow for about 20 minutes of record time and cost about $2,500. In contrast, a recent computer outlet newspaper ad offered 20 Gb hard drives for under $200. Logically, two 20 Gb hard drives working together with updated compression schemes would be far less expensive and hold almost 200 minutes, 10 times more data. That's a whole sporting event, with commercials, on two hard drives. It may also be a full day's news, documentary or commercial shoot. How long does it take for you to shoot 200 minutes of video? And remember, you can dump the bad takes as you go along; it's 200 good minutes.

THE NEW PLAYER, THE INTERNET

A plain and simple Internet dial-up was used by this author to transmit material for the first edition of this book. Today, that same connection can be used for transmission of almost flawless full-motion broadcasts, but as with everything else, the workability is soon followed by improvements for practical applications. Many stations have made their material available through the Internet, and some Web sites offer their news stories for assembly into other newscasts. Free Web browsers and software are being used to view them, too. It seems as if more and more companies are coming out with modems that can transmit full motion broadcasts, and like acquisition, storage and retrieval devices, will keep getting faster and better in a very short time. The information demand and acquisition "dike" has been broken. Information flow is getting much easier.

Even the means of transmitting signals to a station have become faster and easier through digital. For long-distance signal movement, why *not* use the Internet? The use of high-speed lines, more and more of which are becoming available, will do just fine.

For shorter-distance wireless transmission, a new transmission scheme using Compressed Orthagonal Frequency Division Multiplex (COFDM) has been embraced by news broadcasters (see The How and Why of COFDM) Simply stated, it is the transmission of many packets of data through a myriad of carriers numbering in the hundreds, only a few handfuls of which need to be received for reception and reassembly of the signal. COFDM has been successfully demonstrated at NAB and many other places, including live ENG. Those who have tried it have witnessed abilities to transmit and receive as no other a/v signal has been in the past—including from a moving vehicle in one manufacturer's tests. COFDM is actually obstruction-friendly and given its digital nature, looks great (or has no signal at all), without multipath distortion, fading, or containing other distortions broadcasters have become used to in analog transmission.

Mix that with compression schemes which allow for fractioned-time transfer, such as the multiple speed transfer time offered in Sony's Betacam SX format, and users can send from places previously dark at a fraction of the transmission time. It's similar to a small computer whose processing time has been significantly reduced by a faster processor.

COFDM-equipped news vehicles can transmit signals using a much smaller directional or omnidirectional transmission assembly than the conventional directional antenna-topped mast. The vehicles using the technology at NAB used an antenna only a few feet high, and drove under canopies, through tunnels, around buildings and in traffic with very few unacceptable signal distortions. Using masts on ENG vehicles may not be necessary in the future if receive sites and signal strength are set up in certain ways, which provides a cost savings and added safety benefit.

COFDM transmission also requires less power to transmit a quality signal, as power doesn't make the signal better as it does with analog. COFDM also allows for fixed as well as mobile transfer of information, so crews could conceivably transmit one location's material while traveling to the next. This can be a real plus for that great friend of news, speed. With line-of-sight requirements eliminated, moving while transmitting is possible, and distortions such as reflections are eliminated, it rids remote telecasting of many challenges associated with analog.

Another aspect of the movement of data will affect ENG, too: wireless data transmission through cell phones or other wireless interfaces. Pictures and many other data packets are being transmitted through small wireless interfaces at the present time, and some computers even have built-in cameras allowing real-time video to those at the other end of the data stream. Proof of the viability of transmission interfaces usually is followed by marketization and then the improvement in the devices, and frankly, with the size of the processors in camera-equipped computers, there is no reason that there can't be a broadcast-quality camcorder with the computer inside capable of logging on and dumping its data via wired or wireless interfaces as needed.

Cell phone transmission and reception has improved and evolved into digital networks that offer cell phone use with active digital processing. Handheld units are also used as discrete network walkie-talkies, which may represent another means of discrete data transfer. As indicated above, once digital, many "fade" factors disappear and error correction appears. The question becomes how fast and how much can be placed on the circuit.

Earlier editions of this particular section of the book indicated that the future would contain wired interfaces, for ISDN line "nodes" throughout cities, so crews could feed data directly back to receive centers. With the extremely rapid advancements in wireless transmission, however, wire or fiber nodes will be more impractical as time goes on. More wireless development is going on as this is being written than at any other time on the planet, and wired nodes will probably never need to be built. As development of the need for wireless becomes more defined, or those with vision dream on, even more will be invented. For instance, laptop computer modems with wireless interfaces are very common, and the demand for them continues to increase.

The future of ENG will center around portability, wireless transmission sent from anywhere, computer processed, meta-tagged, archived, retrieved in an instant to be sent or simply inserted live as the situation warrants, to or from a moving vehicle, to or from a base station, or in a direct feed right to the viewer's home. The pendulum swings from hardware-rich potential awaiting applications to application-rich dreams awaiting hardware. That's news.

LPTV STRUGGLES TO SURVIVE
MARK J. PESCATORE

While the transition to digital television has challenged broadcasters with a variety of technical and economic issues, no group of stations has felt the effects more than low power television (LPTV). Many LPTV stations provide their communities with local programming, covering events and issues that other broadcasters ignore. By the time the DTV transition is complete, however, hundreds of LPTV stations could be forced off the air. New legislation has provided some relief, but many LPTV stations still face a grim future.

LPTV IN PERSPECTIVE

Although LPTV stations have been around for almost 20 years, many people who do not have an LPTV station in their market are not familiar with the services these stations provide. In most cases, programming broadcast by an LPTV station is not provided in its market through any other broadcast outlet. According to the FCC, there were 2,190 LPTV stations as of July 1, 1999, licensed in the United States. Comparatively, the FCC also reported 4,915 low power UHF and VHF translators, 1,229 full-power UHF and VHF commercial stations, and 370 full-power UHF and VHF educational stations. Alaska has the most LPTV stations, 250, which are part of a statewide educational network. The other LPTV stations are operated by some 700 licensees in more than 700 towns and cities, with an estimated two-thirds of the stations serving rural communities.

Although LPTV does have its roots in translator services, and the two services have similar technical specifications and regulations, the two entities are defined differently by the FCC. According to the 1982 FCC Report and Recommendations in the Low Power Television Inquiry, television translators are low-powered broadcast stations that receive a broadcast signal on one channel and retransmit it on another channel to viewers in remote areas outside the signal's original broadcast area. In contrast, LPTV stations have the option of rebroadcasting syndicated programming or airing original programming. As their name implies, LPTV stations have set limits of signal strength that are significantly lower than full-power stations. While they are considered a "secondary service" (yielding at all times to interference issues with full-power stations), they enjoy relatively few programming regulations or requirements.

LPTV MEETS DTV

To protect the existing broadcast system in the United States, the FCC decided that an NTSC signal would be simulcast along with an HDTV signal for full-power stations during the DTV transition. Full-power broadcasters would then temporarily require a second 6 MHz channel for their DTV signals. As a result, individuals unable to afford new HDTV televisions could continue to enjoy television service.

These additional frequencies for full-power broadcasters are part of the problem LPTV stations are facing during the DTV transition. In an already crowded spectrum (in some areas of the country), full-power stations will require two channels until at least 2006. That means LPTV stations, as secondary services, may be removed to make room for the new DTV channels of existing full-power stations. Although Polar Broadcasting, Inc. challenged the FCC with regard to this course of action in 1994, the U.S. Court of Appeals District of Columbia Circuit upheld the FCC's decision.

Though the FCC recognized the potentially significant impact on LPTV in its Sixth Further Notice of Proposed Rule Making in 1996, it commented, "...we believe on balance that the benefits and innovations to be derived from these actions outweigh this impact." Further, the FCC determined it was necessary to maintain LPTV's secondary status, because limited spectrum space in major markets would require some LPTV displacement (either switching channels or ceasing operation) if full-power stations were to receive a second channel for DTV transmissions.

The FCC estimated that 55 to 65 percent of existing LPTV stations would be able to maintain operations, but even losing 20 percent (a conservative number based on these early FCC estimates), more than 400 LPTV stations across the country could conceivably be shut down. Keith Larson, who was part of the original LPTV task force and is now assistant bureau chief for engineering at the FCC Mass Media Bureau, said the FCC had no firm basis for estimating a final figure for lost LPTV stations. He confirmed there will be some disruption of LPTV service, but it will more likely be in urban areas where the LPTV audience has access to full-power stations and spectrum space is more crowded.

LPTV LEGISLATIVE LIFELINES

Thus, in the name of DTV progress, LPTV was faced with elimination in major markets. Despite appeals from LPTV broadcasters, the FCC maintained that secondary service LPTV stations would not be eligible for DTV licenses initially due to insufficient spectrum space. However, the Commission did note that LPTV stations were not necessarily excluded from converting to DTV; they simply would not be provided a second channel.

In an effort to keep as many LPTV stations on the air as possible, the FCC provided relief opportunities for displaced stations and loosened broadcasting restrictions. First, the FCC authorized LPTV stations to apply for a replacement channel without being subject to competing applications when it has been determined that the station will be displaced. Some interference rules were also relaxed for LPTV stations, including some restrictions on LPTV channel placement. The FCC also maintained a policy to limit initial DTV licenses to existing full-power broadcasters, which prevents new stations from entering a market and interfering with current LPTV stations. Finally, LPTV stations were provided a "power boost" for the first time, as new regulations allow no limit on transmitter output power, though stations are only permitted an effective radiated power (ERP) of 3,000 watts for a VHF station or 150,000 watts for a UHF station.

What many LPTV broadcasters really wanted, however, was the security of equal billing with full-power stations; in other words, they wanted primary status. According to Sherwin Grossman, president of the Community

DTV IN THE REAL WORLD

UNDERSTANDING DIGITAL

PRE-PRODUCTION

PRODUCTION

AUDIO

GRAPHIC & COMPOSITING

POST PRODUCTION

DELIVERY & DUPLICATION

ENGINEERING & TRANSMISSION

APPENDIX

GLOSSARY

Broadcasters Association (CBA), if LPTV remained a secondary service, it would eventually cease to exist. Responding to DTV's imminent effect on LPTV broadcasters, on April 21, 1998, the CBA petitioned the FCC to establish Class A status and award it to certain LPTV stations (as well as translators) to prevent displacement. The proposal would provide LPTV stations "primary spectrum user status, within their principal service contours, against all later authorized full power and low power stations."

The CBA also built a number of conditions into its petition, so not all LPTV stations were eligible (which means not all LPTV stations would be protected from DTV displacement). LPTV stations that qualified for Class A status would only include stations that had essentially mirrored the minimum operating schedule of a full-power station for at least three months and had included at least three hours per week of local or specialized programming not available from other stations in the area. Under the proposed rules, Class A LPTV stations would be permitted to convert from analog to digital, as well as request a second channel for its digital signal, provided the station did not cause interference to other primary stations. Although it was not enacted, the Community Broadcasters Protection Act of 1998 was recommended unanimously by the Senate Commerce Committee in October 1998. The bill had been opposed by full-power broadcasters concerned with additional competition for advertising revenue.

The Community Broadcasters Protection Act of 1999 was introduced in the House of Representatives on February 2, 1999, with similar justifications and restrictions to the 1998 Senate report. The bill did not require the FCC to issue a second channel to LPTV stations for the DTV transition, but provisionally allowed the FCC to grant the additional licenses barring any interference issues. LPTV stations could also elect to convert to DTV on their current channels at the end of the DTV transition.

This time, LPTV broadcasters had reason to celebrate, as the Community Broadcasters Protection Act of 1999, part of the Intellectual Property and Communications Omnibus Reform Act of 1999, was signed into law on November 29, 1999 by President Bill Clinton (the same spending package also gave satellite providers permission to retransmit local television signals). In the law, Congress recognized both the programming services provided by these broadcasters, as well as the economic difficulties they faced (money lenders don't necessarily welcome secondary broadcasters with open arms). Now, the FCC must establish a Class A license for qualifying LPTV stations, subject to the same terms and renewal standards as full-power stations.

After a long political struggle, at least some LPTV stations will be granted primary status instead of elimination as a result of the DTV transition. Legislation is in place, but debate continues regarding LPTV's peculiar position. Granted, LPTV station operators were aware of their secondary status when they signed on, but no one could have reasonably predicted the overwhelming need for spectrum space during the DTV transition.

Should LPTV be punished because full-power broadcasters need additional spectrum space temporarily, and should only select stations be given primary status? Conversely, should full-power broadcasters have to compete with new Class A stations as a result of the new legislation? LPTV stations in rural areas are expected to be relatively untouched by DTV as compared to urban stations; does this imply that LPTV stations in urban areas have less importance because of their location? Should local programming and other programming options be withheld from viewers because they live in a certain geographic region? While industry opinions vary widely, these questions can only be answered definitively through the legislation of the federal government and the actions of the FCC.

WATCHING TV ON AN HDTV: THE GOOD, THE BAD AND THE UGLY

MICHAEL SILBERGLEID

As the editor of DigitalTelevision.com, I purchased an HDTV monitor in 1999 to get a front-row seat for the DTV transition. So far, my reaction is mixed. Although the monitor provides the potential for exceptional images, broadcasters and cable system operators need to recognize the new challenges of the technology.

I bought a 34-inch diagonal direct view flat 16:9 CRT monitor, primarily because it actually fit in my entertainment center with a half-inch to spare on each side. (Of course it took three of us to lift all 181 pounds of it into position, but it was worth the strain.) Inputs were the cable tuner via a VCR, DVD (s-video), computer (s-video), and a set-top box (component-Y/Pb/Pr).

The first images I saw happened to be a cable station with decent reception. I was amazed. Then I watched a standard definition DVD via a consumer s-video cable that was line doubled in the set. In a word, it was stunning. I had never seen pictures like this in a consumer environment, especially in my own living room. I invited a technologically curious friend to watch some DVDs, and he's just purchased an HDTV projection set. It is true: once you see HDTV you want it (even if it's only line doubled). That is, until you stumble onto a signal with poor reception.

On my cable system, SCI FI Channel routinely provides a clean image. When it airs a movie in letterbox, it is a sight to behold on my HDTV monitor, even if I am blowing up the picture to fit (more on a problem with this

DTV IN THE REAL WORLD
UNDERSTANDING DIGITAL
PRE-PRODUCTION
PRODUCTION
AUDIO
GRAPHIC & COMPOSITING
POST PRODUCTION
DELIVERY & DUPLICATION
ENGINEERING & TRANSMISSION
APPENDIX
GLOSSARY

later). WNET, one of my local PBS member stations, looks just as good. But channels with impulse noise, herringbone patterns, and other signal degradations do not translate well to the line-doubled world of HDTV. In fact, doubling the lines also means doubling the problems—they become twice as bad.

Your best defense against delivering poor signal quality is a digital infrastructure. You need to be producing, storing and sending out the best signal possible. Monitor the cable system, and not just at your station. How does it look at home to average viewers? Ask your staff to critically look at your signal via cable when they are home. If something in the signal looks bothersome, imagine how it looks upconverted or line doubled on an HDTV. Communicate with the cable system. Let them know that you are checking on the quality of the signal that they are sending to your viewers. Work with them to evaluate what they send and receive (maybe that is the problem).

Consumer H/DTV is far from a perfect science. But with all things, it comes down to how picky you are. The biggest complaint after picture quality: the station/network logo bugs.

Where does your bug sit? Have you seen where it sits if someone is watching on an HDTV? If they stretch or otherwise justify the picture, your bug will just get wider. But what if they zoom in for full 16:9, losing the top and bottom of the screen image? What if they zoom to fill the screen when you are running a program in letterbox?

Every bug I have seen sits just inside the 16:9 area. When I zoom in to fill the screen, I only see the top third of the bug. It looks like "stuff" in the corner of my picture, not a station or network identification. SCI FI Channel's animated bug is the worst, as it literally looks like white ants (real bugs) crawling around the corner of my screen.

IN THE SPECS BUT NOT IN THE STREAM

Watching real HDTV (or as real as a consumer monitor will allow) is more stunning than a line-doubled DVD. Using a set-top box hooked up to my local cable system, I was able to receive the 8-VSB signals of HBO and WCBS-DT.

First, there *is* a visible difference between a line-doubled DVD and 1080i HDTV, with HDTV being the clear winner. But there are some drawbacks to the system.

There are still parts of the ATSC specification that are not complete or that are not being implemented. Current 8-VSB receivers lack dual-stream audio capability even though manufacturers know that broadcasters are already allowed to use it. Broadcasters, of course, *can't* use dual-stream audio, because it might mean viewers would get no dialogue or no music and sound effects. Present receivers also lack conditional access, copy protection, data applications, and even, perhaps, cable-TV channel compatibility and the ability to display closed captions. Agreements were reached in February 2000 on technical standards for direct connection of digital TVs to cable systems and on-screen program guides. The ATSC data-broadcast specification is expected to be approved in April 2000.

Start thinking about how your viewers will be viewing your signal in the next few years. After all, many retailers reported heavy demand for HDTV monitors and sets during the 1999 holiday season. Viewers will be in a 16:9 DTV world sooner than we thought.

THE DTV CONSUMER

MICHAEL GROTTICELLI

With the turn of a new century, consumer electronics manufacturers are excited about the potential of DTV. After being accused of stalling the rollout of affordable digital receivers, manufacturers are making a real effort to educate prospective DTV customers with in-store information and network TV advertising. In an attempt to jump-start DTV set sales, they're also lowering the price.

The number of "digital-ready" sets sold as of December 1999 was around 125,000 units, mostly without DTV receivers. In comparison, more than 40 million analog sets were sold in 1999. Several CE companies have stated that 2000 is the year when the one millionth DTV set will be sold. To reach their goal, prices will have to drop to about $2,000, various transmission issues will have to be solved, and more regularly scheduled programming will have to become available.

Initial product offerings from consumer electronics manufacturers for digital television in 1998 were big (40 to 60 inches), clumsy rear-projection boxes—employing the 16:9 aspect ratio—that did little to generate consumer interest. The latest generation of sets, somewhat smaller in size and less costly, look to change that, as was evidenced by a new line of digital sets in a variety of prices that were displayed at the Consumer Electronics Show in January 2000.

Also on the market are a wide range of PC-based TV tuner cards that are capable of displaying full HDTV resolutions on appropriate multiscan monitors. Indeed, multiscan monitors with TV tuners are being made even larger to accommodate progressive scan signals on sets that look like traditional TVs.

As more advanced digital scan conversion and other proprietary imaging techniques have been built into newer digital sets, image quality has noticeably improved, as has inherent audio features. Most live HDTV events are now produced in Dolby Digital AC-3 (5.1 channel) and these new sets (in conjunction with the appropriate home audio system) really enhance the sound experience.

DTV IN THE REAL WORLD

UNDERSTANDING DIGITAL

PRE-PRODUCTION

PRODUCTION

AUDIO

GRAPHIC & COMPOSITING

POST PRODUCTION

DELIVERY & DUPLICATION

ENGINEERING & TRANSMISSION

APPENDIX

GLOSSARY

Digital TVs now available generally fall into three main categories: integrated high definition sets that include a digital receiver and display; digital set-top boxes designed to work with HD and standard definition (SD) digital displays (and, in some cases, with current analog sets); and DTV-capable displays that, with the addition of a digital set-top box, offer a complete DTV system.

The market is also starting to see a new generation of direct-view CRT displays, from 27 to 40 inches, third-generation front- and rear projection CRT models, and LCD-based monitors that provide incredible pictures and Dolby Digital surround sound at a slightly reduced cost. There are even digital sets in the 4:3 aspect ratio at a much more affordable price. Since price is an issue with consumers, the economies of scale that have cut the cost of other consumer electronics devices will certainly apply to digital receivers as well.

Heretofore, strategies for DTV receivers in home theaters have seen companies offering a large-screen "digital ready" display and making available—at extra cost—a separate set-top box that decodes analog signals and displays them as digital. Audio has been offered via Dolby Pro Logic surround. The strategy is that these "upscale" consumers can watch big, beautiful analog pictures now, and later, when more programming becomes available, they can purchase a decoder box to watch digital signals at HDTV resolutions.

These decoder boxes will also prolong the life of current analog sets, as consumers will be able to buy and watch digital programming in analog on their NTSC set. The benefit of these boxes, besides addressing the legacy issue, is that they can also be outfitted with internal hard drives and special software, from companies like Microsoft, Wink Technologies, OpenTV, Replay TV, TiVo, and others, that enables a wide range of interactive capability, virtual VCR-like features, and "personal TV" services. Since the set-top is connected to the Internet, this software can be upgraded with or without the subscriber's knowledge, thereby eliminating obsolescence.

Although we've heard a lot of talk about the eventual convergence of the TV and the computer, companies looking to take advantage of these new interactive opportunities are being careful to create a comfortable "lean back" technology, not a "lean forward" one. As Microsoft founder Bill Gates said in his keynote address at the CES show, "People will continue to watch TV as they always have, they'll just have access to any number of separate devices via a home network."

The market is also beginning to see a new generation of DTV sets that feature built-in decoders that receive all ATSC formats and display them as a 1080-line, interlaced signal. The notion of a progressive scan receiver is certainly a viable alternative, as several companies have shown affordable, progressive-scan monitors.

Direct Broadcast Satellite (DBS) providers DirecTV and Echostar have also made arrangements with CE manufacturers to have satellite IRDs installed at the factory, so that consumers will have instant access to DBS services—including HDTV channels, interactive games, Internet access and E-commerce services. Thomson is one company that has led the way in this area, providing a built-in DirecTV decoder.

Several companies are offering flat-screen plasma displays that the average consumer may interpret to be a digital receiver, although these beautiful-looking models are currently analog receivers. Some companies have developed digital, 720-line, progressive-scan flat screens, but at this point are far too expensive to be considered a serious contender to the more traditional digital sets.

Additional advances have been made in the area of DTV set tuners that enable sets to lock onto and receive a specific digital channel. Most notably, a company called Microtune has developed MicroTuner, the world's first single-chip, silicon-based broadband tuner. The company managed to take what was once a cumbersome, steel component technology of the 1950's and place it onto a single chip that offers an integrated, universal solution for high-speed media delivery over digital cable, satellite and terrestrial transmission. It has been engineered with patented techniques to solve the packed-spectrum challenges of today's DTV landscape. Microchips like these will enable reliable reception on the smallest of devices, such as a watch or miniature Sony Watchman.

The one issue that has clouded the DTV reception picture is the use of 8-VSB modulation as part of the ATSC's DTV standard in the U.S. There have been some tests that have shown that the COFDM modulation system (used in Europe and elsewhere around the world) does a better job of distributing a terrestrial signal to indoor antennas. Although there are advantages to both modulation schemes, it has become clear that until this issue is solved—either with the newer generation of VSB reception chips or with COFDM—consumers will not be eager to buy a digital set if it won't work in their neighborhood.

MEASURING SCREEN SIZE

We currently measure 4:3 TVs using a measure of the diagonal of the screen, but 16:9 TVs pose a problem in being able to compare image size when discussing the diagonal size of the screen. Typically, we may want to know how big of a 16:9 screen we need to match the height of a 4:3 screen (for the same height of screen, a 16:9 screen is 33 percent wider).

Above is the relationship of 4:3 screens to 16:9 screens and to 16:9 letterbox in a 4:3 raster, based on common screen height, as well as the three and six times viewing distance from the screen. (Fox Television uses a three picture height rule for 720-line work and a six picture height rule for 480-line work.)

Screen Height	5	6	7	8	9	10	11	12	13	14	15	16	17	18	19	20	21	22	23	24	25
4:3 diagonal	8	10	12	13	15	17	18	20	22	23	25	27	28	30	32	33	35	37	38	40	42
16:9 diagonal	10	12	14	16	18	20	22	24	27	29	31	33	35	37	39	41	43	45	47	49	51
4:3 letterbox (16:9 in 4:3 raster) diagonal	11	13	16	18	20	22	24	27	29	31	33	36	38	40	42	44	47	49	51	53	56
3 picture heights	1	2	2	2	2	3	3	3	3	4	4	4	4	5	5	5	5	6	6	6	6
6 picture heights	3	3	4	4	5	5	6	6	7	7	8	8	9	9	10	10	11	11	12	12	13
Screen Height	26	27	28	29	30	31	32	33	34	35	36	37	38	39	40	41	42	43	44	45	46
4:3 diagonal	43	45	47	48	50	52	53	55	57	58	60	62	63	65	67	68	70	72	73	75	77
16:9 diagonal	53	55	57	59	61	63	65	67	69	71	73	75	78	80	82	84	86	88	90	92	94
4:3 letterbox (16:9 in 4:3 raster) diagonal	58	60	62	64	67	69	71	73	76	78	80	82	84	87	89	91	93	96	98	100	102
3 picture heights	7	7	7	7	8	8	8	8	9	9	9	9	10	10	10	10	11	11	11	11	12
6 picture heights	13	14	14	15	15	16	16	17	17	18	18	19	19	20	20	21	21	22	22	23	23

Note: All numbers rounded to the nearest whole number

Chart: Fox Television

Comparison of 4:3 and 16:9 screen sizes.

CONNECTING TO THE FUTURE

The Consumer Electronics Association (CEA, formerly known as CEMA) had been proceeding with four technical solutions to link cable and other set-top boxes to DTV receivers. This issue has still not been decided and agreed on by the industry, although the 1394 ("FireWire") interface is favored by most parties involved. Once this standard is decided (which could be as early as Spring 2000, when FCC Chairman William Kennard has threatened to mandate specs), manufacturers will include a 1394 interface on most of the monitors they sell. Consumers who buy a DTV set in the future will be able to receive digital cable and use their DTV sets with other digital technologies, such as DBS, DVD players, digital VCRs and computers.

In February 2000, the National Cable Television Association (NCTA) and the CEA reached an agreement on two of four issues holding up cable reception over digital TVs: technical standards for direct connection of digital TVs to cable systems and on-screen program guides. Unresolved are disputes over licensing terms for copy protection technology and labeling of TV sets without two-way digital connections to other consumer devices. The Federal Communications Commission, which has been pressing both sides for months to resolve the DTV-cable compatibility dispute, praised the partial agreement but warned that it would still consider proposed rules for copy protection and labeling.

The biggest limiting factor to displaying true HDTV right now is the masking screens employed on CRT-based displays. These screens, that define a picture's color and sharpness but also limit the amount of light that is displayed, currently can only display about 700 to 800 lines of resolution. Thus, a person with a set that claims to display 1080 lines is not getting the full HDTV experience. This will change with time (and indeed is starting to) as technology improves and prices for components come down.

In the meantime, there's no doubting that when consumers see HDTV, they want it. They anticipate the day when their TV is more than just a TV; it will evolve into the center of a home network that's totally interconnected with the rest of the house. However, consumers also understand the costs involved and probably won't embrace DTV technology until it becomes affordable.

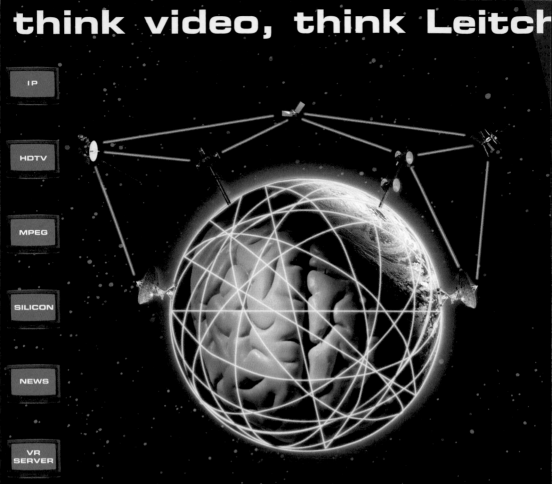

UNDERSTANDING DIGITAL 2

No one can say who first considered a base-two (binary) number system. The concept appeared in abu-Ja'far Mohammed ibn-Musa al-Khowarizmi's (an early-Ninth-Century mathematician in the court of Mamun in Baghdad) work, but it had certainly also been known to earlier thinkers. Long before the first electronic computer graphics or music devices, machines operating on binary mathematical principles created both graphics and music. One such music machine, an ancient form of an organ, was excavated at a Roman archeological site just north of Budapest.

It wasn't until the Twentieth Century, however, that binary mathematics was applied to the recording, transmission, or manipulation of sounds or pictures. The problem was largely technological. First, there wasn't even electronic sound (let alone pictures) to record, transmit, or manipulate until the end of the Nineteenth Century. Second, the circuitry required to digitize even a simple telephone call didn't exist until shortly before that feat was achieved in 1939 (analog-to-digital converters slowed things down; digitally generated speech and music predated the digitization of sound, just as computer graphics predated the digital video timebase corrector and international standards converter).

Scientists working on digital signals weren't even able to use today's common term for the little pieces of information they dealt with until 1948. In July of that year, in the Bell System Technical Journal, *Claude Shannon, considered by many the creator of information theory, credited J. W. Tukey with suggesting a contraction of the words* binary digit *into* bit. *But the word* digital *definitely comes from the Latin* digitus, *which means fingers and toes, making the first digital effects finger shadow puppets on a wall, and the first digital compression a squeezed finger or toe.*

—Mark Schubin

> *This chapter is divided into two sections—basic and advanced theory. Therefore, it can be read in three different ways—basic only, basic and advanced, and advanced only. Start where you think you need to based on your own knowledge, jumping ahead or back if you desire. Digital can be a tough subject, even if it is just ones and zeros.*

UNDERSTANDING DIGITAL: THE BASICS

MICHAEL SILBERGLEID

In order to understand digital, you must first understand that everything in nature, including the sounds and images you wish to record or transmit, was originally analog. The second thing you must understand is that analog works *very* well. In fact, because of what analog and digital are, a first-generation analog recording can be a better representation of the original images than a first-generation digital recording. This is because digital is a coded approximation of analog. With enough bandwidth, a first-generation analog VTR can record the more "perfect" copy.

Digital is a binary language represented by zeros (an "off" state) and ones (an "on" state). Because of this, the signal either exists (on) or does not exist (off). Even with low signal power, if the transmitted digital signal is higher that the background noise level, a perfect picture and sound can be obtained—on is on no matter what the signal strength.

THE LANGUAGE OF DIGITAL: BITS & BYTES

Bit is short for **B**inary dig**it** and is the smallest data unit in a digital system. A bit is a single one or zero. Typically 8-bits make up a byte (although byte "words" can be 10-bit, 16-bit, 24-bit, or 32-bit).

In an 8-bit system there are 256 discrete values. The mathematics is simple: It is the number two (as in binary) raised to the power of the number of bits. In this case $2^8=256$. A 10-bit system has 1,024 discrete values ($2^{10}=1,024$). Notice that each additional bit is a doubling of the number of discrete values.

Here's how this works, as each bit in the 8-bit word represents a distinct value:

$$
\begin{array}{ccccccccc}
1 & 1 & 1 & 1 & 1 & 1 & 1 & 1 \\
\times 128 & \times 64 & \times 32 & \times 16 & \times 8 & \times 4 & \times 2 & \times 1 \\
128 + & 64 + & 32 + & 16 + & 8 + & 4 + & 2 + & 1 & = 255
\end{array}
$$

While 11111111 is equivalent to 255, keep in mind that 00000000, which is equivalent to 0, is the first value, so there are 256 discrete values.

```
10100011 is equivalent to 163:

  1        0        1        0        0        0        1        1
 x128     x64      x32      x16      x8       x4       x2       x1
 128   +   0   +   32   +   0   +    0   +    0   +    2   +    1   =   163
```

The more bits, the more distinct the value. For example, a gray-scale can be represented by 1-bit which would give the scale two values ($2^1=2$): 0 or 1 (a gray-scale consisting of white and black). Increase the number of bits to two-bits and the gray-scale has four values ($2^2=4$): 0, 1, 2, and 3, where 0=0 percent white (black), 1=33 percent white, 2=67 percent white, and 3=100 percent white. As we increase the number of bits, we get more accurate with our gray-scale.

In digital video, black is not at value 0 and white is neither at value 255 for 8-bit nor 1,023 for 10-bit. To add some buffer space and to allow for "superblack" (which is at 0 IRE while regular black is at 7.5 IRE), black is at value 16 while white is at value 235 for 8-bit video. For 10-bit video, we basically multiply the 8-bit numbers by four, yielding black at a value of 64 and white at a value of 940.

Also keep in mind that while digital is an approximation of the analog world—the actual analog value is assigned to its closest digital value—human perception has a hard time recognizing the fact that it is being cheated. While very few expert observers might be able to tell that something didn't look right in 8-bit video, 10-bit video looks perfect to the human eye. But as you'll see in Chapter 4: Audio, human ears are not as forgiving as human eyes—in audio most of us require at least 16-bit resolution—while experts argue that 20-bit, or ultimately even 24-bit technology needs to become standard before we have recordings that match the sensitivity of human hearing.

DIGITIZING: ANALOG TO DIGITAL

To transform a signal from analog to digital, the analog signal must go through the processes of sampling and quantization. The better the sampling and quantization, the better the digital image will represent the analog image.

Sampling is how often a device (like an analog-to-digital converter) samples a signal. This is usually given in a figure like 48 kHz for audio and 13.5 MHz for video. It is usually at least twice the highest analog signal frequency (known as the *Nyquist criteria*). The official sampling standard for standard definition television is ITU-R 601 (short for ITU-R BT.601-2, also known as "601").

For television pictures, eight or 10-bits are normally used; for sound, 16 or 20-bits are common, and 24-bits are being introduced. The ITU-R 601 standard defines the sampling of video components based on 13.5 MHz, and AES/EBU defines sampling of 44.1 and 48 kHz for audio.

Quantization can occur either before or after the signal has been sampled, but usually after. It is how many levels (bits per sample) the analog signal will have to force itself into. As noted earlier, a 10-bit signal has more levels (resolution) than an 8-bit signal.

Errors occur because quantizing a signal results in a digital approximation of that signal.

WHEN THINGS GO WRONG: THE LSB & MSB

Things always go wrong. Just how wrong is determined by when that "wrong-ness" occurred and the length of time of that "wrongness."

Let's take an 8-bit byte as an example:

10100011 is equivalent to 163

MSB							LSB
1	0	1	0	0	0	1	1
x128	x64	x32	x16	x8	x4	x2	x1
128 +	0 +	32 +	0 +	0 +	0 +	2 +	1 = 163

The "1" on the far right that represents the value 1 is called the least significant bit (LSB). If there is an error that changes this bit from "1" (on) to "0" (off), the value of the byte changes from 163 to 162—a very minor difference. But the error increases as problems occur with bits more towards the left.

The "1" on the left that represents the value 128 is called the most significant bit (MSB). An error that changes this bit from "1" (on) to "0" (off) changes the value of the byte from 163 to 35—a very major difference. If this represented our gray-scale, our sample has changed from 64 percent white to only 14 percent white.

An error can last short enough to not even affect one bit, or long enough to affect a number of bits, entire bytes, or even seconds of video and audio.

If our error from above lasted in duration the amount of time to transmit two bits, the error can be anywhere from minor (if it is the LSB and the bit to its left) to major (if it is the MSB and the bit to its right).

Where and how long errors occur is anyone's guess, but as you'll see below in Error Management, digital gives us a way to handle large errors invisibly to the viewer.

A WORD ABOUT RATIOS OR WHERE DID ALL THOSE NUMBERS COME FROM?

GLEN PENSINGER

Ratios such as 4:2:2 and 4:1:1 are an accepted part of the jargon of digital video, a shorthand taken for granted and sometimes not adequately explained.

With single-channel, composite signals such as NTSC and PAL, digital sampling rates are synchronized at either two, three, or four times the subcarrier frequency. The shorthand for these rates is 2fsc, 3fsc, and 4fsc, respectively.

With three-channel, component signals, the sampling shorthand becomes a ratio. The first number usually refers to the sampling rate used for the luminance signal, while the second and third numbers refer to the rates for the red and blue color-difference signals.

A 14:7:7 system would be one in which a wideband luminance signal is sampled at 14 MHz and the narrower bandwidth color-difference signals are each sampled at 7 MHz.

As work on component digital systems evolved, the shorthand changed. At first, 4:2:2 referred to sampling luminance at 4fsc (about 14.3 MHz for NTSC) and color-difference at half that rate, or 2fsc.

Sampling schemes based on multiples of NTSC or PAL subcarrier frequency were soon abandoned in favor of a single sampling standard for both 525- and 625-line component systems. Nevertheless, the 4:2:2 shorthand remained.

In current usage, "4" usually represents the internationally agreed upon sampling frequency of 13.5 MHz. Other numbers represent corresponding fractions of that frequency.

A 4:1:1 ratio describes a system with luminance sampled at 13.5 MHz and color-difference signals sampled at 3.375 MHz. A 4:4:4:4 ratio describes equal sampling rates for luminance and color difference channels as well as a fourth, alpha key signal channel. A 2:1:1 ratio describes a narrowband system that might be suitable for consumer use and so on.

The shorthand continues to evolve. Contrary to what you might expect from the discussion above, the 4:2:0 ratio frequently seen in discussions on MPEG compression does not indicate a system without a blue color-difference component. Here, the shorthand describes a video stream in which there are only two color difference samples (one red, one blue) for every four luminance samples. Unlike 4:1:1, however, the samples in 525 line systems don't come from the same line as luminance, but are averaged from two adjacent lines in the field. The idea was to provide a more even and averaged distribution of the reduced color information over the picture.

(See Chapter 3: Pre-Production, for a comparison of resolutions for different videotape and disk formats.)

VIDEO COMPRESSION

GLEN PENSINGER

S ome people say that compressing video is a little like making orange juice concentrate or freeze-dried back-packing food. You throw something away (like water) that you think you can replace later. In doing so, you gain significant advantages in storage and transportation and you accept the food-like result because it's priced right and good enough for the application. Unfortunately, while orange juice molecules are all the same, the pixels used in digital video might all be different.

Video compression is more like an ad that used to appear in the New York City subway which said something like: "If u cn rd ths, u cn get a gd pying jb" or personalized license plates that don't use vowels (nmbr-1). You understand what the message is

DTV IN THE REAL WORLD

UNDERSTANDING DIGITAL

PRE-PRODUCTION

PRODUCTION

AUDIO

GRAPHIC & COMPOSITING

POST PRODUCTION

DELIVERY & DUPLICATION

ENGINEERING & TRANSMISSION

APPENDIX

GLOSSARY

without having to receive the entire message—your brain acts as a decoder. Email is taking on this characteristic with words such as l8r (later) and ltns (long time no see).

WHY COMPRESS?

There is a quip making the rounds that proclaims "compression has never been shown to improve video quality." It's popular with folks who think compression is a bad compromise. If storage costs are dropping and communication bandwidth is rapidly increasing, they reason, why would we want to bother with anything less than "real" video? Surely compression will fall by the wayside once we've reached digital perfection.

Other people, like Avid Technology VP Eric Peters, contend that compression is integral to the very nature of media. The word "media," he points out, comes from the fact that a technology, a medium, stands between the originator and the recipient of a message. Frequently that message is a representation of the real world. But no matter how much bandwidth we have, we will never be able to transmit all of the richness of reality. There is, he argues, much more detail in any source than can possibly be communicated. Unless the message is very simple, our representation of it will always be an imperfect reduction of the original. Even as we near the limits of our senses (as we may have with frequency response in digital sound) we still find there is a long way to go. People perceive many spatial and other subtle clues in the real world that are distorted or lost in even the best digital stereo recordings.

Furthermore, the notion of quality in any medium is inherently a moving target. We've added color and stereo sound to television. Just as we start to get a handle on compressing standard definition signals, high definition and widescreen loom on the horizon. There will never be enough bandwidth. There is even a Super High Definition format that is 2048x2048 pixels—14 times as large as NTSC.

Perhaps former Tektronix design engineer Bruce Penny countered the quip best when he said, "Compression does improve picture quality. It improves the picture you can achieve in the bandwidth you have."

COMPRESSION BASICS

Compression comes in a number of flavors, each tailored for a specific application or set of applications. An understanding of the compression process will help you decide which compression method or group of methods are right for you.

COMPRESSION RATIO

The essence of all compression is throwing data away. The effectiveness of a compression scheme is indicated by its "compression ratio," which is determined by dividing the amount of data you started with by what's left when you're through.

Assuming a high definition camera spits out around one billion video bits a second, and this is ultimately reduced to something around 18 million bits for broadcast in the ATSC system, the compression ratio is roughly 55:1.

However, don't put too much stock in compression ratios alone. On a scale of meaningful measures, they rank down somewhere with promised savings on long distance phone calls. To interpret a compression ratio, you need to know what the starting point was.

For a compression system that puts out a 25 megabit per second (Mbps) video stream, the compression ratio would be about 8.5:1 if the starting point was 485x740 pixels, 4:2:2, 10-bit sampled, 30 frames per second (fps) pictures. If, however, the starting video was 480x640, 4:1:1, 8-bit, 30 fps, the ratio would be about 4.5:1.

LOSSLESS VERSUS LOSSY

There are two general types of compression algorithms: lossless and lossy. As the name suggests, a lossless algorithm gives back the original data bit-for-bit on decompression.

One common lossless technique is "run length encoding," in which long runs of the same data value are compressed by transmitting a prearranged code for "string of ones" or "string of zeros" followed by a number for the length of the string.

Another lossless scheme is similar to Morse Code, where the most frequently occurring letters have the shortest codes. Huffman or entropy coding computes the probability that certain data values will occur and then assigns short codes to those with the highest probability and longer codes to the ones that don't show up very often. Everyday examples of lossless compression can be found in the Macintosh Stuffit program and WinZip for Windows.

Lossless processes can be applied safely to your checkbook accounting program, but their compression ratios are usually low—on the order of 2:1. In practice these ratios are unpredictable and depend heavily on the type of data in the files.

Alas, pictures are not as predictable as text and bank records, and lossless techniques have only limited effectiveness with video. Work continues on lossless video compression. Increased processing power and new algorithms may eventually make it practical, but for now, virtually all video compression is lossy.

Lossy video compression systems use lossless techniques where they can, but the really big savings come from throwing things away. To do this, the image is processed or "transformed" into two groups of data. One group will, ideally, contain all the important information. The other gets all the unimportant information. Only the important stuff needs to be kept and transmitted.

PERCEPTUAL CODING

Lossy compression systems take the performance of our eyes into account as they decide what information to place in the important pile and which to discard in the unimportant pile. They throw away things the eye doesn't notice or won't be too upset about losing.

Since our perception of fine color details is limited, chroma resolution can be reduced by factors of two, four, eight or more, depending on the application.

Lossy schemes also exploit our lessened ability to see detail immediately after a picture change, on the diagonal or in moving objects. Unfortunately, the latter doesn't yield as much of a savings as one might first think, because we often track moving objects on a screen with our eyes.

PREDICTIVE CODING

Video compression also relies heavily on the correlation between adjacent picture elements. If television pictures consisted entirely of randomly valued pixels (noise), compression wouldn't be possible (some music video producers and directors are going to find this out the hard way—as encoders lock-up). Fortunately, adjoining picture elements are a lot like the weather. Tomorrow's weather is very likely to be just like today's, and odds are that nearby pixels in the same or adjacent fields and frames are more likely to be the same than they are to be different.

Predictive coding relies on making an estimate of the value of the current pixel based on previous values for that location and other neighboring areas. The rules of the estimating game are stored in the decoder and, for any new pixel, the encoder need only send the difference or error value between what the rules would have predicted and the actual value of the new element. The more accurate the prediction, the less data needs to be sent.

MOTION COMPENSATION

The motion of objects or the camera from one frame to the next complicates predictive coding, but it also opens up new compression possibilities. Fortunately, moving objects in the real world are somewhat predictable. They tend to move with inertia and in a continuous fashion. In MPEG, where picture elements are processed in blocks, you can save quite a few bits if you can predict how a given block of pixels has moved from one frame to the next. By sending commands (motion vectors) that simply tell the decoder how to move a block of pixels already in its memory, you avoid resending all the data associated with that block.

INTER- VERSUS INTRA-FRAME COMPRESSION

As long as compressed pictures are only going to be transmitted and viewed, compression encoders can assign lots of bits into the unimportant pile by exploiting the redundancy in successive frames. It's called "inter-frame" coding.

If, on the other hand, the video is destined to undergo further processing such as enlargement, rotation and/or chromakey, some of those otherwise unimportant details may suddenly become important, and it may be necessary to spend more bits to accommodate what post production equipment can "see."

To facilitate editing and other post processing, compression schemes intended for post usually confine their efforts within a single frame and are called "intra-frame." It takes more bits, but it's worth it.

The Ampex DCT videocassette format, Digital Betacam, D9 (formerly Digital-S), DVCPRO50, and various implementations of Motion-JPEG are examples of post production gear using intra-frame compression. The MPEG 4:2:2 Profile can also be implemented in an intra-frame fashion.

SYMMETRICAL VERSUS ASYMMETRICAL

Compression systems are described as symmetrical if the complexity (and therefore cost) of their encoders and decoders are similar. This is usually the case with recording and professional point-to-point transmission systems. With point-to-multipoint transmission applications, such as broadcasting or mass program distribution where there are few encoders but millions of decoders, an asymmetrical design may be desirable. By increasing complexity in the encoder, you may be able to significantly reduce complexity in the decoders and thus reduce the cost of the consumer reception or playback device.

TRANSFORMS

Transforms manipulate image data in ways that make it easier to separate the important from the unimportant. Three types are currently used for video compression: Wavelets, Fractals, and the Discrete Cosine Transform or DCT.

Wavelets—The Wavelet transform employs a succession of mathematical operations that can be thought of as filters that decompose an image into a series of frequency bands. Each band can then be treated differently depending on its visual impact. Since the most visually important information is typically concentrated in the lowest frequencies in the image or in a particular band, they can be coded with more bits than the higher ones. For a given application, data can be reduced by selecting how many bands will be transmitted, how coarsely each will be coded and how much error protection each will receive.

The wavelet technique has advantages in that it is computationally simpler than DCT and easily scalable. The same compressed data file can be scaled to different compression ratios simply by discarding some of it prior to transmission.

The study of wavelets has lagged about 10 years behind that of DTC, but it is now the subject of intensive research and development. A Wavelet algorithm has been chosen for coding still images and textures in MPEG-4, and another is the basis for the new JPEG-2000 still image standard for which final approval is expected in 2001 (ISO 15444). More applications are likely in the future.

Fractals—The fractal transform is also an intra-frame method. It is based on a set of two dimensional patterns discovered by Benoit Mandelbrot at IBM. The idea is that

figure 1. Fractal patterning.

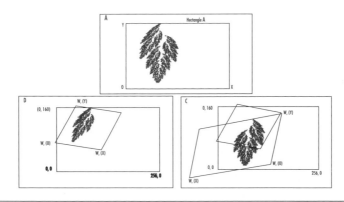

you can recreate any image simply by selecting patterns from the set and then appropriately sizing, rotating and fitting them into the frame (see figure 1). Rather than transmitting all the data necessary to recreate an image, a fractal coder relies on the pattern set stored in the decoder and sends only information on which patterns to use and how to size and position them.

The fractal transform can achieve very high compression ratios and is used extensively for sending images on the Internet. Unfortunately, the process of analyzing original images requires so much computing power that fractals aren't feasible for realtime video. The technique also has difficulties with hard-edged artificial shapes such as character graphics and buildings. It works best with natural objects like leaves, faces and landscapes.

DCT—The discrete cosine transform is by far the most used transform in video compression. It's found in both intra-frame and inter-frame systems, and it's the basis for JPEG, MPEG, DV and the H.xxx videoconferencing standards.

Like wavelets, DCT is based on the theory that the eye is most sensitive to certain two-dimensional frequencies in an image and much less sensitive to others.

With DCT, the picture is divided into small blocks, usually 8 pixels by 8 pixels. The DCT algorithm converts the 64 values that represent the amplitude of each of the pixels in a block into 64 new values (coefficients) that represent how much of each of the 64 frequencies are present.

At this point, no compression has taken place. We've traded one batch of 64 numbers for another and we can losslessly reverse the process and get back to our amplitude numbers if we choose—all we did was call those numbers something else.

Since most of the information in a scene is concentrated in a few of the lower-frequency coefficients, there will be a large number of coefficients that have a zero value or are very close to zero. These can be rounded off to zero with little visual effect when pixel values are reconstituted by an inverse DCT process in the decoder.

THE IMPORTANCE OF STANDARDS

The almost universal popularity of DCT illustrates the power of a standard. DCT may not be the best transform, but once a standard (either de facto or de jure) is in wide use, it will be around for a long time. Both equipment-makers and their customers need stability in the technologies they use, mainly so they can reap the benefits of their investments. The presence of a widely accepted standard provides that stability and raises the performance bar for other technologies that would like to compete. To displace an accepted standard, the competitor can't just be better, it must be several orders of magnitude better (and less expensive won't hurt either).

The incorporation of DCT techniques in the JPEG and MPEG standards and subsequent investment in and deployment of DCT–based compression systems have ensured its dominance in the compression field for a long time to come.

M-JPEG—JPEG, named for the Joint Photographic Experts Group, was developed as a standard for compressing still photographic images. Since JPEG chips were readily available before other compression chip sets, designers who wanted to squeeze moving pictures into products such as computer-based nonlinear editing systems adapted the JPEG standard to compress strings of video frames. Motion-JPEG was born.

Unfortunately, the JPEG standard had no provision for storing the data related to motion, and designers developed their own proprietary ways of dealing with it. Consequently, it's often difficult to exchange M-JPEG files between systems.

Not long after the JPEG committee demonstrated success with still images, the Motion Picture Experts Group (MPEG) and DV standardization committees developed compression standards specifically for moving images. The trend has been for these newer motion standards to replace proprietary M-JPEG approaches.

A new JPEG-2000 still image standard using wavelet compression is being finalized. An extension of this standard (expected in 2001) may include a place to store data specifying the order and speed at which JPEG-2000 frames can be sequenced for display. This feature is designed to accommodate rapid sequence, digital still cameras and is not intended to compete with MPEG, however, it's conceivable that a new, standardized motion JPEG could emerge.

DV—The DV compression format was developed by a consortium of more than 50 equipment manufacturers as a consumer digital video cassette recording format (DVC) for both standard and high definition home recording. It is an intra-frame, DCT-based, symmetrical system.

Although designed originally for home use, the inexpensive DV compression engine chip set (which can function as either encoder or decoder) has proved itself versatile enough to form the basis for a number of professional products including D9, DVCAM and DVCPRO. Both D9 and DVCPRO have taken advantage of the chipset's scalability to increase quality beyond that available in the consumer product.

At 25 Mbps, the consumer compression ratio is about 5:1 with 4:1:1 color sampling. D9 and DVCPRO50 use two of the mass-market compression circuits running in parallel to achieve a 3.3:1 compression ratio with 4:2:2 color sampling at 50 Mbps. DVCPROHD and D9HD (scheduled to debut in 2000) are technically capable of recording progressive scan standard definition or interlaced and progressive HDTV at 100 Mbps. Similar extensions are possible beyond 100 Mbps and DV compression is not limited to video cassette recording, but can be applied to a range of compressed digital video storage and transmission applications.

MPEG—MPEG has become the 800–pound gorilla of compression techniques. It is the accepted compression scheme for all sorts of new products and services, from satellite broadcasting to DVD to the new ATSC digital television transmission standard, which includes HDTV.

MPEG is an asymmetrical, DCT compression scheme which makes use of both intra- and inter-frame, motion compensated techniques.

One of the important things to note about MPEG is that it's not the kind of rigidly defined, single entity we've been used to with NTSC or PAL, or the ITU-R 601 digital component standard.

MPEG only defines bit streams and how those streams are to be recognized by decoders and reconstituted into video, audio and other usable information. How the MPEG bit streams are encoded is undefined and left open for continuous innovation and improvement.

You'll notice we've been referring to MPEG bit streams in the plural. MPEG isn't a single standard, but rather a collection of standardized compression tools that can be combined as needs dictate. MPEG-1 provided a set of tools designed to record video on CDs at a data rate around 1.5 Mbps. While that work was underway, researchers recognized that similar compression techniques would be useful in all sorts of other applications.

The MPEG-2 committee was formed to expand the idea. They understood that a universal compression system capable of meeting the requirements of every application was an unrealistic goal. Not every use needed or could afford all the compression tools that were available. The solution was to provide a series of Profiles and Levels (see figure 2) with an arranged degree of commonality and compatibility between them.

LEVELS		SIMPLE	MAIN	4:2:2	SNR SCALABLE	SPATIAL SCALABLE	HIGH
	HIGH		4:2:0 1920 x 1152 80 Mbps I, P, B				4:2:0, 4:2:2 1920 x 1152 100 Mbps I, P, B
	HIGH-1440		4:2:0 1440 x 1152 60 Mbps I, P, B			4:2:0 1440 x 1152 60 Mbps I, P, B	4:2:0, 4:2:2 1440 x 1152 80 Mbps I, P, B
	MAIN	4:2:0 720 x 576 15 Mbps I, P	4:2:0 720 x 576 15 Mbps I, P, B	4:2:2 720 x 608 15 Mbps I, P, B	4:2:0 720 x 576 15 Mbps I, P, B		4:2:0, 4:2:2 720 x 576 20 Mbps I, P, B
	LOW		4:2:0 352 x 288 4 Mbps I, P, B		4:2:0 352 x 288 4 Mbps I, P, B		

PROFILES

figure 2. MPEG-2 Profiles and Levels.

Profiles And Levels—The six MPEG-2 Profiles gather together different sets of compression tools into toolkits for different applications. The Levels accommodate four different grades of input video ranging from a limited definition similar to today's consumer equipment all the way to high definition.

Though they organized the options better, the levels and profiles still provided too many possible combinations to be practical. So, the choices were further constrained to specific "compliance points" within the overall matrix. So far, 12 compliance points have been defined ranging from the Simple Profile at Main Level (SP@ML) to the High Profile at High Level (HP@HL). The Main Profile at Main Level (MP@ML) is supposed to approximate today's broadcast video quality.

Any decoder that is certified at a given compliance point must be able to recognize and decode not only that point's set of tools and video resolutions, but also the tools and resolutions used at other compliance points below it and to the left. Therefore, an MP@ML decoder must also decode SP@ML and MP@LL. Likewise, a compliant MP@HL decoder would have to decode MP@H14L (a compromise 1440x1080 pixel HDTV format), MP@ML, MP@LL and SP@ML.

As with MP@H14L, not all of the defined compliance points have found practical use. By far the most common is MP@ML. The proposed broadcast HDTV systems fall within the MP@HL point.

Group Of Pictures—MPEG achieves both good quality and high compression ratios at least in part through its unique frame structure referred to as the "Group of Pictures" or Gop (see figure 3). Three types of frames are employed: 1) intra-coded or "I" frames; 2) predicted "P" frames which are forecast from the previous I or P frame; and 3) "B" frames, which are predicted bidirectionally from both the previous and succeeding I or P frames. A GoP may consist of a single I frame, an I frame followed by a number of P frames, or an I frame followed by a mixture of B and P frames. A GoP ends when the next I frame comes along and starts a new GoP.

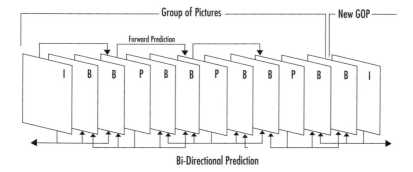

figure 3. MPEG-2 Group of pictures showing I, P, and B frame relationships.

All the information necessary to reconstruct a single frame of video is contained in an I frame. It uses the most bits and can be decoded on its own without reference to any other frames. There is a limit to the number of frames that can be predicted from another. The inevitable transmission errors and small prediction errors will add up and eventually become intolerable. The arrival of a new I frame refreshes the process, terminates any accumulated errors and allows a new string of predictions to begin.

P frames require far fewer bits because they are predicted from the previous I frame. They depend on the decoder having the I frame in memory for reference.

Even fewer bits are needed for B frames because they are predicted from both the preceding and following I or P frames, both of which must be in memory in the decoder. The bidirectional prediction of B frames not only saves lots of bits, it also makes it possible to simulate VCR search modes.

The Simple Profile does not include B frames in its toolkit, thus reducing memory requirements and cost in the decoder. All other profiles include B frames as a possibility. As with all MPEG tools, the use, number and order of I, B and P frames is up to the designer of the encoder. The only requirement is that a compliant decoder be able to recognize and decode them if they are used.

In practice, other standards that incorporate MPEG such as DVB and ATSC may place further constraints on the possibilities within a particular MPEG compliance point to lower the cost of consumer products.

COMPRESSION RATIO VERSUS PICTURE QUALITY

Because of its unique and flexible arrangement of I, P and B frames, there is little correlation between compression ratio and picture quality in MPEG. High quality can be achieved at low bit rates with a long GoP (usually on the order of 12 to 16 frames). Conversely, the same bit rate with a shorter GoP and/or no B frames will produce a lower quality image.

Knowing only one or two parameters is never enough when you're trying to guess the relative performance of two different flavors of MPEG.

4:2:2 PROFILE

As MPEG-2 field experience began to accumulate, it became apparent that, while MP@ML was very good for distributing video, it had shortcomings for post production. The 720x480 and 720x526 sampling structures defined for the Main Level ignored the fact that there are usually 486 active picture lines in 525-line NTSC video and 575 in 625-line PAL.

With the possible exception of cut transitions and limited overlays, lossy compressed video cannot be post-processed (resized, zoomed, rotated) in its compressed state. It must first be decoded to some baseband form such as ITU-R 601. Without specialized decoders and encoders designed to exchange information about previous compression operations, the quality of MP@ML deteriorates rapidly when its 4:2:0 color sampling structure is repeatedly decoded and re-encoded during post production.

Long GoPs, with each frame heavily dependent on others in the group, make editing complex and difficult. And, the MP@ML 15 Mbps upper data rate limit makes it impossible to achieve good quality with a short GoP of one or two frames.

Alternative intra-frame compression techniques such as DV and Motion-JPEG were available. But many people thought that if the MPEG MP@ML shortcomings could be corrected, the basic MPEG tools would be very useful for compressing contribution-quality video down to bit rates compatible with standard telecom circuits and inexpensive disk stores. And so they created a new Profile.

As its name suggests, the 4:2:2 Profile (422P@ML) uses 4:2:2 color sampling which more readily survives re-encoding. The maximum number of video lines is raised to 608. And the maximum data rate is increased to 50 Mbps.

Noting the success of the new profile for standard definition images, the Society of Motion Picture and Television Engineers used MPEG's 422P@ML as a foundation for SMPTE-308M, a compression standard for contribution quality high definition. It uses the MPEG tools and syntax to compress HDTV at data rates up to 300 Mbps.

SMPTE submitted 308M to MPEG to help guide their work on a high level version of 422P. The documents for MPEG 422P@HL have been completed. The two standards are independent, but fully interoperable. The principal difference is that SMPTE 308M specifies an encoder constraint, requiring a staircase relationship between GoP and bitrate. Longer GoPs are permitted only at lower bitrates. MPEG places no restrictions on encoders and any combination of bitrate and GoP is permissible.

MPEG-4

With work on MPEG-1 and MPEG-2 complete, the Experts Group turned its attention to the problems posed by interactive multimedia creation and distribution. MPEG-4 is the result. It is not intended to replace MPEG 1 or 2, but, rather, builds on them to foster interactivity. Like MPEG-2, it is a collection of tools that can be grouped into profiles and levels for different applications. Version one of the MPEG-4 standard is already complete, and the ink is drying fast on version two.

In committee jargon, MPEG-4 provides a Delivery Multimedia Integration Framework (DMIF) for "universal access" and "content-based interactivity." Translated, that means the new toolkit will let multimedia authors and users store, access, manipulate and present audio/visual data in ways that suit their individual needs at the moment, without concern for the underlying technicalities.

It's a tall order. If accepted in practice, MPEG-4 could resolve the potentially unmanageable tangle of proprietary approaches we've seen for audio and video coding in computing, on the internet and in emerging wireless multimedia applications. Toward that end, it borrows from videoconferencing standards and expands on the previous MPEG work to enhance performance in low bitrate environments and provide the tools necessary for interactivity and intellectual property management.

What really sets MPEG-4 apart are its tools for interactivity. Central to these is the ability to separately code visual and aural "objects." Not only does it code conventional rectangular images and mono or multi-channel sound, but it has an extended set of tools to code separate audio objects and arbitrarily shaped video objects.

A news anchor might be coded separately from the static background set. Game pieces can be coded independently from their backgrounds. Sounds can be interactively located in space. Once video, graphic, text or audio objects have been discretely coded, users can interact with them individually. Objects can be added and subtracted, moved around and re-sized within the scene.

All these features are organized by a DIMF that manages the multiple data streams, two-way communication and control necessary for interaction.

Both real and synthetic objects are supported. There are MPEG-4 tools for coding 2D and 3D animations and mapping synthetic and/or real textures onto them.

DTV IN THE REAL WORLD

UNDERSTANDING DIGITAL

PRE-PRODUCTION

PRODUCTION

AUDIO

GRAPHIC & COMPOSITING

POST PRODUCTION

DELIVERY & DUPLICATION

ENGINEERING & TRANSMISSION

APPENDIX

GLOSSARY

Special tools facilitate facial and body animation. Elsewhere in the toolkit are methods for text-to-speech conversion and several levels of synthesized sound.

A coordinate system is provided to position objects in relation to each other, their backgrounds and the viewer/listener. MPEG-4's scene composition capabilities have been heavily influenced by prior work done in the Internet community on the Virtual Reality Modeling Language (VRML), and there is formal coordination between MPEG and the Web3d Consortium to insure that VRML and MPEG-4 evolve in a consistent manner.

Unlike VRML, which relies on text-based instructions, MPEG- 4's scene description language, Binary Format for Scenes (BIFS), is designed for real-time streaming. Its binary code is 10 to 15 times more compact than VRML's, and images can be constructed on the fly without waiting for the full scene to download.

Coding and manipulating arbitrarily shaped objects is one thing. Extracting them from natural scenes is quite another. Thus far, MPEG-4 demonstrations have depended on chromakey and a lot of hand work.

In version 2, programming capabilities will be added with MPEG-J, a subset of the Java programming language. Java interfaces to MPEG-4 objects will allow decoders to intelligently and automatically scale content to fit their particular capabilities.

The standard supports scalability in many ways. Less important objects can be omitted or transmitted with less error protection. Visual and aural objects can be created with a simple layer that contains enough basic information for low resolution decoders and one or more enhancement layers that, when added to that base layer, provide more resolution, wider frequency range, surround sound or 3D.

MPEG-4's basic transform is still DCT and quite similar to MPEG 1 and 2, but improvements have been made in coding efficiency and transmission ruggedness. A wavelet algorithm is included for efficient coding of textures and still images. MPEG-4 coding starts with a Very Low Bitrate Video (VLBV) core, which includes algorithms and tools for data rates between 5 kbps and 64 kbps. To make things work at these very low bit rates, motion compensation, error correction and concealment have been improved, refresh rates are kept low (between 0 and 15 fps) and resolution ranges from a few pixels per line up to CIF (352x288).

MPEG-4 doesn't concern itself directly with the error protection needed in specific channels such as cellular radio, but it has made improvements in the way payload bits are arranged so that recovery will be more robust. There are more frequent resynchronization markers. New, reversible variable length codes can be read forward or backward like a palindrome so decoders can recover all the data between an error and the next sync marker.

For better channels (something between 64 kbps and 2 Mbps), a High Bitrate Video (HBV) mode supports resolutions and frame rates up to Rec.601. The tools and algorithms are essentially the same as VLBV, plus a few additional ones to handle interlaced sources.

While MPEG-4 has many obvious advantages for interactive media production and dissemination, it's not clear what effect it will have on conventional video broadcasting and distribution. MPEG-2 standards are well established in these areas. For the advanced functions, both MPEG-4 encoders and decoders will be more complex and, presumably, more expensive than those for MPEG-1 and 2. However, the Studio Profile of MPEG-4 is expected to have an impact on high-end, high-resolution production for film and video.

MPEG-4 STUDIO PROFILE

At first glance, MPEG-4's bandwidth efficiency, interactivity and synthetic coding seem to have little to do with high resolution, high performance studio imaging. The MPEG-4 committee structure did, however, provide a venue for interested companies and individuals to address some of the problems of high-end image compression.

When you consider realtime electronic manipulation of high resolution moving images, the baseband numbers are enormous. A 4000 pixel by 4000 pixel, 4:4:4, YUV/RGB, 10-bit, 24 fps image with a key channel requires a data rate in excess of 16 Gbps. Even the current HDTV goal (just out of reach) of 1920x1080 pixels, 60 progressive frames and 4:2:2, 10-bit sampling requires just under 2.5 Gbps. Upgrade that to 4:4:4 RGB, add a key channel and you're up to about 5 Gbps. It's easy to see why standards for compressing this stuff might be useful.

The MPEG-4 committee was receptive to the idea of a Studio Profile, and their structure provided an opportunity to break the MPEG-2 upper limits of 8-bit sampling and 100 Mbps data rate. The project gathered momentum as numerous participants from throughout the imaging community joined in the work. Final standards documents are expected by the end of 2000.

A look at the accompanying table shows three levels in the proposed new profile. Compressed data rates range between 300 Mbps and 2.5 Gbps. With the exception of 10-bit sampling, the Low Level is compatible with and roughly equivalent to the current MPEG-2 Studio Profile at High Level.

The Main Level accommodates up to 60 frames progressive, 4:4:4 sampling, and 2048x2048 pixels. The High Level pushes things to 12-bit sampling, 4096x4096 pixels and up to 120 frames per second. The draft standard is expected to include provisions for key channels, although the number of bits for them were still in question as of this writing.

Although you can't have everything at once (a 12-bit, 120 fps, 4:4:4:4, 4096x4096 image isn't in the cards), within a level's compressed data rate limitations, you can trade resolution, frame rate, quantizing and sampling strategies to accomplish the task at hand.

Like all MPEG standards, this one defines a bitstream syntax and sets parameters for decoder performance. For instance, a compliant High Level decoder could reproduce a 4096x4096 image at 24 frames per second or a 1920x1080 one at 120 fps. At the Main Level, a 1920x1080 image could have as many as 60 fames per second where a 2048x2048 one would be limited to a maximum of 30 fps.

As a part of MPEG-4, the Studio Profile could use all the scene composition and interactive tools that are included in the lower profiles. But high-end production already has a large number of sophisticated tools for image composition and manipulation, and it's not clear how or if similar components of the MPEG-4 toolkit will be applied to the Studio Profile.

One side benefit of a Studio Profile in the MPEG-4 standard is that basic elements such as colorimetry, macroblock alignments and other parameters will be maintained all the way up and down the chain. That should help maintain quality as the material passes from the highest levels of production all the way down to those Dick Tracy wrist receivers.

THE OTHER MPEGs

MPEG 7 and 21 are, thankfully, not new compression standards, but rather attempts to manage motion imaging and multimedia technology.

MPEG-7 is described as a Multimedia Content Description Interface (MCDI). It's an attempt to provide a standard means of describing multimedia content. Its quest is to build a standard set of descriptors, description schemes and a standardized language that can be used to describe multimedia information. Unlike today's text-based approaches, such a language might let you search for scenes by the colors and textures they contain or the action that occurs in them. You could play a few notes on a keyboard or enter a sample of a singer's voice and get back a list of similar musical pieces and performances.

If the MPEG-7 committee is successful, search engines will have at least a fighting chance of finding the needles we want in the haystack of audio visual material we're creating. A completed standard is expected in September 2000.

MPEG-21 is the Group's attempt to get a handle on the overall topic of content delivery. By defining a Multimedia Framework from the viewpoint of the consumer, they hope to understand how various components relate to each other and where gaps in the infrastructure might benefit from new standards.

The subjects being investigated overlap and interact. There are network issues like speed, reliability, delay, cost performance and so on. Content quality issues include things such as authenticity (is it what it pretends to be?) and timeliness (can you have it when you want it?), as well as technical and artistic attributes.

Ease of use, payment models, search techniques and storage options are all part of the study, as are the areas of consumer rights and privacy. What rights do consumers have to use, copy and pass on content to others? Can they understand those rights? How will consumers protect personal data and can they negotiate privacy with content providers? A technical report on the MPEG-21 framework is scheduled for mid-2000.

THE MISSING MPEGs

Since we've discussed MPEG 1, 2, 4, 7 and 21, you might wonder what happened to 3, 5, 6 and the rest of the numbers. MPEG-3 was going to be the standard for HDTV. But early on, it became obvious that MPEG-2 would be capable of handling high definition and MPEG-3 was scrapped.

When it came time to pick a number for some new work to follow MPEG-4, there was much speculation about what it would be. (Numbering discussions in standards work are like debates about table shape in diplomacy. They give you something to do while you're trying to get a handle on the serious business.) With one, two and four already in the works, the MPEG folks were on their way to a nice binary sequence. Should the next one be eight, or should it just be five? In the end, they threw logic to the winds and called it seven. Don't even ask where 21 came from (the century perhaps?).

SOME FINAL THOUGHTS

Use clean sources. Compression systems work best with clean source material. Noisy signals, film grain, poorly decoded composite video—all give poor results. Preprocessing that reduces noise, shapes the video bandwidth and corrects other problems can improve compression results, but the best bet is a clean source to begin with. Noisy and degraded images can require a premium of 20 to 50 percent more bits.

Milder is better. Video compression has always been with us. (Interlace is a compression technique. 4:2:2 color sampling is a compression technique.) It will always be with us. Nonetheless, you should choose the mildest compression you can afford in any application, particularly in post production where video will go through multiple processing generations.

Compression schemes using low bit rates and extensive inter-frame processing are best suited to final program distribution.

More is better. Despite the fact that there is only a tenuous relationship between data rate and picture quality, more bits are usually better. Lab results suggest that if you acquire material at a low rate such as 25 Mbps and you'll be posting it on a non-linear system using the same type of compression, the multigeneration performance will be much better if your posting data rate is higher, say 50 Mbps, than if you stay at the 25 Mbps rate.

Avoid compression cascades. When compressed video is decoded, small errors in the form of unwanted high frequencies are introduced where no high frequencies were present in the original. If that video is re-encoded without processing (level changes, zooming, rotation, repositioning) and with the same compression scheme, the coding will usually mask these errors and the effect will be minimal. But if the video is processed or re-encoded with a different compression scheme, those high frequencies end up in new locations and the coding system will treat them as new information. The result is an additional loss in quality roughly equal to that experienced when the video was first compressed. Re-coding quality can be significantly improved by passing original coding parameters (motion vectors, quantization tables, frame sequences, etc.) between the decoder and subsequent encoder. Cascades between different transforms (i.e. from DCT based compression to Wavelets and vice versa) seem to be more destructive than cascades using the same transform. Since Murphy's Law is always in effect, these losses never seem to cancel each other, but add rapidly as post production generations accumulate.

Quality is subjective. Despite recent advances in objective measures, video quality in any given compression system is highly dependent on the source mate-

DTV IN THE REAL WORLD

UNDERSTANDING DIGITAL

PRE-PRODUCTION

PRODUCTION

AUDIO

GRAPHIC & COMPOSITING

POST PRODUCTION

DELIVERY & DUPLICATION

ENGINEERING & TRANSMISSION

APPENDIX

GLOSSARY

rial. Beware of demonstrations that use carefully selected material to achieve low bit rates. Be sure to see what things look like with your own test material covering the range of difficulty you expect in daily operation.

Bandwidth based on format. The total ATSC bandwidth is 19.39 Mbps, which includes audio, video and other data. As the image quality is increased, more bandwidth is needed to send the image, even though it is compressed. Below is a list of popular distribution formats and the approximate bandwidth they will require (30 fps for interlace, 60 fps for progressive).

1080i: 10 to 18 Mbps (10 with easy clean film material, easy clean video material may be a little higher, sports will require 18, all material will require 18 on some of the earlier encoders).

720p: 6 to 16 Mbps (low numbers with talking heads and films, sports may be acceptable under 16 Mbps).

480p: 4 to 10 Mbps (low number highly dependent on customer expectation that this a very high quality 16:9 image).

480i: 2 to 6 Mbps (could average under 3 Mbps with good statistical multiplexing).

ERROR MANAGEMENT

GLEN PENSINGER

Things will go wrong. You can count on it. When they go wrong in digital recording and transmission, bits are corrupted and the message is distorted. The effect of these distortions varies with the nature of the digital system.

With computers, there is a huge sensitivity to errors, particularly in instructions. A single error in the right place and it's time to reboot. With video and audio the effect is more subjective.

If a single video or audio bit has been corrupted, the effect depends on the significance of that bit. If it's the least significant bit in a sample, chances are the effect will be lost in the noise and won't even be noticed. If it's one of the more significant bits, there will probably be a pop in the sound or an unwanted dot in the picture. If the error occurs in a sync word, you could lose a whole line or frame. With compressed video, an error in just the right place could disrupt not only one frame but a long string of frames.

CAUSES OF ERROR

There are lots of reasons why errors occur. The error environment inside a piece of equipment is usually pretty benign. Manufacturers can control noise, crosstalk and other potential interference so that, for all intents and purposes, there will be no errors. Broadcast channels, on the other hand, can be downright hostile. There is all sorts of noise caused by everything from circuitry to lightning to your neighbor's power tools.

Magnetic recording provides lots of opportunity for mischief, too. Small random errors can affect single bits, and isolated large bursts of errors can disrupt a whole array of bits in an area that is otherwise error-free. Errors can be caused by random noise in heads and replay circuits, or losses of head-to-tape contact resulting from imperfections in the magnetic coating, small bits of dust from the media itself and/or improper storage and handling (that unboxed cassette that's been lying in a bag of fries on the dashboard of the news truck all day).

Even an environment as seemingly safe as the inside of a memory chip can have problems. The tiny wells of capacitive charge that represent zeros and ones can be discharged by alpha particles from the natural radioactive decay of the chip's own materials. Statistically this is only going to happen once every 30 years or so, but with thousands of chips in a large memory bank, the probability rises to an error every few minutes.

Every digital channel has its own set of problems, and the solutions applied will be different for each type of channel. There are, however, four broad stages common to all error management schemes:
- Error Avoidance and Redundancy Coding
- Error Detection
- Error Correction
- Error Concealment

Error Avoidance And Redundancy Coding—The first steps in error management constitute a sort of preprocessing in anticipation of the errors to come. Much of this is simply good engineering, doing as much as we can to avoid errors. We design circuitry to minimize noise and crosstalk. We find bad spots on hard discs and lock them out. We see to it that there is enough transmit power and a good enough antenna to ensure an adequate signal–to–noise ratio at the receiver. We keep the cassette out of the fries and off the dashboard.

Error Detection—Next comes some really clever engineering called "redundancy coding." Without it, error detection would be impossible. Detection is one of the most important steps in error management. It must be very reliable. If you don't know there has been an error, it doesn't matter how effective your other error management techniques are.

Redundancy codes can be extremely complex, but we can use a very simple one, the parity check, to explain the idea. Like all redundancy codes, the parity check adds bits to the original data in such a way that errors can be recognized at the receiver. Consider the example in figure 4. Here we have a series of four-bit data words to which a fifth "parity" bit has been added. By adding a zero or a one, the parity bit ensures that there will be an even number of ones in all the coded data words. If the error detection circuitry in the receiver sees an odd number of ones, it knows an error has taken place.

Error Correction—In our simple parity example, when the receiver sees an odd number of ones, it knows that an error has occurred in one of the four-bit data bits. But it doesn't know which bit is wrong. The error can be corrected by asking for a retransmission of the corrupted data word.

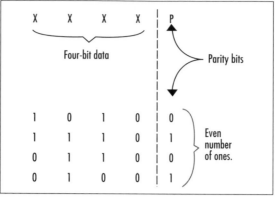

figure 4. Parity coding.

Retransmission requests are commonly used to correct errors in computing, but they're a luxury we can't afford with realtime video and audio. We need the bits when we need them, and we can't interrupt the flow for a retry. We need a scheme that can correct errors.

A "crossword parity check" is a simple example of a redundancy code that can identify which bit is corrupted so that it can be fixed. In figure 5, parity bits are added to both rows and columns. If a single bit is distorted, one row check and one column check will fail (an odd number of ones again) and the bad bit will be at the intersection of the column and row. If there's a one in the corrupted location, it can be corrected to a zero and vice versa.

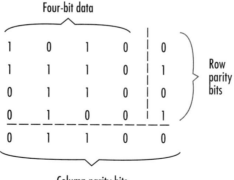

figure 5. Crossword parity check.

The simple examples we've used here can only detect single bit errors. Corruption of two or more bits will easily confuse them. More sophisticated techniques such as the Reed-Solomon and Trellis codes used in digital recording and broadcasting require more bits and more complex math to correct a larger number of errors, but the basic idea remains the same. Bits are added to the basic data stream at the front end in such a way that errors can be identified and corrected at the back.

Unfortunately, any scheme has a finite number of errors it can correct. Closely spaced bursts of errors are a common occurrence, and a burst can screw up more data than even the best coding can fix. Sometimes data can be interleaved during transmission or recording to improve a system's chances in the face of such bursts.

Consider an error correction scheme that can only correct up to four bad data words in a row. It must work in a channel where six–word error bursts are common. What happens if we change the order of our data words so that adjacent words in the original data are no longer adjacent in the transmission channel? Error bursts will still affect six adjacent words in the channel, but when those words are put back into their original order at the other end, it's unlikely that there will be four bad words in a row and the correction scheme can correct the errors.

Error Concealment—No matter how elegant the coding, errors will occur that cannot be corrected. The only option is to conceal them as best we can.

One example of error concealment is the dropout compensation used in analog video recorders. During playback, when a dropout is detected, the dropout compensator inserts some video from the previous line into the hole created by the loss of signal. Since adjacent lines usually contain similar video, the idea works fairly well.

That basic idea has been refined and improved in digital systems. With digital audio, the simple fix is to approximate a lost sample by interpolating a value from samples on either side. A more advanced method makes a spectral analysis of the sound and inserts samples with the same spectral characteristics. If there are too many errors to conceal, then the only choice is to mute.

With digital video, missing samples can be approximated from adjacent ones in the same line, those on adjacent lines and/or ones in previous and succeeding fields. The technique works because there is a lot of redundancy in a video image. If the video is compressed, there will be less redundancy, concealment may not work as well, and error correction will become even more important.

In any case, when both correction and concealment capabilities are exceeded in video, the options are to either freeze the last frame or drop to black.

Concealment techniques aren't limited to recording and transmission. They're even being used in cameras. Thomson's 1657D digital camera uses it to correct defective CCD pixels. Although defective pixels are rare, they do occur, and the Thomson Dynamic Pixel Correction system continuously analyzes the image, detects bad pixels and automatically interpolates a new value for them from surrounding pixels in realtime.

TRADEOFFS

It can be argued that, since redundancy codes add bits to the stream, they reduce storage capacity or channel bandwidth. That's not true if they're properly designed for the channel in question.

Consider magnetic recording. With a properly designed redundancy code, the signal-to-noise ratio of the channel can be reduced because an increased number of errors can be overcome by the error correction system. Cutting track width in half will reduce signal-to-noise ratio by 3 dB, but it doubles storage capacity. With the doubled capacity, it's not difficult to accommodate the extra bits added by the correction scheme.

A properly designed error management system is always worth much more than the bits it consumes.

UNDERSTANDING DIGITAL: ADVANCED THEORY
CRAIG BIRKMAIER

To understand the emerging world of digital television, one must let go of preconceptions rooted in the history of analog television. A world where the image acquisition, transmission, and consumer display components of the broadcast system are tightly coupled. A world where one size fits all.

The NTSC transmission standard was designed to deliver a resolution of approximately 21 cycles per degree (cpd) over a viewing field of just under 11 degrees—a resolution of 22 cpd is considered to be a sharp image for people with average visual acuity. In studies where viewers are shown video images on displays with varying sizes and resolutions, and are given the opportunity to select a *preferred viewing distance*, they will typically choose the distance that produces a sharp image.

In order to deliver the NTSC viewing experience, the engineers who designed the standard assumed that we would watch a 19-inch diagonal display at an average viewing distance of seven picture heights, a distance of about six to seven feet. If we increase the size of the display, to cover a larger portion of the field of view, the limitations of the NTSC standard quickly become apparent. In reality, the NTSC one-size-fits-all approach only delivers a sharp image when the display covers less than 11 degrees of the field of view.

Theater screens typically cover a 30- to 50-degree field of view; special venue theaters such as Imax may cover a 180-degree field of view. The move to high resolution electronic imaging systems deals, in large measure, with the ability to cover a significantly greater portion of the field-of-view, with what is perceived as a sharp and accurate image.

In order for digital television to satisfy the desired goal of screens that cover a larger portion of the field of view, we need to deliver more information to the viewer, not more resolution. It's better to think of the requirements for larger displays in the same terms as a *picture window* in the family room. If we make the window larger, we get to see more of the back yard; the resolution remains constant.

The DTV display in the family room should do the same, providing a sharp image at the designed viewing distance for the installation. Thus, the choice of an appropriate level of resolution for a consumer display will depend on the viewing environment (the application) and the available budget.

In the emerging digital world, acquisition, transmission and display are not connected. Images will be captured at many spatial resolutions (size) and temporal rates (images per second, both interlace and progressive). Content will be composed by intermixing visual objects from many sources, and it will be encoded for distribution at many levels of resolution. Ultimately, the content will be decoded and scaled for presentation on screens that come in many sizes and resolutions.

While digital television provides an appropriate technical foundation for a system without rigid video formats—i.e., resolution independence—it's more practical to design the system with several levels of resolution in a logical progression. This is the approach taken by the engineers who designed the ATSC digital television standard; the number of lines increases by a factor of 1.5 between each level.

Figure 6: The Sharper Image, and figure 7: Sm., Med., Lg., provide a visual framework to assist with your understanding of how the ATSC formats can be used to deliver the DTV viewing experience.

This bewildering array of possibilities takes digital video and broadcasting into an entirely new realm. A world where the digitized representations of *all* forms of media can be encoded for delivery as streams of packetized data. When these digital bit streams are decoded, images will be scaled for presentation to match the requirements of the viewing application and the resolution of the digital television appliance where the content is being consumed—the TV set in the family room or the den, the direct view CRT or LCD screens of personal computers, or the next generation of network computers and home theater systems with large projection screens, or plasma displays that hang on the wall.

To understand digital television, it is helpful to understand the ways in which the human visual and auditory systems acquire images and sound. From this, we can better understand the analog and digital processes that are being carefully tuned to emulate the way we see and hear. These processes are intimately related to the way we will sample images and sound, and compress this data for delivery using digital transmission techniques.

WHAT YOU SEE IS WHAT YOU GET

In the physical world, what we *see* and what we *hear* are analog in nature. Sound is a continuous phenomenon, the result of the modulation of our ear drums by moving air molecules. Sight is a continuous phenomenon, the result of a continuous flow of photons into the receptors of the human visual system. How we see and hear is the basis for how visual and aural data can be compressed—with parts of that information "thrown away."

The human visual system relies on multiple image receptors to deal with the diversity of environments that it encounters: cones are utilized for color image acquisition over a wide range of illumination levels; rods are utilized for monochrome image acquisition at low illumination levels.

The cones are organized into three broad groups of receptors that are sensitive to light in specific spectral bands; while these bands have significant overlaps, they

DTV IN THE REAL WORLD

UNDERSTANDING DIGITAL

PRE-PRODUCTION

PRODUCTION

AUDIO

GRAPHIC & COMPOSITING

POST PRODUCTION

DELIVERY & DUPLICATION

ENGINEERING & TRANSMISSION

APPENDIX

GLOSSARY

How much resolution does a television system need to produce a sharp image?

The level of resolution required to deliver a sharp image is directly related to the size of the screen and the viewing distance. When viewed from the designed viewing distance of seven picture heights, NTSC appears sharp. Step closer, say three picture heights, and you will see the limitations of the NTSC standard.

The ATSC standard supports three levels of spatial resolution for the transmission of 16:9 images, as illustrated above. This image has been carefully constructed to illustrate the relative resolution of the three format families, using frame based image sampling (progressive scan). It does not reflect the loss of vertical resolution that results from interlaced image sampling or display.

If you have average visual ability, this simple test will demonstrate the relationship between resolution and viewing distance. If this image is viewed from three picture heights —about eight inches—1920x1080 should appear sharp; you should be able to see the samples in the 704x480 image and steps on the curves in the 1280x720 image. At five picture heights—about 13 inches—1280x720 should appear sharp; and at seven picture heights— about 19 inches—704x480 should appear sharp.

roughly conform to the red, green and blue portions of the spectrum. Red and green receptors each outnumber blue receptors by a factor of 2:1. The disbursement of these receptors is not uniform; thus, spatial perception deals with a complex matrix of receptor types and cognitive processing by the brain.

The center of the visual field, an area called the fovea, contains 30,000 to 40,000 cones (no rods). Central vision enables us to see detail, while peripheral vision is tuned to detect change, i.e., temporal events.

It takes several hundred milliseconds for the foveal image receptors to capture a detailed image; thus the eye must either be viewing a static scene or it must track a moving object to perceive high resolution.

Evidence suggests the massive amount of information collected by our visual and auditory sensors is *digitized* and processed by the brain, allowing us to discriminate among content of interest and content that can be ignored. In essence we learn how to filter the input from the physical world—to see and hear in a very selective manner.

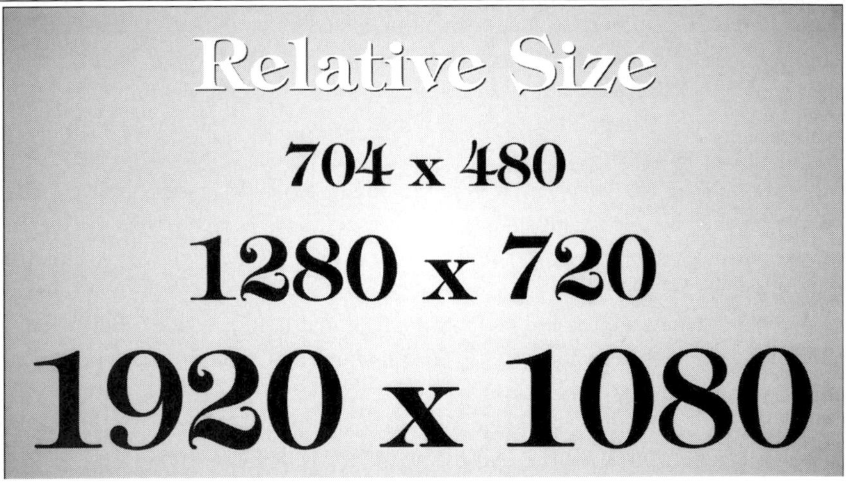

DTV IN THE REAL WORLD

UNDERSTANDING DIGITAL

PRE-PRODUCTION

PRODUCTION

AUDIO

GRAPHIC & COMPOSITING

POST PRODUCTION

DELIVERY & DUPLICATION

ENGINEERING & TRANSMISSION

APPENDIX

GLOSSARY

Relative Size

704 x 480

1280 x 720

1920 x 1080

figure 7.
Sm. Med. Lg.

Television displays already come in many sizes; now we are adding a confusing new variable to the buying decision—display resolution. As you saw in figure 6, viewing distance determines the resolution requirements for a display, regardless of its size. The goal is to deliver a sharp image—approximately 22 cycles per degree of field of view—at the intended viewing distance.

This figure illustrates how resolution requirements increase with the field of view covered by the display. Imagine that the numbers above represent pieces of three screens, all in the same plane (equal distance between viewer and screens). The numbers are all the same height, when the measurement is expressed as a percentage of total picture height.

The width and height of the 720–line display is 1.5 that of the 480–line display; in turn, the width and height of the 1080–line display is 1.5 times that of 720–line display. Under these conditions, as in this illustration, the size of the samples presented to the observer are equal, thus the displays should deliver equivalent perceived sharpness.

How should you choose a DTV display? Measure the space for the display and the average viewing distance. When shopping, look at displays that fit the space and your budget, then judge image quality at the intended *viewing distance.*

The process of capturing sound and images, and processing what is captured to create television programs, has strong parallels. The pragmatic goal of any electronic- or film-based delivery medium is to emulate the ways in which our auditory and visual receptors, and our brains, determine *which* information to throw away.

The image compression techniques that enabled the first six decades of analog television broadcasting provided limited control over the process of selecting which information to keep, and which information to throw away.

With digital television, we can *tweak* the system in new ways. We can be more selective about the information we throw away and the important bits we pass along to the human visual and auditory systems.

CONSERVING BANDWIDTH IN AN ANALOG WORLD

Like the sensors of the human visual system, a television camera produces an abundance of information. Today's interlaced, broadcast-quality cameras typically employ three CCD sensors, producing red, green and blue outputs, each with 6 to 8 MHz of analog information. Unfortunately, stuffing 18 to 24 MHz of analog signals into a 6 MHz NTSC, or 8 MHz PAL channel was a bit tricky at the time these standards were created. The engineers who designed analog television had to throw away a great deal of information.

NTSC and PAL are analog video compression systems, designed to deliver a reasonable balance between static and dynamic resolution. The approximate 3:1 compression is achieved primarily by limiting color resolution and high frequency luminance detail.

The RGB signals are added in a mathematical matrix to produce full bandwidth luminance and color difference signals. These signals are then filtered, limiting the luminance (Y) frequency response to approximately 4.2 MHz in NTSC and 6.0 MHz in PAL. The color or chroma difference signals (I and Q for NTSC, U and V for PAL) are filtered more aggressively, leaving only 1.5 MHz for I and 0.5 MHz for Q in NTSC, 1.5 MHz for U and V in PAL. Thus, color resolution is reduced to approximately one-quarter of the luminance resolution.

Unlike film, where a light source passes through a complete image frame, projecting the image onto a screen, television systems must deliver images as part of a continuously modulated signal that can be decoded by an inexpensive television appliance.

In the early part of this century, when our analog television systems were designed, the technology was not available to store and then display a complete image frame. The solution was to deliver the images using line scanning techniques, synchronized with the modulated television signal. As an image was being scanned by a camera, it was encoded, transmitted, decoded and scanned onto the display.

These line scanning techniques are tightly coupled with the characteristics of the CRT-based display technology available to the designers of television systems during the first half of this century. To produce an image, an electron beam is scanned across the inside face of a CRT covered with phosphors. In any one spot, the phosphors will illuminate, then decay, causing the light intensity to modulate or flicker. Thanks to an attribute of the human visual system called persistence of vision, we are able to integrate the information delivered by the scanning spot, creating the illusion of watching moving pictures.

There are many ways to scan a CRT display. Two methods have become commonplace: interlaced and progressive scanning. With interlaced scan, one half of the image—a video field—is reproduced by scanning all of the even lines in a frame, then the other field is reproduced by scanning all of the odd lines in a frame. With progressive scan, the first line of a frame is scanned across the top of the screen, then each successive line is scanned until the entire frame has been reproduced.

The use of interlace provided a well–balanced solution for the delivery of television images to early CRT displays. Some static resolution was sacrificed, compared to a progressive display with the same number of lines; however, the dynamic resolution was improved by delivering 50 or 60 pictures (fields) each second, versus 25 or 30. (Note that with the addition of color, the NTSC frame rate was modified to 29.97 frames/59.94 fields per second; for convenience, the 30 frame/60 field notation will be used throughout this book.)

Unfortunately, interlace imposes other compromises on image quality, compromises which have become evident as image acquisition and display technology have evolved up to, and beyond, the limits of the NTSC and PAL television standards.

With interlaced scanning, a video frame is acquired in two temporal sampling periods (each field making up the frame is captured at a slightly different moment in time); a frame therefore includes a mixture of spatial and temporal information. This makes it difficult to extract a temporally coherent still image from a video stream—this is why most video still stores allow the user to choose between a still frame and a still field. It also increases the complexity of temporal rate and spatial resolution transformations—for example, standards conversion between NTSC and PAL, and the image scaling and rotation techniques used in digital video effect systems. As we will see later in this chapter, the use of interlaced scanning also increases the complexity of the digital video compression techniques that form the basis for virtually all emerging digital television standards.

Interlace was an effective compression technique in an era dominated by analog technology and CRT displays. The use of interlaced scanning in new digital television systems has been highly contested, especially by the computer industry, which moved to the exclusive use of progressive scan display technology over the past decade. Whether the use of interlace will continue in new high resolution video formats remains to be seen. One thing is certain: broadcasters and videographers must deal with both forms of scanning during the migration to digital television.

DECOUPLING DIGITAL TELEVISION APPLIANCES
FROM ITS ANALOG HERITAGE

The emerging display technologies most likely to replace the CRTs in direct view and projection television displays have more in common with frame-based film projection than a line scanning system. Liquid crystal (LCD), plasma, and digital light processor (a.k.a. digital micromirror device) displays all have fixed sample sites that remain illuminated for essentially the entire field or frame duration. If two fields are combined to display a complete frame, the eye sees two temporal samples at the same time; this can cause severe image quality degradation. For proper display, the images must be de-interlaced, turning fields into frames by doubling the number of lines, approximating the missing information as close as possible. De-interlacing will also be required for progressively scanned CRT displays.

One of the major benefits from the move to digital television comes from the use of frame buffer memory in the receiver. The ability to buffer several video frames in memory is a critical requirement for the digital video compression techniques that will be used to squeeze high definition television into a 6 MHz (US) or 8 MHz (Europe) terrestrial broadcast channel.

Digital television receivers and set-top boxes designed to decode all of the ATSC (Advanced Television Systems Committee) Table 3 formats (see Glossary), will produce images at 480, 720 and 1080 lines. Both interlaced and progressive scanning techniques are used in the 480 and 1080 line format families (the 720 line format is progressive only). After decoding these images, they must be scaled for presentation at the resolution of the local display and, if necessary, de-interlaced.

In addition, DTV receivers will decode data and create raster images for display. These images may be displayed in lieu of video programs, in portions of the screen not occupied by the main program, or overlaid onto the video program(s).

Applications such as electronic program guides, news and weather services, sports scores, and closed captioning are examples of data broadcast services. Many proponents of data broadcasting hope to deliver new forms of content based on the technology and standards developed for the Internet and World Wide Web.

DIGITIZING THE IMAGE

The process of capturing images and converting them into bits involves two critical steps: sampling and quantization.

As the term implies, sampling is the periodic measurement of analog values to produce image samples. All film and electronic imaging systems utilize sampling to some extent.

The spatial resolution of film is limited by the density of grains of photosensitive dyes (image samples), while temporal resolution is limited by the frame rate and shutter angle (exposure time per frame period).

Analog video has always been sampled vertically because of the use of line scanning techniques. In a horizontal line scanning system, static and dynamic resolution are determined by several factors:

- Horizontal resolution is limited by the frequency response and frame rate of the system.
- Vertical resolution is limited by the sampling frequency—the number of lines per field or frame and the frame rate.

To digitize an image, we sample the analog video waveforms produced by a line scanning tube camera, or line and frame array image sensors.

Both line and frame array sensors sample images in three dimensions: horizontal, vertical and time. Line array sensors are used to scan still images, such as a film frame or the image on a photographic print or document.

With a tube-based image sensor, sampling takes place over the field or frame period, as the image accumulating on the sensor is scanned. The temporal skew from the first to the last sample in an interlaced video frame is 1/30th (NTSC) or 1/25th (PAL) of a second; samples on adjacent lines have a temporal skew of 1/60th or 1/50th of a second.

Modern CCD image sensors are frame-based capture devices. All of the sensor sites are capturing an image frame for the same portion of the temporal sampling period. Electronic shuttering is possible as the CCD sensor can dissipate charge (shutter closed) for a portion of the field or frame period, then accumulate charge (shutter open) to simulate the desired shutter speed.

The charges that accumulate during the frame sampling period are shifted to read-out registers. The CCD then produces an analog signal by scanning out the samples over time; this is analogous to the way a film frame is scanned.

A CCD can be designed to produce either an interlaced or a progressive scan output; some can output both. For a progressive scan output, every line is scanned. For an interlaced output, the charges on adjacent lines are summed to produce a video field. In the first field period, lines 1 and 2, 3 and 4, etc., are summed; in the second field period lines 2 and 3, 4 and 5, etc., are summed to provide the one line offset between fields.

Interlaced analog signals can be digitized with excellent results, as we have seen with the ITU-R 601 digital component sampling standard. Analog and digital component processing are now used as intermediate steps in the process of creating high quality analog NTSC and PAL signals, and digitally encoded MPEG-2 bit streams.

The static and dynamic resolution of a digitized image stream is directly related to the sampling frequency and the level of quantization applied to each sample.

QUANTIZATION

If we are capturing a document with black text on a white background, it is sufficient to represent the samples with a single bit: if the bit is set to 0 we have white, if it is set to 1 we have black. If we wish to capture an image with intermediate values, for example a gray scale that changes from white to black, we will need many values or quantization steps to represent each sample. With 8-bit quantization, we can represent 256 levels of gray; 10-bits provide 1,024 discrete quantization steps.

The number of quantization levels determines the accuracy with which a sample can be represented. More quantization steps provide greater accuracy and the ability to reproduce the small levels of difference between samples in smooth gradients (see figure 8: Quantization Levels).

Sampling is, at best, an approximation of the analog world. The actual level being sampled may differ from the sample value for a number of reasons. Even if the sampling system were perfectly accurate, a quantization error of one-half step is still possible. Sampling systems are rarely that accurate; in the real world, an error of a full quantization step is quite probable. To improve sampling accuracy we can *oversample* the image, then resample to the sample grid we will use for distribution.

The bit that determines the choice between two adjacent quantization levels is called *the least significant bit*. It is difficult for the human visual system to detect single-step quantization errors in systems with good dynamic range (typically eight or more bits per sample). Thus in uncompressed systems, the least significant bit can be used to encode additional information without significantly impacting image quality.

In addition to errors introduced during sampling, subsequent image processing and encoding can introduce the following quantization errors:
• Rounding errors when samples are manipulated.
• Conversion of the samples into a representation with fewer quantization levels.
• Bit rate reduction techniques.

As we will see later in this chapter, selectively quantizing certain information within an image forms the basis for many of the video compression techniques used in digital television.

SAMPLING THEORY

The sampling frequency establishes limits on the spatial and temporal frequencies that an imaging system can reproduce without the introduction of perceptible alias-

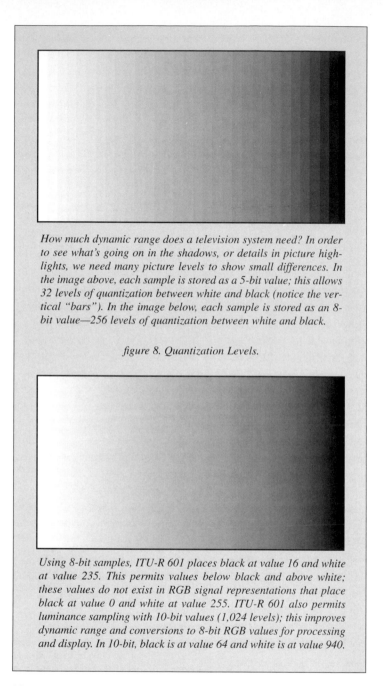

*How much dynamic range does a television system need? In order
to see what's going on in the shadows, or details in picture highlights, we need many picture levels to show small differences. In
the image above, each sample is stored as a 5-bit value; this allows
32 levels of quantization between white and black (notice the vertical "bars"). In the image below, each sample is stored as an 8-
bit value—256 levels of quantization between white and black.*

figure 8. Quantization Levels.

*Using 8-bit samples, ITU-R 601 places black at value 16 and white
at value 235. This permits values below black and above white;
these values do not exist in RGB signal representations that place
black at value 0 and white at value 255. ITU-R 601 also permits
luminance sampling with 10-bit values (1,024 levels); this improves
dynamic range and conversions to 8-bit RGB values for processing
and display. In 10-bit, black is at value 64 and white is at value 940.*

ing artifacts. In terms of spatial resolution, sampling theory indicates that the highest spatial frequency we can reproduce—without aliasing—will be slightly less than
one-half the sampling frequency.

Let's use the ITU-R 601 component digital sampling specifications as an example. This specification is based on multiples of a 3.375 MHz sampling rate, a num-

ber carefully chosen because of its relationship to both NTSC and PAL. Two levels of quantization are permitted for the luminance component: 8- and 10-bit. The color difference components are quantized at 8-bit.

The sampling frequency for the luminance (Y) component of the signal is 13.5 MHz. Thus, the upper limit on the spatial frequencies that can be represented will be slightly less than 6.75 MHz. This is sufficient for the 6.0 MHz luminance bandpass of PAL, and represents significant horizontal oversampling relative to the 4.2 MHz luminance bandpass for NTSC.

The sampling frequency for the color difference components, R-Y and B-Y, is 6.75 MHz. Thus the upper limit on the spatial frequencies that can be represented will be slightly less than 3.375 MHz. This is significantly higher than the 1.5 MHz bandpass for the color components in both PAL and NTSC. This additional color resolution is quite useful in the generation of color mattes, providing yet another reason to use component rather than composite video signals in the video composition process.

A notation system has been adopted to describe the relative sampling frequencies for the luminance and color difference components of the digital video signal; this notation is referenced to the 3.375 MHz basis for the ITU-R 601 standard. The luminance sampling frequency is four times the base frequency; the color difference sampling frequency is two times the base frequency. Thus this sampling relationship is know as 4:2:2, representing luminance and each color difference component. These sampling parameters are used in the D1, D5, D9, Digital Betacam and DVCPRO50 tape formats.

The notation 4:4:4 indicates that each of the signal components is sampled at 13.5 MHz. This corresponds to the signals produced by the individual image sensors, thus the 4:4:4 notation is often used for either YUV or RGB components.

The notation 4:1:1 indicates that the color difference components have one-quarter the resolution of the luminance signal; this correlates well with luminance and color resolution delivered by NTSC and PAL. 4:1:1 sampling is used in the consumer DV format and the 25 megabit per second (Mbps) versions of DVCPRO and DVCAM.

In the production environment, it is often useful to store a matte channel that can be used to overlay portions of an image in a video composition. The matte can be based on color information in the original image (a chromakey), luminance information in the original image (a luminance key) or a linear control signal (an alpha channel or linear key).

Linear key and alpha channel signals typically have the same sample structure as the luminance or Y channel portion of the signal; however, the number of quantization levels may be reduced. The value of an alpha channel sample is used to establish the level of blending or transparency for the image samples (Y, R-Y, B-Y) in the same spatial location. The number of quantization levels in the alpha channel determines the number of levels of transparency available; to reproduce smooth gradients, such as shadows, it is typical to represent alpha channels with 8-bit values (256 levels of transparency). The standard notation for an alpha channel is to append it to the image sampling notation: 4:4:4:4 and 4:2:2:4 indicate images with full resolution alpha channels.

As all of the sample representations described to this point are based on interlaced scanning, it is important to note that the color sub-sampling affects only horizontal resolution. All of these systems sample luminance and both color difference components on every line.

As we learned earlier, the underlying rationale for color sub-sampling is based in the limits of human visual perception. These limits exist for both horizontal and vertical resolution, although research indicates that the visual system is forgiving of inequalities in H and V resolution in the range of 2:1 to 1:2.

One of the major reasons that today's interlaced video systems do not attempt to limit the vertical color resolution is the mixing of spatial and temporal information between the fields that make up a frame. It is nearly impossible to accurately separate the temporal and spatial information, and to predict the information that was not sampled in the first place. Proper sub-sampling of vertical color resolution involves the same complexity, and inherent limitations, found in devices used for temporal and spatial resampling, including standards converters, digital video effect systems and display processors that de-interlace and double or quadruple the number of lines.

By comparison, with film and progressive scan image acquisition, it is relatively easy to sub-sample vertical color resolution, thereby eliminating more information that the human visual system does not process.

Unfortunately, this creates a rather nasty problem with the notation system used to describe color sub-sampling. What is the accepted notation for a system that reduces *both* horizontal and vertical color resolution by one-half?

4:2:2 is probably the most accurate description, but it's already taken. For reasons that are not obvious, the notation used for this form of color subsampling is 4:2:0. This is the designated sampling structure for the MPEG-2 video compression that will be used for digital television broadcasts.

Before we leave the subject of image sampling, a brief discussion about the advantages of oversampling are in order. In his book, *The Art of Digital Video* (1990, Focal Press) John Watkinson makes the point that television systems have evolved from times when many of the freedoms of modern image acquisition and display technology were not available.

> *"The terrestrial broadcast standards of today were designed to transmit a signal which could be fed to a CRT with the minimum processing. The number of lines in the camera, the number of lines in the broadcast standard and the number of lines in the display were all the same for reasons of simplicity, and performance fell short of that permitted by sampling theory. This need no longer be the case.*
> *Oversampling is a technique which allows sampled systems to approach theoretical performance limits more closely. It has become virtually universal in digital audio, since at the relatively low frequencies of audio it is easy to implement. It is only a mater of time before oversampling becomes common in video."*

While less efficient from the viewpoint of bandwidth requirements, oversampling has much to offer in terms of high quality image acquisition and subsequent processing. The video industry is unique in that the same sampling grid is typically used for image acquisition, processing, transmission, and display. To prevent aliasing, an optical low pass filter is generally placed between the lens and image sensor(s), limiting the spatial frequencies present to less than half of the sampling frequency. To properly reconstruct the image, a similar low pass filter should be placed in front of the display to eliminate the aliasing artifacts it may produce. Unfortunately, viewers might object if manufacturers placed such a filter over the display, so we live with these aliasing artifacts.

It is not likely that viewers will purchase separate displays for each of the formats in the ATSC digital television standard, or that manufacturers will offer low-cost displays that synchronize to each of the 36 formats defined by the standard. Even if the display could operate in more than one format, the problem of combining images from multiple sources—to support picture-in-picture, for example—would still exist.

Therefore, it is likely that the display component of a digital television system will operate with image refresh parameters that provide optimal image quality for that display, and that all of the transmission formats will be re-sampled in the receiver to match those parameters. This will require de-interlacing and other forms of image processing in the receiver.

Bottom line: The best way to assure that high quality images are presented on screens that come in many sizes and resolutions is to encode only the highest quality images for transmission. This does not necessarily mean the highest resolution images, although oversampling, relative to the resolution eventually encoded for distribution, will pay many dividends in the emerging digital world.

AN INTRODUCTION TO DIGITAL VIDEO CODING

We are now prepared to begin the discussion of digital video encoding techniques, otherwise known as digital video compression or bit rate reduction.

Digital video encoding is based on a *toolbox* approach to the problem. A variety of coding techniques are available from the toolbox; appropriate tools can be selected and employed to match application and bandwidth requirements. These digital video coding tools can be divided into several broad categories:

Lossless: Ensures that the original data is exactly recoverable.

Lossy: The original data is not completely recoverable. Coding is based on the theory that small quantization errors in the high-frequency components of the image are not perceptible by the human visual system.

We can further divide digital video coding into spatial and temporal coding techniques:

Self-referential or Intra-frame: Bit rate reduction is based entirely on redundancy within the image that is being coded.

Predictive or Inter-frame: Bit rate reduction is based on the redundancy of information in a group of pictures (a small number of consecutive video frames). Motion compensated prediction is typically used, based on reference frames in the past and the future. Redundant information is removed by coding the differences between a

DTV IN THE REAL WORLD

UNDERSTANDING DIGITAL

PRE-PRODUCTION

PRODUCTION

AUDIO

GRAPHIC & COMPOSITING

POST PRODUCTION

DELIVERY & DUPLICATION

ENGINEERING & TRANSMISSION

APPENDIX

GLOSSARY

prediction of the image data within a frame and the actual image data.

Lossless coding techniques have an obvious advantage, in that the original sample data can be recovered without the introduction of quantization errors. Unfortunately, these techniques do not provide enough compression efficiency to meet the bandwidth constraints further down the digital video food chain.

There are several lossless coding techniques employed in digital video compression systems. The first is run length encoding (RLE). This technique counts the number of samples along a line with the same value; this value and the number of samples—the run length—are stored, followed by the next run, etc. The efficiency of this technique is scene-dependent. A smooth gradient in the vertical direction encodes very efficiently, as every sample along a line is the same. A smooth gradient in any other direction does not compress at all, as every sample on every line is different. One of the goals of the compression techniques we are about to examine is to increase the runs of identical pixel values to improve the efficiency of this lossless encoding technique.

Reversible transforms are employed in virtually all image coding techniques in common use today. In essence, the sample data is transformed into a different representation that has advantages in terms of compression efficiency. If the transformed data is not modified, the transform can be reversed, recovering the original data.

Entropy coding is, from a historical perspective, one of the oldest data compression techniques. The Morse Code for telegraphy is an example of an entropy code. The most common letter (in English) is **E** so it gets the shortest code (one short tone—a dot). **Q** is much less common, so it is assigned a long code (two long tones, one short tone, one long tone—dash-dash-dot-dash). This speeds up transmission on average.

Lossy coding techniques throw information away. Typically, the sample data is subjected to a reversible transform; the transformed data is then quantized to eliminate small differences, then run length and entropy coded. When the process is reversed, the sample data is reconstructed, hopefully with only minimal degradation.

INTRA–FRAME VIDEO CODING

The discrete cosine transform (DCT) is currently the most widely used transform for video compression. The wavelet transform has also enjoyed popularity for intraframe video coding; however, it does not lend itself as well to the inter–frame compression techniques that provide much of the efficiency in MPEG video compression. The DCT is the basis for the intra–frame coding techniques used in JPEG, Motion-JPEG and MPEG, as well as many video recording formats including, D9 Digital Betacam, DV, DVCAM and DVCPRO.

MPEG is the acronym for the Moving Picture Experts Group, which creates standards under the auspices of the International Telecommunications Union and ISO (International Standards Organization). This standards group has close ties with JPEG—the Joint Photographic Experts Group—which develops standards for the compression of still images.

As video is nothing more than a succession of still images, a variation called Motion-JPEG or M-JPEG is used for intraframe video compression. Because of low cost implementations and the need to access each frame easily for frame-accurate edits, M-JPEG is currently the compression codec of choice for the majority of non-linear video editing systems.

The DCT is a reversible transform that converts sample data from spatial order into frequency order; if the resulting coefficients are not quantized, the process can be inverted, returning the original data set. If coefficients have been quantized, they can still be passed through the transform multiple times without further loss; this attribute is very important, as with reasonable care, it enables images to pass through multiple DCT-based compression codecs without additional degradation.

The DCT is applied to small eight-by-eight sample regions of the luminance and color difference components that make up an image. By breaking the image up into small blocks, the effect of the transform is localized. The block structure also plays an important role in the motion-compensated prediction techniques used for inter-frame coding.

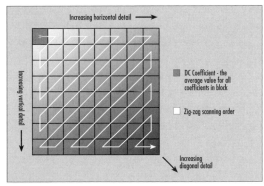

figure 9. Ordering of DCT coefficients.

When the DCT is applied, sample data is transformed from the spatial domain—the horizontal and vertical locations of the pixels–into the frequency domain. The resulting DCT coefficients are arranged on the basis of the spectral content of the samples. In figure 9: Ordering of DCT Coefficients, we see how the sample information has been reordered in the frequency domain. The upper left corner of the eight-by-eight matrix of transform coefficients contains the DC coefficient; this is the average value for the entire block. This is the only coefficient required to represent a solid block of luminance or color information.

Moving away from the DC coefficient to the right, we find coefficients that differ from the DC coefficient based on increasing horizontal frequency content. Moving down, we find increasing vertical frequency content. Large differences typically indicate the presence of high frequency edge information within a block. Small differences typically indicate gradual changes, such as the subtle shifts in luminance or color in the sky. As you will see, small differences are actually more difficult to deal with than large ones.

Since image information is localized with the DCT blocks, it tends to be highly correlated. The transform will typically produce a limited number of spectral coefficients, leaving many holes in the data (coefficients with a value of "0"). These holes are eliminated using run length coding—coefficients are read out in zigzag order to maximize the run lengths of "0" coefficients.

Huffman (entropy) coding of the coefficients is used for additional data reduction. Lower frequency coefficients, which tend to occur frequently, are given short codes; higher frequency coefficients, which occur less frequently, are given longer codes.

The DCT transform and entropy coding do not cause any loss of picture information. As information content typically changes from scene to scene, the amount of data produced by the DCT for each frame varies with scene content. Unfortunately, for the most demanding video images, the DCT yields, on average, a 2:1 compression ratio. Many nonlinear editing systems now handle the bandwidth peaks required for 2:1 compression, and thus can support the *lossless* mode available in M-JPEG codecs.

To achieve higher levels of compression, it is necessary to *quantize* the DCT coefficients in a nonlinear fashion. This is where the DCT has major advantages over NTSC's analog compression techniques, and where the MPEG, M-JPEG and DV family tree begins to branch.

NTSC uses filtering techniques to limit the maximum frequency of the luminance and color components of the signal—without regard to the total amount of information in the image. Based on the spectral content of video images, we find that significant portions of the NTSC signal contain little or no information. Add to this the portions of the signal that contain synchronizing information for the CRT display, and we see that there is plenty of room left in which to squeeze more information about the images, including high frequency details that are removed by the bandpass filters.

With the DCT, it is possible to quantize coefficients on a selective basis; high frequency detail can be preserved for most scenes. The quality of the resulting images depends on two factors: the total information content in the image and the target bit rate. If the level of quantization is held constant, the bit rate of the compressed image stream will vary based on the information content. If the bit rate is held constant, the level of quantization must vary to compensate for changes in the information content of the images.

Quantization of DCT coefficients is accomplished by dividing the coefficients by values contained in a quantization or Q-Table. Dividing by 1 leaves a coefficient unchanged; dividing by larger numbers reduces the differences between coefficients. This reduces the number of different coefficients, and thus improves compression efficiency.

Q-tables can be tuned to achieve specific compression levels, or for specific kind of image information. JPEG and M-JPEG use the same Q-table for all of the DCT blocks (usually 8x8 pixels) in an image. Thus like NTSC, the table *filters* every block the same. DV and MPEG allow the Q-table to be adjusted for each macroblock in the image—a macroblock is small group of DCT blocks, typically four blocks or 16x16 pixels. Based on image statistics derived by passing the image through the DCT transform, the level of quantization can be adjusted for each macroblock, allocating more bits to the most demanding regions of the image.

The highly selective quantization process puts the coded bits into the frequencies to which our visual system is most sensitive, while limiting the bits that code the higher frequencies to which we are less sensitive. Used in *moderation*, the quantization of DCT coefficients is a highly effective compression technique.

The presence of high frequency transitions within a DCT coding block—such as those that occur in text and graphics—influences all of the coefficients within that block. To properly decompress the image without artifacts, each coefficient must be restored to its original value. If many coefficients are modified in the quantization process, the result will be the periodic disturbance of the pixels around the high frequency transition. This is referred to as quantization noise.

High quality analog or digital component video, sampled at rates comparable with ITU-R 601, can typically be encoded with compression ratios in the range of 2:1 to 5:1, with no visible loss in image quality. As the level of quantization increases, we begin to see noise around high frequency edges.

Another defect of the quantization process, which is often more noticeable than the high frequency quantization noise, occurs when there are subtle changes within a region of the image, for example in the sky, or in smooth gradients. Higher levels of quantization will eliminate the small differences, causing the entire block to become a solid rather than a gradient. As a result, the region will take on a quilted appearance. If we quantize at even higher levels, the entire image will break down into *blocking* artifacts, resembling pixelation.

If we quantize the DCT too coarsely, the end result is the generation of quantization noise. It is somewhat ironic that *noise* is the most significant barrier to high quality, DCT-based compression. Noise appears as very high frequency information, with no correlation to the samples that are being encoded. When the DCT is presented with a noisy signal, compression efficiency can be severely impacted.

This is one of the principal reasons that new digital video acquisition formats digitize and compress image samples before they are recorded. When applied properly, intraframe digital compression techniques can be used to preserve the highest levels of image quality.

INTER–FRAME VIDEO CODING

When the DCT is used in conjunction with prediction-based **inter–frame** video coding techniques, we enter the sometimes bizarre world of MPEG. Unlike intra–frame techniques, which require approximately the same performance for encoding and decoding, the MPEG encoding/decoding process is highly asymmetrical. Significantly greater processing power is required to *encode* an MPEG data stream than to *decode* it.

MPEG-1 and MPEG-2 were developed to encode moving pictures at a variety of bit rates—from what some consider near-VHS quality at 1.5 Mbps to near-HDTV quality at 15 to 30 Mbps. MPEG-1 is optimized for the coding of video frames at low bit rates (1 to 3 Mbps); MPEG-2 is optimized for the coding of video fields or frames at higher bit rates (3 to 10 Mbps for SDTV, 15 to 30 Mbps for HDTV).

Intra– and inter–frame video coding tools, along with audio encoding techniques and a data transport protocol, are part of what has become known as the MPEG-2 *toolbox*. Specific combinations of tools, optimized for various performance and application requirements, are known as *profiles*. For example, MPEG-2 Main Profile at Main Level (MP@ML) supports sample rates—for the active area of the video image—of up to 10.4

samples per second; MP@ML is optimized to handle existing digital video formats based on the ITU-R 601 sampling specifications. The difference in sample rates, 10.4 million versus 13.5 million, relates to the time spent sampling the video blanking intervals.

In order to achieve the higher levels of compression required to squeeze HDTV into a 6 to 8 MHz channel, we need to eliminate temporal redundancy. The interframe or temporal coding tools used by MPEG are based on a technique called Differential Pulse-Code Modulation (DPCM). The DPCM coding loop lies at the heart of MPEG coding techniques.

Differential PCM comes out of the intuitive concept that sending the *difference* between two things takes less information, or bandwidth, than sending the two things themselves. For example, if a television picture is stationary, why should we send the same picture over and over again, 60 times a second? Why not just send the *difference* between successive pictures?

If we can predict, with reasonable accuracy, what a frame will look like, the differences will be significantly smaller than the frames themselves—for still images the differences will consist primarily of noise or film grain. This provides a significant boost in compression efficiency when compared with intraframe compression techniques.

MPEG specifies three types of "pictures" that can be coded into a data stream:

Intra-coded picture (I): The original image is encoded using information only from itself. DCT compression techniques are used to code the image frame, or two interlaced fields. I pictures provide access points to the data stream.

Predictive-coded picture (P): A picture coded using motion-compensated prediction from a past reference picture. The difference between the actual image and the predicted image is encoded using DCT compression techniques.

Bidirectionally-predictive coded picture (B): A picture coded using motion-compensated prediction from past and future reference pictures. The difference between the actual image and the predicted image is encoded using DCT compression techniques—it is not an average of the previous and future frame. B pictures provide the most efficient coding, however, a third memory buffer is required in addition to the buffers for past and future reference (I and P) pictures. Fast search modes are facilitated by ignoring B pictures.

MPEG streams can be coded using I frames only, I and P frames, I and B frames or I, P and B frames. The coding of I frames only is, in fact, virtually identical to the intraframe coding techniques discussed in the previous section.

MPEG profiles for program distribution utilize 4:2:0 sampling, IP or IPB frames, and the bit rate constraints described at the beginning of this section. The MPEG-2 Studio Profile was created for production and contribution quality video encoding. This profile permits the use of 4:2:2 sampling, any combination of I, P and B frames, and bit rates of up to 50 Mbps. For example, the Sony Betacam SX format employs 4:2:2 sampling, I and B frames, and a bit rate of 18 Mbps.

The syntax of MPEG data streams is arranged in a layered hierarchy. Starting at the bottom of the hierarchy and working up:

Block: An eight-row by eight-column orthogonal block of pixels. This is the basic unit to which the discrete cosine transform is applied.

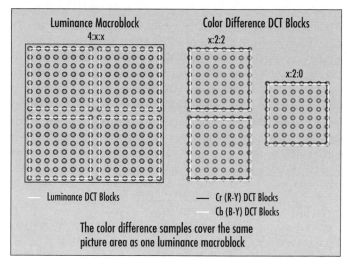

figure 10. MPEG color sampling.

Macroblock: In the typical 4:2:0 picture representation used by MPEG-2, a macroblock consists of four 8x8 blocks of luminance data (arranged in a 16x16 sample array) and two 8x8 blocks of color difference data which correspond to the area covered by the 16x16 section luminance component of the picture (see figure 10: MPEG Color Sampling). The macroblock is the basic unit used for motion compensated prediction.

Slice: A series of macroblocks. A slice is the basic synchronizing unit for reconstruction of the image data and typically consists of all the blocks in one horizontal picture interval—typically 16 lines of the picture.

Picture: A source image or reconstructed data for a single frame or two interlaced fields. A picture consists of three rectangular matrices of eight-bit numbers representing the luminance and two color difference signals.

Group of pictures (GoP): A self-contained sequence of pictures that starts with an I frame and contains a variable number of P and B frames.

The MPEG coding loop requires one or two frames of the video stream to be stored in memory, providing the reference image(s) for motion compensated prediction. Predicted frames require a second or third memory buffer.

A significant amount of the computational work in MPEG involves motion estimation—searching for matching macroblocks in two frames, to determine the direction and distance a macroblock has moved between frames (motion vectors).

Decoders use these motion vectors to reposition macroblocks from the reference frames, assembling them in a memory buffer to produce the predicted image. The encoder also contains a decoder, which is used to produce the predicted image; this prediction is *subtracted* from the original uncompressed frame, hopefully leaving only small differences. These differences are encoded using the same DCT-based techniques used to encode I frames.

The MPEG coding loop is more efficient when it can see what things look like in the future. When we start coding a new picture sequence with an I frame, moving objects obscure the background behind them; there is no way to predict what those background pixels will look like until they are revealed. If we skip forward a few frames, and we can learn two very important things: 1) what the pixels that are revealed look like; 2) the motion vectors for the objects that moved.

An MPEG encoder must have multiple frame buffers to allow it to change the order in which the pictures are coded. This is known as the **coding order**. With one frame of buffer memory forward predictions can be used to create the next P frame. With two frames of buffer memory bi-directional predictions can be used to create one or more B frames between the reference I and P frames.

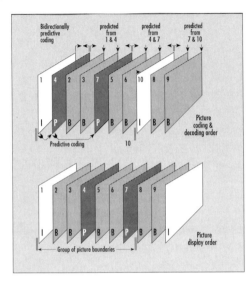

figure 11.
The MPEG coding loop.

An encoder that works at less-than-realtime rates has no problem in cheating time. It just fills its buffers with a bunch of pictures, then codes them out of order. In order to peek into the future, a realtime MPEG encoder must introduce a period of latency between the actual time of an event and the time you see it—the latency is equal to the number of frames of delay built into the encoder (this will make off-air monitoring during live news remotes almost impossible).

If a non-realtime encoder runs into a tough coding sequence, it can slow down and do a better job of motion estimation. But a realtime MPEG encoder has a finite amount of time to make encoding decisions and thus may make some compromises—either more picture artifacts or a higher data rate for the same picture quality.

A group of pictures (GoP) begins with an I frame. A GoP can be a single I frame, or it may include a variable number of P and/or B frames. GoP lengths typically increase with the frame rate of the source material, and they tend to be longer with progressive scan source material.

A new GoP begins with the next I frame: this frame may be unrelated to the previous GoP—e.g., when there is a scene cut—or it may be a continuation of the previous GoP. Because images are coded out of order, B frames that are predicted from an I frame in the following GoP are included in that GoP (see figure 11: The MPEG Coding Loop).

When a GoP contains P and B frames and after the I frame is coded, we skip ahead a few frames and code a P frame. A forward prediction is created, based on the I frame. With I and P frames in the buffers we can now make accurate predictions about the B frames that are in-between. Again, we predict what these frames should look like, then encode the differences from the actual image.

An MPEG decoder uses the reference I and P picture data and motion vectors to re-construct the B pictures. The difference information is then added to the predictions to reconstruct the images that will be displayed.

All of the serialized processes that are required for an MPEG encoder can be run on general-purpose computational engines. In most cases these *software* encoders are allowed to take as much time as they need to obtain maximum image quality.

Realtime encoders may take advantage of the slice level of the MPEG syntax to divide the image into sections that can be encoded in parallel. Each slice of the image is encoded using a separate processor, and several additional processors are used to keep track of information that is moving between slices. Early realtime MP@ML encoders used as many as 14 parallel processors to encode the image.

The coding of interlaced images requires an additional layer of sophistication, due to the temporal skewing between the fields that make up each frame. When the fields are combined, the skewing between samples interferes with the normal correlation between samples—the skewing looks like high frequency edge information.

M-JPEG systems avoid this problem by coding individual video fields; they treat the interlaced video information as if it were 50 or 60 video frames with half the number of lines. While MPEG could use the same approach, there are more efficient ways to deal with interlace; MPEG-2 added several techniques to deal with the coding of interlaced video images.

The first is adaptive field/frame-based coding at the macroblock level. An MPEG macroblock contains four DCT coding blocks. When significant skewing is detected within the DCT blocks, the samples from one field are moved into the two upper blocks while the samples from the other field are moved into the lower blocks. This improves the correlation of image data, significantly improving the coding efficiency of each DCT block (see figure 12: Field/Frame DCT Coding).

The combination of quantization at the macroblock level and field/frame based macroblock coding, on average, allows intraframe MPEG-2 coding a 2:1 improvement in compression efficiency over M-JPEG. This may eventually lead to the use of I frame MPEG-2 coding in video editing applications as the cost of MPEG encoders decline.

The second technique, added in MPEG-2 to deal with interlace is adaptive field/frame-based motion prediction. This complements the use of adaptive field/frame-based block coding, allowing separate motion vectors to be generated for the blocks that make up each field.

The MPEG specification does not define how encoding decisions are to be made. It only specifies what an MPEG-compliant bit stream must look like. Thus, it is up to the manufacturers of encoders to *differentiate* themselves in the marketplace based on

This figure illustrates the field/frame based DCT coding techniques employed in MPEG-2 for the coding of interlaced frames. The images in this diagram were captured off of a cable television feed and have been enlarged to show their sampling structure. Because of horizontal motion between fields periods, there is significant skewing in the samples. By reordering the samples within a macroblock, it is possible to improve coding efficiency.

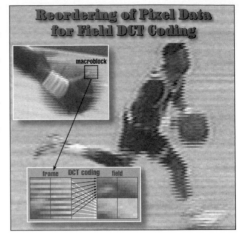

figure 12. Field/frame DCT coding.

major feature/benefit criteria: price; realtime versus non-realtime operation; and picture quality versus bit stream data rate.

Interframe coding provides a major boost to compression efficiency over intraframe techniques; this is especially true with non-realtime coding, where motion estimation can be given enough time to reach full efficiency, and scenes can be examined and the coding parameters modified to deal with specific scene content.

By eliminating the redundancy in portions of the image that are stationary, more bits can be used to reduce the quantization of DCT coefficients. Thus MPEG compression can typically operate with compression ratios in the range of 10:1 to 50:1.

The downside to the use of MPEG compression at highly constrained bit rates is that image quality may vary with scene content. When there is little motion, more high frequency coefficients are preserved and the image will be sharper. Scenes with rapid motion and lots of image detail—for example a pan from one end of the court to the other during transitions in a basketball game—may stress the encoder. This may result in the loss of resolution and increased quantization noise, or in the worst case, blocking artifacts. Fortunately, as long as the level of artifacts is not too severe, these fluctuations in image quality correlate well with the static and dynamic resolution capabilities of the human visual system.

MPEG also has problems dealing with certain common video production effects, notably the *dissolve* and *fade-to-black*. During these effects, every sample is changing with each new field or frame; there is little redundancy to eliminate. The cross dissolve is further complicated by the co-location of two images with objects moving in different directions.

Work is already underway on MPEG-4, which will deal with more advanced techniques to encode multiple image objects for transmission and compose these objects locally for display.

WHAT ABOUT AUDIO CODING?

Unlike video, audio is a continuous signal. There is no frame rate, no temporal redundancy to eliminate except when things go silent. Like video, the spectral content of audio varies over time, and with it, the information content of the signal at any moment. As with the video compression techniques described previously, the goal of the Dolby Digital/AC-3 compression algorithm, chosen by the ATSC for audio coding, is to pack information into the transmission channel more efficiently.

The Dolby Digital/AC-3 compression algorithm can encode from 1 to 5.1 channels of source audio from a PCM (Pulse-Code Modulation) representation into a serial bit stream at data rates ranging from 32 kbps to 640 kbps. The 0.1 channel refers to a fractional bandwidth channel intended to convey only low frequency (subwoofer) signals. Four channels provide surround sound and the fifth center channel delivers dialog.

The audio encoders are responsible for generating the audio elementary streams which are encoded representations of the baseband audio input signals. The flexibility of the transport system allows multiple audio elementary streams to be delivered to the receiver. These streams can include complete audio programs or a separate audio program for music and natural sound that can be mixed with dialog in multiple languages, enhanced audio for the hearing impaired, program related commentary and emergency audio messaging.

At the receiver, the transport subsystem is responsible for selecting which audio streams to deliver to the audio subsystem. The audio subsystem is responsible for decoding the audio elementary streams back into baseband audio.

The Dolby Digital/AC-3 algorithm achieves high compression efficiency by coarsely quantizing a frequency domain representation of the audio signal. For example, an uncompressed 5 Mbps audio program with 5.1 channels will typically be compressed to 384 Kbps—a 13:1 compression ratio.

The audio compression system consists of three basic operations. In the first stage, the representation of the audio signal is changed from the time domain to the frequency domain. As with video, this is a more efficient domain in which to perform psychoacoustically based audio compression.

The resulting frequency domain coefficients are then encoded. The frequency domain coefficients may be coarsely quantized, because the resulting quantizing noise will be at the same frequency as the audio signal, and relatively low signal-to-noise ratios are acceptable due to the phenomenon of psychoacoustic masking. The bit allocation operation determines, based on a psychoacoustic model of human hearing, the actual SNR (signal-to-noise ratio) that is acceptable for each individual frequency coefficient. The frequency coefficients can then be quantized to the necessary precision to deliver the desired SNR and formatted into the audio elementary stream.

The Dolby Digital/AC-3 encoding system chosen for the ATSC standard is one of several alternatives for the delivery of enhanced audio service and surround sound, that will coexist in the emerging world of digital television. The MPEG-2 standard includes tools for the coding of a variety of audio formats. MPEG-2 audio is used on DVD (as is Dolby Digital/AC-3), and may be used in some areas of the world for terrestrial broadcasts.

Like Dolby Digital/AC-3, the MPEG-2 audio tools permit the coding of multichannel audio. The basic stereo mix is encoded to be compatible with the MPEG-1 audio standard. Support is provided for a variety of multi-channel and surround systems including Dolby Pro Logic. These modes include: three channel, with a center dialog channel; four channel, with a center channel and single surround channel for rear speakers; 5.1 channels with center channel, separate right and left surround channels and subwoofer channel; and 7.1 channels, like 5.1 with the addition of right and left center channels for better dialog placement.

DEALING WITH DIGITAL COMPRESSION
IN THE BROADCAST FACILITY

We have completed a behind-the-curtain peek at the video compression techniques that made analog television possible, and the digital techniques that will enable the next generation of digital television broadcasting. We are now entering a transition period where we must deal with both, and begin the process of upgrading broadcast facilities to take full advantage of the new services enabled by digital broadcasting.

One area of concern during this transition period relates to the proper handling of analog and digital video signals in the broadcast facilities: Where and how to use various compression techniques appropriately to maximize the quality ultimately delivered to the viewer, and what to avoid to prevent unnecessary degradation of signal quality.

Perhaps the best way to look at this issue is to consider the use of appropriate video compression techniques as we move from image acquisition, through the production and distribution environments, and finally encode content for digital transmission–the digital video food chain.

From this perspective, the content creation and distribution process looks something like a bandwidth funnel; at certain points along the food chain, we must throw information away to meet bandwidth constraints as we move from acquisition to final program distribution.

As is the case with current digital component systems, the first steps in bit rate reduction will take place during image acquisition. For many applications, it may be desirable to preserve virtually all of the image content within each frame to facilitate subsequent image processing. At this end of the video food chain, we can generally afford more storage bandwidth, thus we can preserve more of the original image information.

The next major squeeze typically takes place when content is encoded for distribution—perhaps through a satellite link—to facilities where it may be subject to further modification. This is often referred to as *contribution quality*. Modifications may include editing and integration with other content; thus, the bit rate reduction techniques used for contribution quality typically reflect these requirements.

Finally, when the content is ready for broadcast, we can take the last step in bit rate reduction. We squeeze what's left into the constrained bandwidth of a digital broadcast channel, or squeeze further to deliver a multiplex of programs and data broadcasts. An HDTV program, originally acquired at a bit rate of 1.2 gigabits per second (Gbps) is compressed by a factor of 66:1 to fit in an 18 Mbps portion of the 19.39 Mbps digital channel. SDTV programs sampled using ITU-R 601 specs will typically be compressed by factors of 20 to 40:1 to produce bit streams in the range of 4 to 8 Mbps.

Unlike the analog television food chain, if we preserve the data—both images and *metadata*—we can maintain quality as content moves from one process to the next.

What is metadata? It is data about the data. This can include ancillary data such as time code, or text-based descriptors of the content. It may also include information about the image processing history, links to the original source and related versions, and encoding decisions that were made the *last time* the images or sound were encoded. Things like the choice of quantization tables for each DCT coding block, and motion vectors.

If we maintain the metadata about the processing history of the content, we can use it to save time and preserve quality when the content is re-encoded. It is only when we modify the data, or throw more data away that the potential for errors exists. The term used to describe these losses is *concatenation errors*.

For example, it may be necessary to convert the representation of an image stream (file format and encoding techniques) when it is transferred from a field acquisition format to a nonlinear editing system. If we are working the same sampling parameters, and both systems use block based DCT coding, it should be possible to effect this transfer with no loss in quality, assuming that the target system does not impose additional bandwidth constraints that require additional quantization of the DCT coefficients.

In order to facilitate this type of file conversion, the bit stream must be decoded to the DCT coefficient level, reversing the entropy coding, quantization and field/frame based ordering of the coefficients. The coefficients can then be re-encoded using the same quantization decisions used when the content was originally encoded.

If the conversion involves moving from an environment with different levels of quantization for each macroblock, to a single level of quantization for each block in the image, we can still preserve all of the DCT coefficients by choosing the table with the lowest level of quantization (highest quality).

A related approach to the minimization of concatenation errors with MPEG-2 compression has been developed by a European research consortium called the ATLANTIC Project. These European broadcasters are trying to deal with the problems of adding information to programs as they move from the network, through regional operations centers, and finally to local transmission facilities.

The ATLANTIC decoding/re-encoding process uses a technique called *Mole Technology*. When an MPEG-2 stream is decoded, the metadata about the encoding decisions is buried in "uncompressed 601" signal; this is accomplished by using the least significant bit of each sample to encode the Mole data. If the content is not modified, the ATLANTIC encoder recognizes the presence of the Mole, and uses the encoded data to exactly reproduce the original encoding decisions. If the mole is disturbed, then the frame or a section of the frame must be re-encoded, with the potential for concatenation errors.

Another approach is to pass MPEG-2 encoded streams through, without modification, and add ancillary data, which can be turned into an image object and composed

DTV IN THE REAL WORLD

UNDERSTANDING DIGITAL

PRE-PRODUCTION

PRODUCTION

AUDIO

GRAPHICS & COMPOSITING

POST PRODUCTION

DELIVERY & DUPLICATION

ENGINEERING & TRANSMISSION

APPENDIX

GLOSSARY

with the MPEG-2 video in the receiver. This approach would require receiver standards that are currently being developed, but may not be deployed in early digital television appliances. The MPEG committee is currently working on the MPEG-4 standard, which provides a syntax for the composition of a video background with multiple video foreground objects and locally generated graphics.

Like HTML, an object oriented method for composing visual information in a remote viewing environment, the MPEG-4 concepts will allow future DTV devices to compose video information in unique ways for local consumption. This is analogous, in many ways, to moving the "master control switcher" into the DTV receiver. Rather than splicing all content into a single program stream for decoding, the receiver will have the ability to switch between sub-streams, e.g., with localized versions of commercials, and to overlay visual objects, such as commercial tags, localized to the receiving site. Transitions such as dissolves and fades can be applied in the receiver, after decoding of the image streams.

At the beginning of this section, I suggested that it would be appropriate to let go of preconceptions founded in analog thinking. Concatenation errors are one of those problems that looks troubling, from an analog perspective, yet may be almost irrelevant in the world of digital television broadcasting.

Out of necessity, analog production techniques evolved as a serialized process. The first generation of digital tape formats and production equipment made it possible to eliminate the quality losses associated with multiple generations of image processing. The first generation of digital nonlinear editing and image composition products turned editing and image composition into a parallel processing task.

Nonlinear systems work with the original bits, acquired with digital formats, or first generation digitized copies. Any composition of any complexity can be created in one additional generation, by decoding each object layer to the original samples, combining all the objects, then compressing the result. The process is non–destructive of the original source. A different version is just a different playback list.

Furthermore, many of these tools are resolution independent. They can be configured to output any format at any resolution, and accept visual objects from many sources, using many encoding formats, at many resolutions.

What other approach could possibly work for a digital broadcast standard with 36 *optional* video formats? From this perspective, it quickly becomes apparent that formats are an artifact of the analog world. Now there is only data.

[No smoke. No mirroring.]

You already have enough to think about when choosing a video server system. So we'll keep it simple. SeaChange is the industry's leading supplier of digital server systems. We offer a full lineup for broadcast, broadband and Internet.

Because we're focused solely on television, our video servers are engineered for your most demanding applications—video on demand, play-to-air, digital advertising, and Internet streaming. Which means you experience substantially better performance, efficiency and reliability for the money—without costly mirroring.

With SeaChange, you can affordably buy into open standards and networked solutions that offer real opportunities for streamlining your single or multichannel operation.

Get all the facts at www.schange.com. And learn why we're playing on 30,000 channels worldwide.

SeaChange
INTERNATIONAL
www.schange.com

HDTV

PESA

**High
Definition
Solutions**

Alliance SD/HD
Digital Master
Control

Cougar HD
32x32 Matrix

Ocelot HD
16x16, 16x8 Matrix

LNS-8 HD
8x2 Matrix

PESA's lineup of HDTV routers is right for today's needs. For maximum flexibility take a look at the new **Cougar HD**. You can start as small as 4x4 and expand to 32x32 with plug-in cards. The PESA **Alliance** Master Control Switcher makes sense for mixed SDTV and HDTV broadcasting too. Ask about PESA's all-new HDTV distribution amplifiers!

Tools for the Transition!

HDTV won't replace all other formats anytime soon. That's why the PESA **Alliance** Master Control Switcher makes so much sense. The **Alliance** is designed for; 1) full-time SDTV; 2) full-time HDTV; or 3) mixed SDTV and HDTV broadcasting. Multi-format technology allows SDTV systems to be upgraded to HDTV, preserving your investment. The PESA **Alliance** also supports multi-channel capability, so you're ready to handle any programming strategy.

PESA's lineup of HDTV routers is right for today's needs. For maximum flexibility take a look at the **Cougar HD**. You can start as small as 4x4 and expand to 32x32 with plug-in cards. The **Ocelot HD** delivers a 16x8 or 16x16 matrix in only 1RU, making it great for field or studio use. The **LNS-8 HD** 8x2 switcher is perfect for monitoring, editing, telecine, and automated applications.

PESA
Switching
Systems

Corporate Sales Office
35 Pinelawn Road, Suite 99E
Melville, NY 11747
Tel: 631-845-5020 Tel: 800-328-1008
Fax: 631-845-5023 www.pesa.com

The pre-production process takes into consideration all that happens until the final product is delivered. But in this new digital age, there are tools to help the producer and videographer with this process. But first a story...

"I want it to look like *Toy Story.*"
This is to be a children's television series...a mixture of 3D animation, puppets and live action. There are to be thirteen, 30-minute programs. The budget is $150,000 per program. The cost of doing just the three to five minutes of animation will be $75,000 per program. Add in actors, sets, costumes, props, crew, equipment, post and everything else you can think of and you're absolutely correct—this show is still *in pre-production, even though we originally told this story in the first edition.*

DIGITAL CAN BE DANGEROUS

MICHAEL SILBERGLEID

Just as with analog, in the digital pre-production process you concern yourself with the final product—whether that be a master videotape or hundreds of distribution copies that you may or may not be responsible for.

But digital technology has made almost anything that can be imagined possible—for a price. Effects in the analog world were limited and simple (or consisted of true-life models), while digital effects can bring the cost of a project to over $10,000 per frame.

So, like nonlinear editing, we think about the final result and work backwards to try and achieve that result.

But through this process, keep something in mind—digital does not mean nonlinear or disk-based, but nonlinear and disk-based do mean digital (a clarification is needed here for accuracy: laserdiscs are nonlinear but they are analog as are phonograph records).

In analog, determining quality was primarily a function of the camera, microphone and videotape format chosen. In digital it is similar, but tape "format" concerns have been replaced with concerns for the digital format—the resolution of the video signal itself. The same way you have learned the quality restrictions of analog tape formats, you'll have to learn the differences between resolutions such as 4:1:1 and 4:2:2:4 and when each is appropriate.

While there is no generational loss with digital video, there is the possibility of a loss of resolution. For example, if footage is acquired in 4:2:2, later transferred to 4:1:1 (or acquired in 4:1:1), and then digitally broadcast as 4:2:0, what actually is broadcast is sort of like 4:1:0. Based on the current definition of 4:2:0—i.e. 1/2 horizontal and 1/2 vertical resolution relative to luminance, this is true. Going from 4:2:2 to 4:1:1 causes the color difference signals to be reduced from 1/2 to 1/4 of the horizontal luminance resolution. The vertical resolution of the color difference signals are the same for both 4:2:2 and 4:1:1—i.e. the same as the vertical resolution of the luma channel. When encoded as 4:2:0, the vertical resolution of the chroma channels is reduced by 1/2. Thus the net result will be color difference signals with 1/4 the horizontal resolution and 1/2 the vertical resolution of the luminance channel. However, it may not be proper to call this 4:1:0.

CHOOSING A DIGITAL FORMAT

Just as shooting in VHS and editing in BetaSP will give you VHS quality in a BetaSP format, shooting digital 4:1:1 and posting in 4:2:2 will only give you 4:1:1 resolution in a 4:2:2 format. Your lowest resolution will always be your limiting factor. If you are trying to see the difference between 4:2:2 and 4:1:1, you should be looking at fine chroma detail—eye color, lips, etc.

Keep in mind that, as Patrick Griffis, formerly with Panasonic and now with Microsoft, once said *bits is bucks.* The higher the resolution and bit rate of the format, the more the format will cost to operate. This concept is especially important in transmission—a limited bandwidth system, where there are only a finite amount of bits available each second and compression is used to squeeze the most out of the bits available.

Compression is also used to bring the cost of digital video formats down, so as always, higher quality with more bits and less compression will cost you more.

As with analog, a format is chosen based upon the quality required; but today, producers have to be concerned with not just the how a program will look now, but if the quality of that program will be high enough for that program to continue to be an asset years down the road.

Following are three charts to help you evaluate formats, perhaps the toughest thing when going digital. No chart is as important as how a format looks to your (and your client's) eyes. Without comparison, a format on its own can look excellent to your eye, but comparing formats in a "shoot out" can shock and surprise you as your favorite format falls to the wayside. What is "good enough" for you, may not be "good enough" for your client once they see a better looking format.

CONSUMER VERSUS PROFESSIONAL FORMATS

The consumer DV format has brought inexpensive (at least compared to professional formats) digital quality to the masses. There are also a great many professionals using the consumer DV format. But there can be some serious problems with this practice.

While the "back-end" of every consumer DV camcorder will record the same high quality 4:1:1 signal as a professional DV dockable back, the "front-end" might be dis-

DTV IN THE REAL WORLD

UNDERSTANDING DIGITAL

PRE-PRODUCTION

PRODUCTION

AUDIO

GRAPHIC & COMPOSITING

POST PRODUCTION

DELIVERY & DUPLICATION

ENGINEERING & TRANSMISSION

APPENDIX

GLOSSARY

Comparison of Horizontal Resolutions of Analog and Digital Videotape Formats
(not the only determining factor in format comparisons)

Format	Resolution	Format	Resolution
ATSC Transmission	4:2:0	DVCPRO50 (interlace)	4:2:2
Betacam	2.7:0.9:0.9*	DVCPRO HD	8:2.6:2.6*****
Betacam SP	3:1:1	DVCPRO P	
Betacam SX	4:2:2	(progressive)	4:2:0
Betamax	2:0.3:0.3	DVD	4:2:0
D1 (8-bit)	4:2:2	ED-Beta	4.1:0.3:0.3
D1 SP (10-bit)	4:2:2	HD D5	10.7:5.3:5.3****
D2 (NTSC)	4.7:0.8:0.4**	HDCAM	8:2.6:2.6*****
D3	4.7:0.8:0.4**	HDD-1000	10.7:5.3:5.3
D5 (13.5 MHz		Hi-8	3.33:0.33:0.33
sampling)	4:2:2	ITU-R 601	4:2:2
D5 (18 MHz		Laser Disc	3.7:0.8:0.4**
sampling)	5.3:2.7:2.7	M-II	3:1:1*******
D6	10.7:5.3:5.3***	MPEG IMX	4:2:2
D9/Digital-S	4:2:2	NTSC Transmission	2.8:0.8:0.4
D9 HD	8:2.6:2.6*****	One-inch (Type C)	4:0.8:0.4**/*******
DCT	4:2:2	S-VHS	3.3:0.3:0.3
Digital-8	4:1:1	Super Highband	
Digital Betacam	4:2:2	Beta(max)	2.8:0.3:0.3
DV (NTSC)	4:1:1	SuperBeta	2.5:0.3:0.3
DV (PAL)	4:2:0	U-Matic	2.0:0.3:0.3
DVB Transmission	4:2:0	U-Matic SP	2.8:0.3:0.3
DVCAM (NTSC)	4:1:1	VHS	1.9:0.3:0.3
DVCAM (PAL)	4:2:0		
DVCPRO/D7	4:1:1		

*The specification for Betacam has the high frequencies as much as 6 dB down.
**Depends on NTSC encoder
***Based on sampling rate, D6 would be 22:11:11.
****Based on sampling rate, HD D5 would be 22:11:11.
*****Based on sampling rate, D9, DVCPRO HD and HDCAM would be 16.5:5.5:5.5.
******There are slight differences between the U.S. and NHK versions.
*******Assumes a 6 MHz luminance bandwidth.

appointing. Most of the consumer DV camcorders use only one CCD for imaging. But some use three CCDs just as professional cameras do. But these CCDs are smaller and with less pixels than professional camera CCDs. While broadcasters and videographers debate the usefulness of consumer DV, others are using it successfully. In some circumstances the weaker "front-end" holds up incredibly well, in others it does not. The one aspect that most professionals agree on is that for the best imaging, careful attention must be paid to lighting for the consumer CCDs to produce their best images.

But even though the cost is less than a professional digital camcorder, the potential user of a consumer DV camcorder should thoroughly test the camcorder for usefulness with regard to the anticipated image quality. A few thousand dollars is still a few thousand dollars.

4:3 VERSUS 16:9

Do you go wide? If so, do you protect for 4:3? Do you pan and scan? Do you letterbox? Do you know how to shoot wide (see Chapter 4: Production)? And what do you do if you shot in 4:3 but will display in 16:9? Do you use side panels (also known as pillarboxing)? Do you expand the image to 16:9 and risk cutting off something important from the top and/or bottom?

How do you shoot for today while protecting for tomorrow?

Unfortunately, there are no clear answers to these questions. The answers come from your skill as a video professional and from your clients as the recipients of the finished product. They come from asking yourself and your client questions regarding each individual project and how it will be used in the future, not just today. And it is your job to play devil's advocate with your client regarding 4:3 versus 16:9.

Popular Digital Video Recording Formats

Specification/Format	Betacam SP (PWM) (for comparison)	Ampex DCT (700d)	Betacam SX	ComCutter / Editcam	D1	D2	D3
Video S/N	Y: >51dB / R-Y/B-Y: >49dB	Y:55dB	Y: >60dB	Y: 56dB	Y: 56dB	Y: 54dB	Y: 54dB
Bandwidth	Y: 4.5MHz / R-Y/B-Y: 1.5MHz	Y:5.75MHz / Pb/Pr:2.75Mhz	Y:5.75MHz / R-Y/B-Y:2.75Mhz	5MHz +0/-1dB	Y:5.75MHz / R-Y/B-Y:2.75Mhz	5.5MHz +/-3dB, 6MHz +0/-2dB	6.2Mhz
Video Data Rate	—	88Mbps	18Mbps	4.8Mbps	172Mbps	94Mbps	90Mbps
Recording Data Rate	—	124.7Mbps	40Mbps	Up to 90Mbps	225Mbps	115Mbps	115Mbps
Type of Signal/Resolution	Analog Y/R-Y/B-Y / 3:1:1	4:2:2	4:2:2	4:2:2 / AVR-70 and AVR-70H	4:2:2 (component)	4fsc (composite) / 4,7,0.8,0.4	4fsc / 4,7,0.8,0.4
Sampling Rate	—	13.5MHz / 8-bit	13.5MHz / 8-bit	13.5MHz / 8-bit	13.5MHz / 8-bit	14.3MHz / 8-bit	14.3MHz / 8-bit
Compression Type & Ratio	—	2:1 DCT	MPEG-2 4:2:2P@ML / 10:1	M-JPEG Dynamic, up to 4:1	Uncompressed	Uncompressed	Uncompressed
Digital Audio S/N	AFM: >85dB	90dB	90dB	DAT standard	>102dB	>95dB	>105dB
Analog Audio S/N	Longitudinal: >72dB	—	—	—	>42dB (cue)	>50dB (cue)	>44dB (cue)
Digital Audio Freq. Response	AFM: 20Hz-20kHz	20Hz-20kHz	20Hz-20kHz	20Hz-20kHz +1dB	20Hz-20kHz +/-0.5dB	20Hz-20kHz +0.5dB/-1.0dB	20Hz-20kHz
Analog Audio Freq. Response	Longitudinal: 40-15KHz	—	—	—	100Hz-12kHz +/-3dB (cue)	100Hz-12kHz +/-3dB (cue)	100Hz-12kHz (cue)
Wow & Flutter (analog only)	Longitudinal: <0.1%	—	—	—	—	—	—
# of Digital Audio Channels	—	4	4	4	4	4	4
Audio Sampling & Bit Rate	—	48kHz / 20-bit	48kHz / 16-bit	48KHz / 16-bit	48KHz / 20-bit	48KHz / 20-bit	20-bit
# of Analog Audio Channels	4 (2-AFM, 2-Longitudinal)	—	1 cue	0	1 cue	1 cue	0
Incl. Insert Editing All Channels	Y	—	Y	Y	Y	Y	Y
Timecode Type	VITC/LTC	—	VITC/LTC	SMPTE Embedded	VITC/LTC	VITC/LTC	VITC/LTC
Userbits	Y	—	Y	Y	Y	Y	Y
Recording Lengths	5-90	208 max	60-180	30 / 30-96 with 4GB FieldPak	6-94	32-208	63-245
Faster Than Realtime	N	—	Y	Disk-based zero transfer time	N	N	N
Other	Industry analog standard. Specs for metal tape. For oxide tape performance is slightly less.		Certain models can play Betacam SP. Certain models are hybrid with HDD. Encodes with I and B frames.	DNS-11W switchable 4:3 and 16:9 / Ethernet support / built-in IP address, target/host/gateway settings / software upgradeable / Retro-Loop allowing for recording the past few seconds / time-lapse recording up to one frame per day			

Notes: Cue track audio is used during search speeds. 4:2:2 formats have a sampling rate of 13.5 MHz for luminance and 6.75 MHz for color difference/chroma channels. 4:1:1 formats have a sampling rate of 13.5 MHz for luminance and 3.375 MHz for color difference/chroma channels.

For more comparison information, see the joint EBU/SMPTE Task Force report on the Harmonization of Standards for the Exchange of Program Material as Bit Streams, released in 1998, available at www.smpte.org/engr/ebumeet1.html.

Specification/Format	D5	D6	D9 (Digital-S)	Digital Betacam	DVCAM	DVCPRO (D7)	HDCAM
Video S/N	Y: 62dB	Y: >56dB	Y: >55dB	Y: 62dB	Y: >54dB	Y: 60dB	Y: 56dB
Bandwidth	Y: 5.75MHz / R-Y/B-Y: 2.75MHz	Y: 30Mhz / Pb/Pr / 5Mhz	Y: 13.5 / R-Y/B-Y: 6.76 Mhz	Y:5.75Mhz / R-Y/B-Y: 2.75MHz	Y: 5.0MHz / C: 1.5MHz	Y: 5.75MHz / R-Y/B-Y: 1.5MHz	Y: 23MHz / Pb/Pr: 7MHz
Video Data Rate	220Mbps	922Mbps	50 Mbps	95Mbps	25Mbps	25Mbps	—
Recording Data Rate	300Mbps	1.188Gbps	100 Mbps	127.76Mbps	125.2Mbps	99Mbps	180 Mbps
Type of Signal/Resolution	4:2:2	—	4:2:2	4:2:2	4:1:1	4:1:1	8:2.6:2.6 decimated to 3:1:1
Sampling Rate	13.5MHz / 10-bit	— same HDCAM	13.5MHz / 8-bit	13.5MHz / 10-bit	13.5Mhz / 8-bit	13.5Mhz / 8-bit	Y: 74.25MHz/Pb/Pr: 37.125MHz
Compression Type & Ratio	Uncompressed	Uncompressed	DV-DCT / 3.3:1	DCT; 2.34:1	DV-DCT / 5:1	DV-DCT / 5:1	DCT / 7:1 (4.4:1 after 3:1:1)
Digital Audio S/N	>105dB	>90dB	90dB	90dB	>85dB	90dB	>95dB
Analog Audio S/N	>44dB (cue)	—	—	>45dB (cue)	—	—	>40dB (cue)
Digital Audio Freq. Response	20Hz-20kHz	20Hz-20kHz	20Hz-20kHz	20Hz-20kHz	20Hz-20kHz (2 channel) / 20Hz-14kHz (4 channel)	20Hz-20kHz	20Hz-20kHz +0.5/-1.0dB
Analog Audio Freq. Response	—	—	—	—	—	—	90Hz-12kHz +/-3.0dB (cue)
Wow & Flutter (analog only)	—	—	—	—	—	—	—
# of Digital Audio Channels	4	10	2 and 4	4	2 and 4	2	4
Audio Sampling & Bit Rate	48kHz / 20-bit	48kHz / 24-bit	48kHz / 16-bit	48kHz / 20-bit	48kHz/16-bit(2); 32kHz/12-bit(4)	48kHz / 16-bit	48kHz / 20-bit
# of Analog Audio Channels	1 cue	—	2 cue (1+3 and 2+4)	1 cue	0	1 cue	1 cue
Incl. Insert Editing All Channels	Y	Y	Y	Y	Y	Y	Y
Timecode Type	VITC/LTC	VITC/LTC	SMPTE 12M	VITC/LTC	SMPTE/EBU standard	VITC/LTC	VITC/LTC
Userbits	Y	Y	Y	Y	Y	Y	Y
Recording Lengths	32-125	64 max	10-124	6-124	12-184	6-123	22 & 40 / 64 & 124
Faster Than Realtime	N	N	N	N	Y	Y	N
Other	For 18NHz, 8-bit sampling resolution is 5.3:2.7:2.7. Playback D-3. HD processor and HD version available for 8-bit and 10-bit, 1080i / 1035i with optional 525p / 525i downconverter. HD version with 720p / 1080i switchable available.	Philips has a D-6 modification for film work with slightly modified specs and 12 audio channels.	Certain models playback S-VHS, 2 uncompressed VBI lines. On 4 channel machines-audio sample rate converter, PB levels, optional embedded audio/SDI, DMF increases distribution tape time by 20%. Two channel machines can playback and record ch. 1&2 from/to 4 channel machines. HD version with 8 channel audio, 62 min max. 720p/1080i switchable available mid-2000.	Playback Betacam SP.	Playback/record consumer DV. Certain models also playback DVCPRO. One model outputs MPEG-2 4:2:2 P@ML. 25 Mbps.	Playback consumer DV & DVCAM / DVCPRO50 version available for 4:2:2 / DVCPROP version available for 4:2:0 P with 62 min capacity. HD version available with 32 min capacity, 8 channel audio and 6.6:1 DCT compression.	High definition with 525 downconversion available / 4:3/16:9 switchable

All information provided by manufacturers & published information. (A "—" signifies information not supplied.

DTV IN THE REAL WORLD
UNDERSTANDING DIGITAL
PRE-PRODUCTION
PRODUCTION
AUDIO
GRAPHIC & COMPOSITING
POST PRODUCTION
DELIVERY & DUPLICATION
ENGINEERING & TRANSMISSION
APPENDIX
GLOSSARY

Theoretical Comparison of Analog and/or Digital Production, Editing and Delivery to Betacam SP Generation Quality

Shoot	Post	Deliver	Generation Quality (Betacam SP Theoretical Comparison)
Analog	Analog	Analog	3
Analog	Analog	Analog Laser Disc	2
Analog	Analog	Digital	2
Analog	Digital	Analog	2
Analog	Digital	Analog Laser Disc	1
Analog	Digital	Digital	1
Digital	Analog	Analog	2
Digital	Analog	Analog Laser Disc	1
Digital	Analog	Digital	1
Digital	Digital	Analog	1
Digital	Digital	Analog Laser Disc	Better than 1
Digital	Digital	Digital	Better than 1

Notes:
1. Keep in mind that a first generation analog signal can be of better quality than a first generation digital signal since analog is exact, and digital is a representation of the analog signal. See Chapter 1: Understanding Digital, for a more complete explanation.
2. The analog format and digital resolution can alter the theoretical generation quality—I am assuming an analog acquisition and editing format of BetaSP and a digital resolution of 4:2:2. Obviously a third generation VHS tape will look worse than a third generation BetaSP tape.
3. For delivery tapes that are then mass duplicated in VHS, add 1.5 to the Generation Quality (BetaSP Theoretical Comparison).

FILM?

Yes...film. A great percentage of prime time television programs and high-end commercials are shot on film. That is why, in the pre-production process, film is still a valid format for consideration for producing high quality television.

While it used to be that Super 16mm did not have the resolution for high definition television, that is changing. New Super 16mm film stocks and telecine gates get rid of the "grain the size of boulders" problem. Meanwhile, all of us agree that 35mm film is still a beautiful format for acquisition if high definition television is the goal.

Although film is expensive to use (about $400 for 11 minutes of Super 16 film with processing at 24 fps), there are certain instances where film is the only way to go...primarily because of the "film look" (although that can now be digitally duplicated). And what digital technology allows us to do with video, it can also allow us to do with film once digitized.

Super 16 color negative film is now available in 800-foot lengths. This gives the cinematographer the ability to record 22 minutes of Super 16 film at the normal 24 fps without having to change magazines or film. Previously, the longest length available was 400 feet for an 11-minute capacity. Of course some people shoot at a higher frame rate for higher quality—30 fps, 50 fps (in Europe) and 60 fps in the U.S.

Present-day telecines not only output video (both analog and digital), but can output individual film frames as data files that can be archived, and more importantly, manipulated with digital imaging post production tools.

Last year, we saw the introduction of the new HD 1080p/24 format as an international ITU worldwide standard, from which all other formats can be derived. Also called D-Cinema (Digital Cinema) and E-Cinema (Electronic Cinema) by different manufacturers and their supporters, the format is becoming a base platform for HD production at the standard film frame rate. *(Editor's note: While film is projected at*

24 fps, movie theater projectors shutter each individual frame anywhere from twice to four times.)

1080p/24 is in active use with the many of the CBS-HD prime time lineup being mastered in the format as of early 2000 (they are delivered as 1080i/30). The biggest benefit is not needing to undo 3:2 pulldown when needing to transfer to European standards or for mastering a DVD. The 24 fps rate serves as a basis from which all needed formats can be derived, no matter what the frame rate. The 1080 line rate also means that it is fairly easy to produce a 720p transfer or any of the other ATSC Table 3 formats. One of the questions that have been raised is the limitations of the 24 fps rate for fast moving action, so most producers in early 2000 are using the format for dramas, but not for sports or other fast-paced applications.

DIGITAL PRE-PRODUCTION: TOOLS OF THE TRADE
ROBERT M. GOODMAN

Every production starts with an idea. An idea that, sooner or later, will become a treatment, script or set of storyboards. For the simplest productions, a few scribbles on paper may suffice. However, as the complexity of the production increases or if the production values of the final program are important, pre-production planning is critical to success. Digital technology has blurred the line between pre-production, production and post. New tools for pre-production are providing greater control over the entire production process and making it easier for producers to plan for and anticipate production challenges. The benefit of better pre-production planning is the ability to produce programs with higher production values for less money. So, where exactly does pre-production planning begin?

In the past, pre-production began with budgeting and scheduling. The producer or a production manager used the information in the script or storyboards to plan out the production. Digital technology has shifted the start of pre-production to the writing and development phase. The reasons will become clear if you understand the current capabilities of scriptwriting software.

SCRIPTWRITING SOFTWARE
The best scriptwriting software provides a wide range of reports and data for pre-production planning and on set. Before discussing these tools one clarification is in order; "scriptwriting software" is a misnomer. These programs are actually script formatters because even in the digital environment, the writer must provide the creativity and originality necessary for good storytelling.

There are two generally accepted formats for scripts. The screenplay format is widely used because one page, properly formatted, accurately translates into one minute of screen time. The AV format, with separate columns for video and audio, is used for switched multicamera shows. Variations on these two basic formats regularly spring up to suit the needs of a particular producer or program.

There are two types of scriptwriting software: add-on templates or macro programs for popular word processing programs, such as Microsoft Word, and standalone scriptwriting software. The majority of these programs are designed to properly format scripts in the screenplay format. A few programs can also prepare scripts in the AV format (Scriptware and ScriptWerx) or display storyboards in the script (Script Wizard and ScriptWerx). One program, ScriptThing (also sold as Movie Magic Screenwriter) can link scenes to storyboards created in other applications. ScriptThing also has the ability to create and playback interactive scripts for multimedia and game design applications.

Formats aside, scripts are the blueprints for production. All the information necessary to plan a production is embedded in the script. Software designed for scriptwriting tracks this information, which allows producers or production managers to generate reports useful for pre-production and production.

Some reports are simple lists. For example, many programs can generate a list of all the speaking roles or unique locations. More detailed reports are available if the producer or writer marks or tags the props, non-speaking roles, special effects and other special items mentioned in the script. Most of the standalone scriptwriting programs can print this information as a breakdown report on a scene-by-scene basis; all can export the information to Screenplay Systems' Movie Magic Scheduling program, the industry standard for scheduling.

STORYBOARDING

Storyboards are another way of communicating the ideas and intent of the project. If the project is a television commercial, a set of storyboards will often take the place of a script. Directors, art directors and directors of photography prefer to work with storyboards in their pre-production planning process. If you know how to draw, it's easy to create a set of storyboards that will suit your needs. Unfortunately, most of us do not draw well enough to create even the most basic of storyboards, but computer software enables anyone to produce useable storyboards.

Power Production's Storyboard Quick v3.0 uses libraries of pre-drawn 2D figures and locations that can be manipulated to produce basic storyboards. It's simple enough that nearly anyone can use it to improve planning and on-set communications. Storyboard Artist v3.0, a step up in complexity, adds drawing tools, more libraries and the ability to playback a sequence of storyboards. These sequences can be saved as Quicktime or AVI files. This program makes it possible to create simple animatic versions of a project. Artist is also useful for interactive or multimedia program design because storyboards can be linked in any order. The program can save storyboards in HTML format to permit posting them on the Web. Storyboards created by Storyboard Quick or Storyboard Artist can be linked to scripts written with ScriptThing, Movie Magic Screenwriter, Scriptware or Final Draft from within Power Production's software. ScriptThing and Movie Magic Screenwriter can link Storyboard Quick or Artist files to scenes in a script.

Metacreation's Poser v4.0 program is at the other end of the sophistication scale from Storyboard Quick, although Poser is very easy to use. It's a clear demonstration that ease of use has no relationship to sophistication. Poser allows you to manipulate a library of 3D models of the human figure, men, women and children, which can be posed in any position and set in any environment. The models can be clothed from costume libraries which include business and casual attire. Height, weight, size and body type are adjustable. A library of props adds to the realism. You can use a paint program to create an appropriate wardrobe for your characters. Backgrounds or environments can be scanned in from location photographs, the set designer's drawings or pulled from other graphics programs. After the figures have been placed within a space, Poser provides full control over the placement of the camera and lights. The view of the figures automatically changes to reflect the changing perspective of the camera as you move the camera. It's just as easy to predetermine the impact of lighting on a scene because when you move the lights the changes are immediately visible.

Poser v4.0 also produces animation sequences quickly and easily. Simply create a few poses and the program automatically builds all the in-between frames, and output the sequence as a series of numbered frames or as an AVI or QuickTime file. You can choreograph the camera instead of the figures or create sequences in which both the camera and the figures move. The possibilities are endless because of the enormous flexibility built into this program. If you have enough time and storage space on your computer, you could model every scene in your program prior to actually shooting it. Metacreation's Poser, originally developed to make designing 3D characters easier, is equally adept at pushing the concept of storyboarding to its natural limits.

BUDGETING

If your projects require multiple shooting days, it's time to consider using budgeting software. Budgeting programs reduce the time it takes to prepare detailed bids. These tools also prevent future surprises by triggering a lot of "oh yeah, we need that!" and can make the financial side of pre-production less onerous.

Budgeting programs use one of two standard formats: the Association of Independent Commercial Producers (AICP) Film Production Bid Form or the Feature Film format. The AICP form was developed to make it easier for advertising agency producers to compare production quotes from different companies. The Association established a standardized form with preset categories and lines. The AICP form has changed because new technologies have had a big impact on traditional methods in commercial production. The feature film format is less rigid because it must accommodate accounting differences that exist among the major studios.

Feature film budgets use a topsheet or summary page. The topsheet is a list of categories, or accounts, with subtotals and a budget total. This first page is arranged into traditional "above the line" (executives, talent and creative personnel) and "below the line" (craft and technical personnel and production expenses) categories. The distinguishing characteristic of the feature format is that dollar amounts can be entered in any subtotal category on the topsheet; this is impossible to do on most AICP summary pages. The advantage of this approach is that producers and production managers can prepare a quick budget guesstimate for the powers that be. The guesstimate can be substantiated later by forcing the underlying detail lines to add up to the guess.

Are either of these models useful for digital video production? Most producers could benefit from the detail and ability to track costs that are the backbone of these programs. When you're planning a production, a list of line items and categories is a handy reminder of the critical resources you'll need to produce a show. It also makes it harder to forget the little things—such as coffee, fruit and muffins for eight or 50 people every morning for five days—something that can easily slip your mind on a complex production. Forgetting to include the cost of a meal on a one-day shoot with a small crew is a minor miscue; on a shoot with a large crew and cast, simple over-sights can be financially disastrous and threaten the morale of the production team.

The best reasons to use budgeting software are to be able to quickly determine your costs and profits and to prepare a presentable estimate. Budgeting software also makes it easy to play the "what if" games, such as: Is it cheaper to go into overtime or to add a day to the schedule? These programs can help you arrive at the most cost-effective way to produce a project.

Another factor to consider is the IRS rules about independent contractors in production. Most crew personnel have been relegated to employee status. Producers and production companies are responsible for paying FICA (social security taxes) and providing workers' compensation insurance to these freelancers. Budgeting programs accurately estimate the total costs for cast and crew, including fringe benefits such as payroll taxes, workers' compensation, service fees, agent fees and pension and welfare costs. Some fringe benefits may be calculated only on base salary and others on base salary and overtime. It's complicated, but budgeting software makes these calculations headache-free.

AICP OR FEATURE STYLE?

Should you select AICP bidding software or a feature budgeting program? If you work frequently with advertising agencies and plan to do commercial production, invest in an AICP-style bidding program. On the other hand, if you want the flexibility to customize the budget categories to meet your needs and those of your clients, feature film and television budgeting software may be a better fit.

AICP bid software is available as an add-on template for spreadsheet programs, such as Microsoft Excel, or as standalone programs. The AICP approach is to create a bid estimate and then "actualize" the estimate once the job is completed. Actualization is the process of posting invoices to the line items in the bid estimate to determine your actual costs and profit.

Budgets and productions revolve around crew costs, so most AICP programs use a data entry form to input the days, rates, overtime estimates and fringes for the crew. Some programs also use data forms to enter the production company, advertising agency, spot title, and studio/location information required if submitting an AICP bid to an agency. The better programs have a fill command that lets you enter the same number in every row in a column. It's a very fast way to enter the anticipated shoot days or overtime hours for everyone in the crew.

The best AICP budgeting software is also equipped to handle a powerful feature called detail lines, one of the strengths of the AICP form. Detail lines contain information that can be attached to each of the preset lines in the AICP form but which will not appear on the printed bid. These underlying support lines enhance the flexibility of the preset lines.

The information is often used to quickly prepare different budgets. For example, you can use detail lines to compare the cost of shooting Digital Betacam versus DVCPRO, or compare shooting with your A list crew instead of your less expensive B list crew. The Association of Independent Commercial Producers has recently changed the post production categories to reflect changes brought about by digital technology.

Hollywood film budgets are astronomical. Most producers would be thrilled to produce two programs for one percent of what the major motion picture studios spend on one film. Given this disparity, of what possible use is feature film budgeting software for projects with more modest budgets?

The benefit is that this budget format really works for production. The format uses three levels. As you drop down a level, the level of budget detail goes up. The amounts for rates, days and costs are entered at the bottom or detail level. These detail lines are grouped into accounts—the middle level—and the accounts are totaled into categories which appear on the topsheet. The topsheet is the executive summary—a one-page outline—of the budget suitable for clients or your boss.

For example, at the bottom level below an account labeled gaffer (or chief lighting technician), are lines for the gaffer's prep days, shoot days and expenses. The gaffer account is usually grouped with accounts for the other members of the gaffer's crew and with all the electrical/lighting rentals and purchases. On the topsheet, the level directly above the account level, all these accounts could be totaled into a single line called lighting or electrical operations. The total in this category, on the topsheet, would be the sum of all the detail lines in every account that appears under the lighting category.

GLOBALS, SUBGROUPS AND LIBRARIES

The principal advantage of Screenplay System's Movie Magic Budgeting software is the ability to create globals, subgroups and libraries of information for reuse in future budgets. A global is a name that represents a value. You can define this variable and apply it to lines in your budget. For instance, instead of entering the number of planned shoot days for every crew member, simply enter the word "shoot." If you define "shoot" as six days, everyone's day rate is multiplied by six. Change the definition of shoot to five days and all those day rates are multiplied by five. The benefit of this approach should be readily apparent.

Subgroups are groups of detail lines that you can decide to include or exclude with the click of a mouse. You can build subgroups for shooting in different cities, for film versus video, or for the A level or B level crew. For instance, create a series of detail lines under the accounts you normally use, with New York, Chicago and Vancouver crew rates. Each city's detail lines are connected to its respective subgroup. Then, when you need to calculate the cost of doing a job in New York, include the "New York" subgroup and exclude the "Chicago" and "Vancouver" subgroups. The process can be supercharged if you're willing to take the time to build these subgroups. You can also build libraries of information beyond subgroups. The budget forms supplied with these software programs are one type of specialized information library. These pre-built forms are similar to the charts of accounts you'll find in a small business accounting program. Most importantly, budgeting software should make it easy to

DTV IN THE REAL WORLD

UNDERSTANDING DIGITAL

PRE-PRODUCTION

PRODUCTION

AUDIO

GRAPHIC & COMPOSITING

POST PRODUCTION

DELIVERY & DUPLICATION

ENGINEERING & TRANSMISSION

APPENDIX

GLOSSARY

save sections of a budget for reuse in another budget. You shouldn't have to retype all the items and costs associated with a camera rental every time you do a budget. The library concept allows you to enter those details once, save them and then paste that block of information into all of your subsequent budgets. It's another way to reduce the amount of time it takes you to prepare a budget.

UNIONS AND CONTRACTS

Another way to speed up the process is to use the Industry Labor Guide (ILG) database. This program is a database of labor agreements and rates covering all the members of U.S. and Canadian unions working in the film and television industry. An integrated version for Movie Magic is available. You can search the guide by crew position, production type (feature, television, video), department, city and union and automatically post the rates to your budget. The ILG is a reference guide to the rules, rates and fringes due union actors and crews. It covers the contracts for SAG/AFTRA, WGA, DGA, IATSE, IBEW, Teamsters and all of the Canadian unions and guilds. The ILG is invaluable for scheduling and budgeting if you work with union personnel. It's updated quarterly to reflect changes in rates and rules.

Contracts are a reality for every production. From the depiction releases to merchandising rights, producers confront a host of issues that can impact on the eventual profitability of the program. If you're producing a multimillion dollar project, hire the appropriate legal counsel. However, budget often precludes hiring an entertainment attorney to handle all the contracts a producer needs. If that's your situation, Automated Contracts for the Film & Television Industry may be the answer. It's a collection of more than 60 fill-in-the-blank contracts written by Mark Litwak, an experienced Hollywood entertainment attorney. The program is written in Java and uses the Netscape or Explorer browser to automate the process of filling in the relevant information. You can copy the completed contract to your favorite word processor or just print it out. It's best to have an attorney review any contracts before you make a deal, but even a standard contract is better than relying on a handshake and fallible memory.

MAPPING SOFTWARE

When you're looking for locations or trying to move from one location to another, it's easy to get lost. Good directions are important and especially critical when you're producing in an unfamiliar place. Since you have no ground intelligence, you can't spot mistakes. That's when mapping software becomes extremely valuable. Six companies currently produce mapping software in three categories. There are navigation programs for address-to-address directions, street atlases for local maps, and road atlases for city-to-city driving directions.

Four companies—Delorme, Etak, Microsoft and Rand McNally—produce road and/or street atlas programs that work in very similar ways. Navigation programs hadn't had much of an impact in the market until TravRoute Software's Road Trips Door-to-Door, which handles local and city-to-city routing, was introduced. There are few if any major differences between the mapping data in any of these programs, because the primary source of information comes from the U.S. government. Each company enhances that information from a variety of other sources.

The real differences—features, level of detail, ability to customize the maps, and ease of use—are all software-dependent. Rand McNally's TripMaker and TripMaker Deluxe include restaurant and lodging information from the Mobil Travel Guides, as well as a wealth of other leisure travel resources which make the programs very popular. The company's Street Finder and Street Finder Deluxe programs prepare address to address directions by accessing the company's Internet site. All of Rand McNally's products support Palm Pilots and Windows CE PDAs.

Delorme's Street Atlas 7.0 is another of the best-selling mapping software products on the market. You can locate places by name, ZIP code, area code and telephone exchange, or move around the U.S. map with Delorme's compass-like navigator. Street Atlas is fast, easy to use, accurate and GPS and Internet enabled. The program can automatically calculate the fastest route between two places and prepare directions. If you need street-to-street directions, you must first locate the address on Street Atlas' maps because you can only find places in the database by name, ZIP code or area code. Printing an area map is more difficult because of some quirks in the program's design. What you see is not necessarily what prints. Maps can be customized by using Delorme's draw tool to add notes to the map. Street Atlas can import information from Delorme's Phone Search program or any database that's in a comma or tab delimited ASCII format. Those names or places are pinpointed on the map with a note box. These boxes include all the information you choose to import. Maps can be downloaded to your hard drive if you'd prefer to travel without your CD-ROM drive. You can download weather, road construction and special event information from Delorme's Web site. Delorme's road construction information is helpful, but it's not a substitute for listening to the local news.

AAA Map N' Go is Delorme's road atlas product. Like Street Atlas, all of Map N' Go's data arrives on one CD. The user interface for this routing and travel aid program differs from Street Atlas but remains easy to use. Map N' Go v5.0 has GPS capabilities and links to the Internet. The database of travel information included in the program is from the American Automobile Association's extensive resources. Map N' Go is an excellent program that includes street level maps for over 250 cities and complete highway coverage of North America. For production purposes, Map N' Go has major limitations. Journeys must begin at preset locations—the choices are usually the airport, the AAA office and the center of town—and must end at another preset location. The driving directions are clear and consistent. You can customize your route by entering highway preferences (scenic, divided, etc.) or by adding a stop. Map N' Go has the same draw feature as in Street Atlas so you can add notes. The other manufacturers' street atlas and road atlas products are similar. The exact features and ease of use vary from company to company. Maps and routes can be loaded into a Palm Pilot or other PDA.

The standout product for production planning is TravRoute Software's Road Trips Door to Door. Simply enter addresses for the start and end of your trip and press return. Road

Trips Door to Door will prepare detailed driving directions and a map in seconds. It's amazing. Every street in North America is covered on one CD. The program even has data on the directions of one-way streets and on turning restrictions. You can click on the map to add start and end points. You can edit the maps to avoid specific streets, add turn restrictions and update one-way street information. The GPS-enabled version is called Co-Pilot.

Door-to-Door does have quirks. The program allows you to enter or exit limited access highways or toll roads at any point along the road, placing you in the create-your-own exit territory common to chase films. On occasion, the wording of the turning directions can be vague. Digital technology is rarely perfect so remember to review Door-to-Door's directions before you print and duplicate them for a crew. The program's directions can saved and edited with any word processor.

ACCESS TO ANYONE

The Internet is the clearest expression of digital technology in the minds of the public. Does this technology offer any benefits to producers during pre-production? As a research tool, the Internet is unprecedented. It's possible to discover information on nearly every subject under the sun and the expert sources that help build great stories. The only difficulty lies in finding where the information you need is and sorting out the wheat from the chafe. There are a number of excellent shareware programs that allow you to conduct simultaneous searches using multiple Internet search engines and locate what you need quickly. Look for these programs on CNET, tucows or ZDNet to help you cut through the overwhelming clutter on the Internet.

Having a searchable telephone directory of the entire United States makes you feel like you have your finger on the pulse of the planet. Electronic telephone directories that can do reverse searches or sorts by addresses are powerful tools. You can enter an address to display someone's phone number or locate all the neighbors on a block or in a building. In the past, this information was only available on CD-ROMs. Today, anyone can access the information on the Internet.

The power of the Internet has lots of uses in production. Imagine you're shooting outdoors and would like to quiet the barking dog in a house on the street. With your wireless Internet connection, it's a simple matter to find the name and phone number of the homeowner. Use your digital phone to call them and restore peace and quiet to the neighborhood. It's less threatening approach than sending a PA to knock on someone's door, although the owner may wonder how you got their telephone number.

Some Internet telephone directories and the few remaining CD-ROM programs are capable of searching by name, address, phone number and SIC codes, which the government uses to categorize businesses. You can export the information to your contact manager, word processor or database program. For production purposes, find a site that can do reverse searches and has a high degree of accuracy. To test accuracy, look up your phone number and those of a few friends. You may be surprised at the results. Even the best CD directories have only a 90 percent accuracy rate because people move and area codes change rapidly. Yet, the basic task of searching for one phone number or a list of a hundred has become a breeze in this age of Internet-driven commerce.

SUNRISES, BREEZES AND FRONTS ON THE WEB

Speaking of breezes, there's nothing more important when you're shooting outdoors than the weather. Here, too, the Internet provides a wealth of options. The United States National Oceanic and Atmospheric Administration (NOAA) has a Web site that provides up-to-date local and regional forecasts. Free accurate information is available at www.esdim.noaa.gov/weather_page.html. The value for production purposes may be limited because forecasts are only available for the present and following day. The Weather Channel (weather.com) and portals like excite.com and yahoo.com also offer free weather forecasts.

LOGGING TOOLS FOR PRE-PRODUCTION?

Logging is a part of the pre-production process for production and post production. You can simplify the process of logging in the field by using pre-production to build lists of the shots and scenes you plan to shot during production. By building these lists you are also creating a check-off list that ensures all the shots you needed to record are, in fact, recorded. Then, as you're shooting, the only information you need to enter are the timecode ins and outs, take numbers and comments, greatly simplifying the logging process under difficult field conditions.

Despite the advantages logging remains a widely ignored time saver. Few nonlinear manufacturers provide logging software that can be used in the field or that will run apart from the nonlinear workstation. Avid's Media Log is one of the few. Media Log's wide distribution helped make Avid the market leader in nonlinear editing because logging with a low-cost computer makes the process of post faster, cheaper and easier to manage.

There are only three solutions that can be used to log footage for a variety of nonlinear systems. Play's Producer is a handheld field logging hardware/software combination designed to use 3Com's Palm Pilot. The Producer's hardware module connects RS422 (Sony serial protocol) or LANC compatible recorders (including MiniDV camcorders) to the Palm Pilot via cables and has four buttons that can be used for deck control or logging. The software is designed to make field logging as simple and easy as it's likely to get. The Palm Pilot's Hot Sync Manager uploads the log database—with as many as 16 different projects—to Mac or Windows-based computers.

Imagine Product's approach to logging is radically different from Play's approach. Imagine's The Executive Producer (TEP)—designed for field or studio logging—can be purchased with or without Imagine's Automatic Capture Technology. TEP can control VTRs using RS-422 or LANC with converter cables Imagine manufactures. The program can also capture timecode from a wide variety of readers. TEP comes with a variety of preset logging templates, all of which are modifiable. Fields can be resized or moved using the mouse. It's also easy to change the format and content of a field. However, most of the keyboard commands require two hands and the mouse control buttons are too small to make field logging with TEP truly efficient.

Imagine's Automatic Capture Technology (ACT) is designed to overcome this deficit and it's a terrific accomplishment. ACT analyzes the information within the video frame (a video capture device is required), calculates the moment when the information has changed radically, and captures that frame as a representation of the new scene or take. You can log footage unattended and capture frames of video for each scene along with timecode ins and outs, but the type of footage and the shooting style has an impact on ACT's accuracy. Whether you decide to capture frames automatically or manually, you'll still need to enter descriptions and to screen the footage to grade the quality of each take. TEP with ACT transforms logging from a numerical and verbal description exercise to a picture manipulation process that's more like editing than math. Imagine uses a USB video capture device or PC Card capture card to grab frames.

TEP extends the concept of logging software beyond prep and into the post production arena. You can easily rearrange the clips to build a simple EDL complete with storyboards and whatever supplemental material you desire. The printed quality of the storyboards was impressive. Add in the ability to import and export to nearly every nonlinear format and you have a powerful tool that should prove useful for almost any producer or editor.

Another major strength of TEP is its ability to import and export log files for nearly every linear and nonlinear editing systems on the market. It does an excellent job of translating from one format to another. If you edit on more than one nonlinear system, TEP is an extremely useful tool. TEP with ACT, control cables and an image capture device is expensive. Producers who use outside facilities could amortize the expensive over one or two jobs and consistently cut their costs.

Ebside Prodution's Log This offers a simple, inexpensive solution for field or studio logging. There are large mouse buttons to mark ins and outs. The VTR control panel can be displayed for studio logging or hidden during field use. Log This imports and exports logs for Avid, CMX, Edit, Media 100, and Scitex (now Accom) edit systems. It's not fancy, just fast and efficient. Log This is available on the Web at ebside.com.

The future of post production is in production environments with central computer servers capable of storing all the footage for a project networked to desktop computers. Imagine a solution that links the script and storyboards to footage with the same ease that allows a nonlinear editor to connect clips on a timeline. Imagine replacing pre-production storyboards with actual footage or still images from the footage in your timeline. Imagine connecting scenes to the words in a script simply by dragging and dropping the images on a highlighted portion of the script. Imagine moving back and forth between the rough cut and the script or storyboards with ease. It's a future that's real and available. Large organizations are already employing tools to manage video and audio from idea to server-based broadcast. It's only a question of time before these new tools and approaches become available to independent producers and small organizations.

THE PROCESS

The lines between pre-production, production and post are indistinct. Digital and computer technology continues to make the tasks traditionally associated with pre-production easier to accomplish even as the concept of pre-production changes. The current trend is to maximize the information contained in a variety of separate sources, but the future will be to consolidate all the information into a central location. Some things are unlikely to ever change; it's hard to imagine the disappearance of budgeting and scheduling.

IN THE RACE FOR BETTER LENS TECHNOLOGY,
WE'VE OUTDISTANCED THE COMPETITION.

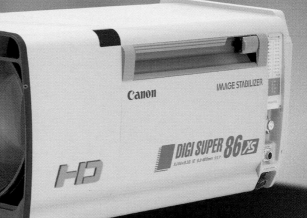

DIGI SUPER 86 *HD*xs
WITH IMAGE STABILIZER.
HDTV/SDTV COMPATIBLE.

INTRODUCING THE 86X FIELD ZOOM WITH IMAGE STABILIZER.

With the introduction of the 86X, Canon and their customers finish first...again. The longest lens ever for HDTV and SDTV, the XJ86x9.3 BIE D is also the first long lens with Image Stabilization. By comparison, the competition finished far behind.

But that's nothing new, considering that Canon was also the first to introduce Internal Focus technology; the first and only broadcast lens company to introduce Image Stabilization technology; the first to use digital technologies in lens control; and much more.

Of course, if you're a Canon customer, impressive firsts are nothing new. They simply re-affirm that you're buying the best. They also provide some serious reasons for everyone to consider buying the technology and support leader. At Canon, we go the distance.

Zoom Ratio	**86X** with image stabilizer
Range of Focal Length (with Extender)	9.3-800mm (18.6-1600mm)
Maximum Relative Aperture (with Extender)	1:1.7 9.3-340mm 1:4.0 at 800mm (1:3.4 18.6-680mm) (1:8.0 at 1600mm)
M.O.D. (from image plane)	3m
Weight	51.8lb (23.5kg)

Same size and weight as our standard field lens.

Maximize Your Camera's Performance.

HDTV YOUR WAY.
Ikegami Has The "Universal" Solution.

The HDK-790D Studio/Field and HDK-79D Portable Companion cameras take the guess work out of choosing production formats. It is now possible to deliver any of the leading HDTV formats directly from one camera system with no external converters. This is made practical by 2.2-million pixel 2/3" CCDs that provide selectable native-interlace and native-progressive read-out modes. Thus, the camera can be switched to provide 1080i, 720p and 480p.

A superior quality NTSC signal is always available from the CCU for simulcast or dedicated applications. Independent adjustment of colorimetry and detail are provided in the HDTV and NTSC signal paths.

Outputs are provided for HDTV and SDTV in both digital and analog. NTSC signals can be independently switched to 16:9, 4:3 side-cut or 4:3 letterbox aspect ratios. Return video supports all these combinations as well, giving the operator a consistent HDTV display in the viewfinder.

Recent breakthroughs in advanced ASIC design provide a high quality all digital solution for camera and CCU. Introduction of new solid-type electrolytic capacitors will improve component life dramatically. Ikegami has again taken the lead in developing the most versatile camera system to address the future needs of HDTV.

HDK-790D　　**HDK-79D**

HDTV

MULTI-FORMAT HDTV CAMERAS•SPECIALTY HDTV CAMERAS•HDTV MONITORS

"Production is production." "Producing in digital is just like producing in analog." "I'm an artist, not a technician." Words of wisdom or famous last words?

Producing in digital is sort of like producing in analog, except that the picture has the potential to be better—much better, and much worse. You might see things you've never seen before, just like hearing a favorite vinyl record or cassette tape on CD for the first time. Some of those things you'll see for the first time won't be good things either—compression artifacts, motion blur, bad 16:9 image composition, and a host of others.

To aid you in this endeavor, please see the digital video production and transmission charts in Appendix A: Digital Television Production & Transmission.

The real world is analog. What you shoot is analog and the way it will be displayed to the viewer is analog. But, as they say, "It's a digital world."

THE LENS: MAKING THE BEST OF AN ANALOG SITUATION

COLETTE CONNOR

Use a cheap lens and your image will suffer. Use a great lens and your image will be great. Use a high definition lens and you'll spend a lot of money, though maybe not as much as you think. Improvements in the evolving technology of lenses have allowed lenses to become smaller in size and weight without sacrificing strength and optical quality.

Today, the best lens that you can buy for video is a high definition lens. And while you may be shooting in standard definition, you can still use a high definition lens if you think it is worth the cost.

The lens is what brings the image to the imager (a single CCD, an optical block with three CCDs, or even an optical block with three tubes). And this lens is an analog device that affects your picture quality first. If part of the image doesn't make it through the lens, it will never make it to the viewer.

Lenses, in fact, contain various elements, and many different kinds of glass are used in their manufacture: the type of glass chosen for a particular lens is designed to pass different frequencies of information, in the form of light waves, to the camera. The higher the resolution, the more information is being passed, and the more complicated and difficult the lens is to make.

The consensus of industry opinion is that as digital television defines itself, high

DTV IN THE REAL WORLD

UNDERSTANDING DIGITAL

PRE-PRODUCTION

PRODUCTION

AUDIO

GRAPHIC & COMPOSITING

POST PRODUCTION

DELIVERY & DUPLICATION

ENGINEERING & TRANSMISSION

APPENDIX

GLOSSARY

definition (HD) lenses will come more and more into use. How expensive will HD lenses be? Will all HD lenses work with the myriad of proposed TV-line formats? How difficult are they to shoot with? What impact does aspect ratio have? Can you use HD lenses on 16:9/4:3 switchable cameras? Are there any benefits to using an HD lens on a standard definition television (SDTV) camera?

HD LENS BASICS

Video camera lenses are designed and manufactured to complement the television system they operate in. The major difference between current NTSC lenses and HD lenses is the amount of information (such as the number of TV lines) the lens has to resolve. The current NTSC standard is 525 TV lines of resolution (480 are active). The higher definition lens, whether it is resolving 480 progressive scan (p), 720p or 1080 interlaced (i) TV lines, has to resolve more information.

In our present TV transmission system everything—including lenses—is referenced by the number of scanning lines and scan rate; 5 MHz, which relates to 400 horizontal TV lines, has been the standard since the beginning of U.S. television. NHK (see below) has recommended that the U.S. television standard be raised from the present 5 MHz for NTSC video up to 9 MHz for HD video, which will cover all of the new formats that are being proposed. Camera lenses that relate to higher scanning rates are already being produced.

16:9 ASPECT RATIO

There is no mandate for digital broadcasting of 16:9 or high definition television. But—and it's a big "but"—consumer TV manufacturers are moving towards or are already producing 16:9 consumer digital TV sets. Only time will tell if consumers will buy the new shape of television. However, when you're talking high definition, you are talking 16:9 aspect ratio.

The granddaddy of HDTV is Japan's NHK television network. This is the "1125" system (shot, broadcast, and received in 16:9 aspect ratio) that is still used throughout the world by HD pioneers, experimental artists and high definition production companies that until recently produced programming almost exclusively for NHK. That high resolution analog "1125" system, with double the number of scan lines of NTSC (1080 active TV lines), calls for extreme attention to detail, especially in the lens. At 1080 TV lines, any deviation in the light results in one-quarter less allowable error in a lens than what is considered allowable error in any current SDTV lens. There's considerably less margin of error in color resolution.

Operationally, HD lenses will be used exactly the same as any lens, but visually—to the cameraperson or to the director—everything changes. Since HD lenses are designed right from start to do 16:9, framing is the first thing you'll notice. After that, the whole look of the system is amazingly crisp, and gives the viewer the feeling that they're right in the picture. Most viewfinders don't have enough resolution to show the difference, but on a monitor (typically at least 17 inches in diameter) everybody will see the difference.

Learning to shoot 16:9, everyone agrees, is practically back-to-school time. (See Framing for Two Worlds that follows.) Your lighting changes, the placement of your cameras change, your camera angles change. The sets have to change because they're going to be wider than they are tall—considerably. Focus also becomes an issue. An HD lens picks up such fine detail that instead of a tight close-up of a talking head, a medium close-up shot will be all the detail you'll need (or want).

A small but growing number of TV stations and independent production companies (particularly documentary producers, at the moment) are hedging their bets by shooting 16:9 high definition, mainly for archiving purposes. That way, their digital 16:9 production can be downconverted or upconverted to any aspect ratio or TV-line format; it's future-proofing their hard work.

HD LENS MANUFACTURING

The basic manufacturing process of an HD lens—from the initial cutting, grinding, and polishing of the glass through to the mechanical and electronic construction—is almost exactly the same as the SD lens process, but the quality control and the specifications are at a higher level. Improvements in the evolving technology of lenses have allowed lenses to become small in size and weight without sacrificing strength and optional quality.

There are over 200 types of glass that can be chosen for a lens (SD or HD) and in any one lens there can be several different kinds of glass. The glass is hand-picked to meet the specifications and the quality needed for high definition. Starting out with a block of glass that looks like a big ice cube, it is then cut into the general shape—a little larger than needed—and then ground into the exact shape desired. The polishing process then begins, from coarse to fine, to finer, to ultra-fine. After that, every element in every lens is coated. For HD lenses, the coatings are specially designed for high definition. According to the model, function, and design of the lens, there will be a number of different kinds of glass in different combinations in one lens, with everything designed to work as a unit. For example, one glass could meet a very high specification in one area, but in another area it's somewhat lacking. The next element put in line will actually correct for the previous elements' problems. In order to reduce chromatic aberrations while increasing the resolution of the product, HD lens manufacturers have tightened mechanical specifications.

Chromatic aberration is very much like errors in color printing: when the registration is off you get blurs and distortion. In video, the three different colors used—generally referred to as "RGB" (red, green and blue)—do not always get through the lens equally (size/frequency, etc.) and that causes blurring. MTF (modulation transfer function), which is a way of expressing reproduction of contrast, happens out toward the edges of the picture, because the colors are not all focusing the same. For instance, all three colors on an edge, out in a corner, may have to overlap each other, and if the red is a thicker line (because it's not quite as focused as the others), fringing occurs.

For digital cameras in general, and HD cameras in particular, lens manufacturing has become even more precise (and more difficult) than ever, because the three CCD "chip" cameras do not allow adjustments to be made in the camera to compensate for any error in the lens. With the old tube cameras an operator could compensate for a registration problem. Now, if the chips are not exactly the same and correctly aligned, you still have a registration problem but no means of correction in the camera. For HD lenses, which must be excruciatingly precise, the manufacturers tried numerous approaches to create correction elements within the lens. Manufacturers are now using super electron beam coating for beam-splitting prisms, which has greatly benefited resolution.

While the glass is being ground and coated, another part of the factory is manufacturing the cams, the focusing sections, and all of the mechanical parts that are necessary inside the lens. These parts are also specifically designed for HD and, again, the specifications are very exact, more than would be necessary for an SDTV lens. When all the parts are made, including the optical parts, they all meet at the assembly line, and the lens-in-the-making goes through many people doing many different jobs and testing many times. And when the last person puts in the last screw and tightens it down, the lens then goes through total quality control testing as a whole system. There could be 20 different elements or more in one of these lenses, all working in conjunction with each other. In the end, the lens has been designed as a system that can provide the finest picture possible.

LINES, FORMATS AND RESOLUTIONS

Canon and Fujinon report their HD lenses will work for both interlaced (i) and progressive (p) scan. The HD lenses being manufactured today will not perform properly on a 1080p system; they will, however, perform on 480p, 720p or 1080i standards. Performing on those lower TV-line formats may be a moot point, according to some sources. Today's HDTV lenses may represent the best quality lenses in the market, but differences in format resolutions may not allow the drastic differences in picture quality you might expect. Comparisons between standards will also be difficult, as results may vary due to camera equipment and formats.

Other lens experts assert that as far as the HD lens is concerned, the format of the camera—whether it's 720p or 480p or 1080i or even 1080p—makes no difference. Format is a camera issue; it's not a lens issue. An HDTV lens has to do with the overall quality of the picture that is transferred to the camera. Once the picture is in the camera, whatever the camera does with it from that point on no longer concerns the lens. The size of the CCD, and the placement of that CCD matters, but what the camera does with the video is essentially the camera's business. According to these experts, if the lens exceeds the system resolution-wise, a shooter is at least guaranteeing the maximum out of that camera system. Some shooters do use HD lenses on SDTV cameras. Reasons vary: some may be trying out the HD lens now so that when they buy an HD camera, they'll already have the lens and be familiar with its uses; other might be trying to squeak every last bit of resolution out of their current cameras.

16:9/4:3 SWITCHABLE CAMERAS

High definition means shooting in a 16:9 aspect ratio, but 16:9 does not mean high definition. The 16:9 aspect ratio is not what distinguishes an HD lens from an SDTV lens; in fact, there are plenty of true 16:9 SDTV lenses available. Instead, the quality of the picture is what truly separates HD lenses from SDTV lenses.

A number of camera manufacturers are touting 16:9/4:3 switchable cameras. These are NTSC 525 TV-line digital cameras equipped with what's called alternately a "minimizer," a "ratio converter," a "retro-zoom," or a "crossover." It's a unit of glass that compensates for the 20 percent angle-of-view lost when you switch from 16:9 to 4:3. On these cameras, when you go to 4:3 you lose wide-angle, and this (0.8mm) wide-angle converter—built into the lens and switchable through a toggle switch on the camera—will give you back what is lost in the camera; to the eye, it will look like you never lost anything.

You can shoot 16:9 on these cameras with any current SDTV lenses. However, when you go back to 4:3, your lens becomes 20 percent more telephoto, and this is true of every camera manufacturer, with the exception of Philips. Most camera manufacturers reduce the chip; the chip starts out as a 16:9 chip, and the edges (sides) are pulled in to make 4:3. The Philips system starts out with a 4:3 chip, and reduces vertically to 16:9 so the angle-of-view is not lost.

Using an HD lens on a 16:9/4:3 switchable camera will not give you high definition. It will give you the best possible picture that a 525-line digital camera could do in 16:9, but switching to 4:3 would result in the same problem that an SDTV lens would have. Without the 0.8 wide converter in the lens, your viewing angle would change. This is a function of the camera system, not the lens; however, Canon now offers HD lenses which can be equipped with the 0.8mm wide-angle converter in the lens.

The two leading manufacturers of broadcast and ENG lenses are, not surprisingly, the leading high definition lens developers, manufacturers, and suppliers. For the last several years Canon has been doing research and development into the high definition lenses used by Sony, Philips and a few other companies. Those lenses were very specialized and almost hand-made, and the price reflected it. A powerful HD telephoto zoom, with a 40X magnification ratio, had a list price of almost a quarter of a million dollars.

The introduction by Sony and Ikegami, among other camera manufacturers, of a standardized 2/3-inch lens-to-camera interface for HD, also called the B4 interface (a standard interface that already existed in the current SDTV cameras and lenses), made the development of more economical lenses possible.

Focal lengths and specs sound familiar on HD lenses, because lens manufacturers designed HD lenses to be as close as possible to SDTV lenses, to make the transition to high definition easier for camera people. The HD lenses are designed to look, feel and operate like the SDTV lenses that shooters currently use, with only some slight differences in focal length. Initially, HD zoom lenses are expected to be the most popular, but fixed focal length HD lenses will become necessary as more film-style work, such as commercials and TV series, will be shot in high definition video.

FRAMING FOR TWO WORLDS

RANDALL PARIS DARK

> 'Twas the night before Christmas and all through the house,
> not a creature was stirring except for the FCC.
> On that fateful night, the visual electronic and computer world
> would be changed forever.
> The future not only became brighter, it became a lot wider as well.

Tuesday, December 24, 1996, the Federal regulators approved digital television standards that will deliver movie-quality television to America's living rooms. The Federal Communications Commission has given television stations the go ahead to deliver incredible digital signals, sharper pictures and up to six-channel CD-quality sound in many different formats. These formats include an aspect ratio of 4:3 and 16:9 as well as high definition TV with an aspect ratio of 16:9. During all this, the broadcaster must also continue to transmit analog TV that has an aspect ratio of 4:3. Confused? Stay tuned. The following formats listed below are production and transmission formats and are not necessarily display formats (in pixels):

- 1920x1080, 16H:9V, square pixel, 24 frames per second, progressive scan
- 1920x1080, 16H:9V, square pixel, 30 frames per second, progressive scan
- 1920x1080, 16H:9V, square pixel, 60 fields per second, interlace scan
- 1280x720, 16H:9V, square pixel, 24 frames per second, progressive scan
- 1280x720, 16H:9V, square pixel, 30 frames per second, progressive scan
- 1280x720, 16H:9V, square pixel, 60 frames per second, progressive scan
- 704x480, 4H:3V, non-square pixel, 24 frames per second, progressive scan
- 704x480, 4H:3V, non-square pixel, 30 frames per second, progressive scan
- 704x480, 4H:3V, non-square pixel, 60 frames per second, progressive scan
- 704x480, 4H:3V, non-square pixel, 60 fields per second, interlace scan
- 704x480, 16H:9V, non-square pixel, 24 frames per second, progressive scan
- 704x480, 16H:9V, non-square pixel, 30 frames per second, progressive scan
- 704x480, 16H:9V, non-square pixel, 60 frames per second, progressive scan
- 704x480, 16H:9V, non-square pixel, 60 fields per second, interlace scan
- 640x480, 4H:3V, square pixel, 24 frames per second, progressive scan
- 640x480, 4H:3V, square pixel, 30 frames per second, progressive scan
- 640x480, 4H:3V, square pixel, 60 frames per second, progressive scan
- 640x480, 4H:3V, square pixel, 60 fields per second, interlace scan

These formats are known as the 18 "ATSC Table 3" formats (see Glossary). Each frame rate has a 1000/1001 frequency change to accommodate NTSC color (24=23.98, 30=29.97, 60=59.94), for a total of 36 formats.

THE FUTURE

Whether you believe HDTV or DTV is coming, going or staying where it is, the bottom line is that the future is Electronic Widescreen High Resolution TV/Computer/Movie Theater. Period. That is evolutionary, not revolutionary. As a species, we have evolved from primitive finger painted drawings in our caves to primitive low resolution moving images (television) in our homes and we will not stop there. Humankind has always wanted bigger, brighter, sharper. (How else can you explain the clothing styles of the 1970's?) This change will affect every one of us, but initially it will have the biggest impact on the broadcasters. And you don't have to take my word for it. The government has told the broadcasters they have to switch from analog to digital television. The clock is ticking.

HDTV is not television as we know it, it is not an NTSC camera shooting in 4:3, low resolution information, nor is it a 2:1 film camera. High definition is another animal, another tool. To say one is better or worse than the other is like saying a Picasso is better than a Henry Moore. It is just different. It has the advantages of film in that it has the wideness in shape and the ability to show incredible contrast and detail. It also has an advantage over NTSC, not only because of the improved resolution, but because you can do something more than the continual 4:3 TV close up when framing shots. Finally, the creatives can frame a much more interesting shot, off centered and allow a shot to be loose enough to give a sense of place.

HDTV/DTV conversion, or at least a statistically-significant, financially-viable deployment of the technology, is the largest marketing challenge in the history of consumer electronics—and whatever happens, it will rock the very economic foundation of the broadcasting industry as we know it today. Unfortunately, HDTV, ATV and now DTV have been regarded as a science project by industry executives. Only now are we beginning to see these broadcast executives react to the business-model issues of HDTV/DTV.

Regarding that business model, one of the key issues surrounding it is the idea of producing in a higher-resolution widescreen (16:9) format and downconverting the center (4:3) section of that image to NTSC in order to provide the feed for the existing (revenue-generating) NTSC channel. I have been producing HDTV since 1986, and for various creative reasons, it is likely that this process will limit the quality of programming in both formats. Again, this issue has been regarded as part of a science project: scalability, interlace-verses-progressive scan, quality of vertical filtering, downconversion, pan-and-scan, etc. But the real issue is: Can you produce compelling programs that are tailored to the strengths and weaknesses of each format through the use of this process? I believe the answer to this question is no.

That being the case, the slow adoption rate of DTV predicted by the consumer electronics industry means two things: First, that the integrity of your NTSC programming must be retained to protect your position in the NTSC marketplace, your primary source of revenue for the next 10 to 20 years, and; second, you must provide high-quality widescreen HDTV programming tailored to the format so that consumers actually perceive a quality difference when evaluating their purchases. In essence, this means that in most cases, you must produce the two streams separately.

NEWS PROGRAMS

Take the case of local news. The most obvious problem here is creation of cross-standard graphics elements. While each station generally invents its own style for presenting these graphics, it is unlikely that a design that works in 4:3 will be optimum when presented in 16:9, and if 16:9-optimized graphics are converted to NTSC-cropped-4:3, any information in the side panels will be lost. And this doesn't even touch on the graphics composition issues created by the wider viewing angle, bigger screen size and closer viewing distance, which are the main differences between true HDTV and widescreen NTSC/SDTV. Much has been said about upconverting the existing news programs in the HDTV world, but once the viewer watches one station's news in HDTV, will they watch the competing station in upconverted NTSC?

FRAMING FOR SPORTS OR
HOW I LEARNED TO PAN AND SCAN LIVE

Over the past 10 years, I have noticed that the aspect ratio of HDTV fits perfectly with many sports. The shape of the playing fields of football, basketball, hockey, and soccer to name a few, is rectangular in design. When soccer is shot in HDTV, you can see more of the field and watch how the team positions itself to attack the opposition. In football you can see both the defensive back and the offensive back in the same shot without having to be completely wide. Not only is the shape of HDTV almost the same as a skating rink, but with HDTV the viewer may finally find the puck in hockey. These sports are a natural for the 16:9 aspect ratio, but there are problems that come with the crossover that will happen during the transition period.

Imagine a basketball game shot in HDTV and downconverted live, edge cropped, because no viewer, let alone no network, would allow letterbox sporting events. There is also a limited amount of space for cameras, so many events will not have the luxury of both HD and NTSC cameras and crews. Therefore, simulcasting using the HDTV equipment as source equipment will be the order of the day. In that scenario, where would the director put the net in the frame? Safe action for NTSC leaves the net almost in the middle of the 16:9 frame. Put the net in the edge of the 16:9 frame and it doesn't even appear in the NTSC feed. Live pan and scan seems to be the immediate compromise. This means that there is a new operator in the mobile. His sole job would be to pan with the action, making sure that the framing of the shot remains in the safe action area at all times, giving the best possible framing in both worlds. Difficult but do-able.

However, with every advantage there are also limitations. Think tennis. The primary camera position is behind the tennis player, where the 4:3 frame works perfectly. The 16:9 frame fights that angle, there is too much air on each side of the court from that camera position. Pan and scan from the end camera would be next to impossible. With a few sports, new camera positions will have to be experimented with and we will have to find new and compelling ways of covering certain sporting events.

EDITING FOR TWO WORLDS

There are many subtle editing issues as we evolve into this new and complex world. Take the case of a comedy program (sitcom) where the editing sets the pace of the show and in large measure determines the comedic timing of a performance. Say you want to edit just after someone enters the shot. Does the edit occur just after the actor enters the 16:9 frame or the 4:3 frame? Which do you compromise? If you edit separately, will the lengths of the scenes be different? Framing and composition for the same show possess new and interesting problems. Picture, if you will, a head to toe shot in 16:9. There is an immediate feel and look to that framing. Now picture the same shot in 4:3. The look completely changes. No editing can change that problem.

Picture a close-up two-shot in 16:9. In NTSC that shot is either a shot that has each face half off the picture or you need to pan and scan the shot in post much like you do when you do film transfers for television release. In a sitcom with bang-bang timing, this would bring new meaning to the words whip pan.

Simulcasted edge–cropped camera moves present an interesting scenario. Pan an actor into the 16:9 frame. As he enters the picture, he starts to talk, while in the 4:3 frame we hear a mysterious voice with no one in the shot. If he waits until he enters the 4:3 frame to speak, the 16:9 audience will think he has forgotten his lines. Zooming in and out would further complicate this already dizzying scenario. Depending on what aspect ratio your television is, the actor may or may not be in the shot at different times during the zoom. Again, what works for one ratio may not work at all in the other.

One possible solution to these problems would be to convert from HDTV (or a lower-resolution 16:9 format) to NTSC using the "letterbox" method. This puts black bars above and below the 16:9 image, or places a single large bar above or below the image. Although this unused area could contain program-related graphics material, experience has shown that the U.S. market is reluctant to accept the smaller images that letterbox provides on a given size display.

For many programs, the network broadcasters and their TV-station partners must maintain two completely separate program streams during the conversion period when legacy-hardware consumers must be protected, or they will have to compromise the creative integrity of the 16:9 program, hardly creating a compelling case for the purchase of new television receivers.

It is not only an issue of who will pay for the transmitters, antennas, towers and distribution infrastructure, but who will pay for the creation of the separate programs, particularly in the early days (the first 10 to 20 years) when the penetration of DTV is projected to be quite limited.

CAN THERE BE COMPROMISES?
A REAL WORLD EXAMPLE: *WOODSTOCK '94*

There seems to be a common fear in the pay-per-view world that viewers will demand their money back on the grounds of "technical problems" if they see black bands because of letterboxing. This usually leads to a decision to air the live event in "edge crop" where the sides of the wide screen image are discarded in the conversion process. Of course, the high definition users are then concerned that the director will focus his attention on the 4:3 area and not use the widescreen (16:9) advantage. That usually leads to concerns over how the person switching the selectable ISO will cover the event for post production.

A settlement was negotiated that not only quieted the concerns, but allowed the pay-per-view broadcasters to test the market in non-prime time and gave the viewers a way of identifying live and delayed broadcasts. The live broadcasts were converted in a compromise 14:9 aspect ratio which allowed the under scan on most receivers to cover the black border on the top and bottom. The backup converters ran in letterbox mode and the NTSC D2 recordings for *Woodstock Overnight* were made from these signals. The *Overnight* replays were made over a stylized background which made the top and bottom area seem to be part of the program, much the same as the sports ticker on CNN Headline News. So the widescreen format was converted from a drawback to an advantage. The promoters seemed happy with this approach, and even agreed not to complain if we had to switch to the letterbox mode in the live broadcast because of equipment failure.

The conventional NTSC mobile unit provided all the available bells and whistles for packaging the program, including digital effects, still store and live graphics. All transmission was standard NTSC and was no way affected by the high definition production. The high definition production was broadcast at a later date in Japan[1].

CONCLUSION

Over the next 10 to 15 years, the creative and technical community will be forced to deal with having to simultaneously transmit the same program using two TV channels, one for programs in the existing analog format and the other in any or all of the new digital formats. There are many difficult issues to be worked out during this period. Some programs will make this transition seamlessly, others will be compromised. But is it impossible to do? No. Simulcasting has a future and upconverting has a limited future. What the real challenge is and what will be truly exciting are the new possibilities—having to re-think existing programs and develop new types of programs. Programs that are best suited to this new format. HDTV and widescreen are enhancing technologies. We are in its infancy, only just beginning to look at the possibilities. Having recently watched a few hours of old black and white television programs, it is easy to see that over the past 30 years we've come a long way. With this exciting new development in Electronic Widescreen High Resolution TV/Computer (television), it is apparent that we still have much to learn—and learn it we must. There is no going back.

SHOOTING HD: MY FIRST TIME

JEFF ALRED

I was approached to demo a high definition camcorder at the ESPN Summer X Games in San Diego, California in 1998. Gladly I accepted the offer; finally I could use the "format of the future" I only read about in college some years ago. My experience as an ENG photographer leaves me with limited digital exposure, so as you can imagine the HD format presented many new challenges. Two of the biggest challenges I ran into while using this format were the aspect ratio and clearer resolution.

ASPECT RATIO

The HDCAM acted much like a Sony 600 or 700, only the viewfinder showed a 16:9 aspect ratio. I picked up the camera and started shooting without too much guidance. I actually passed the camera off to show many different handheld camera operators, and they used the HD camcorder almost instantly. White balance, audio settings and other manual functions were in the same location, so most of my attention could be focused on shooting with a letterbox look instead of the 4:3 aspect ratio I was so used to.

Once I began shooting with the camera, I found myself trying to maximize the whole frame, especially with the extra thirds the format presented to me. Since my proportions were different with this format, I was looking at the "fringes" of the frame rather than the subject I was interviewing. As I overcame the initial newness of the format, I began to utilize the frame to my advantage. I started to use right or left justification of my subject so the editor could use the other two-thirds of the frame for effect or B-roll. I framed shots with specific items in one-third of the frame and the subject sharing the remainder of the frame. This aspect ratio allows the photographer to marry together one or two products with the subject, something that 4:3 just doesn't allow you to do.

When shooting action, it took some getting used to the skinnier, longer frame. At first, I began tilting up and down too slowly, realizing the action was going through my frame twice as fast as I was used to. I really enjoyed having a longer frame, especially for the speed shots where I could let the athletes enter and exit through the whole frame. It was a good method to relate the speed to the fan sitting at home.

CLEARER RESOLUTION

The second major challenge was the clearer resolution presented through the improved scan rate. I was really impressed with the crispness of the picture—even subtle details were clear. We set up an interview where we had to make sure not even a gum wrapper laid on the ground in fear of it being seen by the camera!

When we returned to the edit room to screen the footage, I was amazed every time with how the format translated an image compared to how it looked in person. Most of our interviews were done on location, but this format may cause some headaches for set designers or lighting directors. It really exposes any flaws or patches in set work.

Since this is such a clear and concise image, some shots could tell stories without words. Shots of faces which show the wrinkles of experience, the ripples of muscles during competition—I used them all because the format's resolution is almost truer than life. I also utilized the shutter with this format, and it gave me an image that was almost unexplainable. I thought the format was already impressive, but this function could capture every frame even more crisp than before. I began shooting the majority of my video with shutter, and the reaction from the edit area was equally enthusiastic.

This HD camcorder is very easy to operate. The aspect ratio definitely kept me on my toes, but I found many positive ways to use this format to my advantage once I became comfortable with it. With the clearer resolution and 16:9 aspect ratio, this format will be a favorite of sports producers, because it gives the viewer a fan's perspective, the peripheral vision that has never been previously offered.

REAL-WORLD DIGITAL AND PRODUCTION PROBLEMS

MICHAEL SILBERGLEID

The one good thing that analog and NTSC did for broadcasters and videographers was to hide a multitude of sins. Here's a simple example: If you shoot a black and white glossy photograph, a monitor will show you sharp, highlighted edging. This edging has high frequencies that the camera and monitor can see. But a tape format like VHS doesn't see them at all. So instead of the picture looking as bad as it did on the live monitor, it looks "better" from tape. All the high frequency noise was removed by simply recording on a narrow bandwidth analog tape format. Record that same image in digital (and especially high definition digital), and you'll get all that high frequency "noise" and a worse-looking image.

Another NTSC savior: 30 frames per second interlace. Look at a still frame (not a field) of video with motion not shot using a fast electronic shutter, and you'll see that the object moving is blurry. Even when that object is at rest, the image is not perfect. What this means is, for the most part, that there is not a great difference between the sharpness of the two images. (See figure 1.)

Now do the same test with high definition. What you'll see is a very sharp picture of the object at rest, but blur when it moves. That blur is called motion blur. You can eliminate motion blur by using a high speed electronic shutter, but the video then takes on a strobe-like effect.

figure 1. Motion blur.
Simulation of motion blur in a high definition image. On the left an image shot without helicopter movement in the frame (could also be with movement in the frame but with a high speed electronic shutter). On the right, a simulation of the same image and quality with movement in the frame and no electronic shutter. Motion blur can make high definition look soft.
Photo: WFOR-TV, Miami, Chopper4,©1996, Z'GARCI.

Here's a real-world example: During a demonstration of HDTV, blur was noticed in the image. At first it was thought that the focus was slightly off on a scene of a woman walking down a street towards the camera. Although tight focus on the extra-sharp high definition image will be critical, it was not the problem in this case—motion blur was. As the woman moved up and down in step, her image blurred. This blur would not normally be noticeable in NTSC, but in high definition it was.

It was noted that the scene was shot in interlace and we were also watching an interlace image. When the image was shown in progressive, about one-half of the motion blur was removed. But because of the interlace production and shutter speed of 1/60th of a second, the blur was still noticeable.

By now, we all know that we can no longer use fake props and set pieces or an old-looking studio set with HDTV as the clarity gives away all our tricks and illusions.

Older NTSC sets shot in high definition do not hold up well under the sharp scrutiny of the high definition camera. The sets look cheap. Graffiti on the sets "reads" for the first time and backgrounds begin to look awful. Immediately it was realized that new sets would be needed for high definition production, and traditional NTSC set "tricks" would no longer work. Those "tricks" include fake bookcases with painted-in books, slightly off paint jobs on walls, and other things that producers and designers knew would not be reproduced when going through NTSC.

SHOOT AND PROTECT

You may be shooting for today, but you want to protect for tomorrow's high definition widescreen world.

Today, many productions are shot in 16:9, posted in 16:9 and then center sliced with an aspect ratio converter for the final 4:3 air master. On screen composition is for the 4:3 image, while protecting the 16:9 image.

Keep in mind that shots composed for a 16:9 aspect ratio may look awkward in 4:3 and that if you adjust camera detail for monitoring on an HD monitor, your NTSC picture may look soft. There are always going to be compromises to be made in the world of widescreen and high definition.

16:9 LETTERBOX

A widescreen 16:9 television does not guarantee the premanant exile of letterbox. 16:9 has an aspect ratio of 1.77:1, but a number of motion pictures are produced in an aspect ratio of 2.35:1. To accomodate this wider-than-16:9 image, the motion picture is presented in a letterbox format.

To avoid what many consider to be the annoying black bars of letterbox, Home Box Office has decided to pan-and-scan all newer 2.35 film to high definition transfers to fit within the 1.77 aspect ratio of their HBO HD service. This means approximately 26 percent of the image of a 2.35 motion picture will be lost at any one time. While purists demand that films be shown in their intended aspect ratio, others (like HBO) believe in filling up the screen.

An interesting exercise is to take a DVD that has both a 4:3 pan-and-scan on one side and a 16:9 letterbox on the other (several films, including *Austin Powers: International Man of Mystery*, have been released with this feature). Watch a scene in one format then the other and see if you find what is missing in 4:3 or visible in 16:9 to be of major importance.

14:9: THE GREAT WIDESCREEN COMPROMISE

As you've seen before, 14:9 might answer many of the problems of 4:3 versus 16:9. At the International Broadcasting Convention held in Amsterdam, Holland, The Netherlands in 1996, a paper called "The Simultaneous Transmission Of Widescreen And 4:3 Programmes" by M. L. Bell and H. M. Price was presented. Within this paper was the first major look at the 14:9 compromise, as made by the BBC.

Let's start with production and end with distribution: Our old programs (and our current ones) are 4:3. Our new programs will increasingly be 16:9. We can protect for 4:3, or pan-and-scan for 4:3, or do true 16:9 and letterbox for 4:3.

The BBC had that problem: Simultaneous transmission of widescreen and 4:3.

The BBC and all the U.S. networks know that most viewers dislike letterbox. So how do you show 16:9 on a 4:3?

Their answer—14:9 "half-letterbox." There is minor letterboxing and some minor loss of the edges of 16:9, but the BBC found that most viewers were okay with this format.

Now, how do you present 4:3 material on a widescreen 16:9 television set?

As bad as it sounds, and the BBC admits that there are no easy solutions, it is with side curtains. The picture could be expanded slightly to reduce the curtains, but at the expense of the top and bottom of the frame being cropped.

In the years to come, experimentation will help to further answer these 16:9 and 4:3 questions.

COMPRESSION

Compression is used to make digital video affordable. And the type of compression we use literally throws bits of data away based on how humans visually perceive information. Look at how a format (and its compression scheme) performs under different conditions (lighting, camera movement, subject movement, color saturation, etc.) and judge for yourself.

There are only two issues that can cause you grief with regard to production and compression: overloading your encoder and concatenation.

All of the encoders that you'll be using are realtime encoders. They must compress your video data at a steady rate regardless of the images you shoot. Problems arise when the visual information is too complex for the encoder to handle. All encoders react differently to the data they are given based on the type of encoding (DV, MPEG, M-JPEG) and the compression ratio they must work at.

A scene too complex for an encoder might be one with a quick pan, zoom or dolly. Or one that has lots of motion in it where the image changes dramatically from pixel to pixel and from frame to frame. When an encoder "chokes," two things can happen. It can either freeze up and re-output the last frame of properly encoded video again or it can produce macroblocks—a compression artifact—making a large block of pixels look all the same (color and brightness). (See figure 2.)

Decoders can also "choke" since they need to work in realtime as well, and suffer from the same symptoms.

Practice with your encoder (your camcorder or deck) will let you see what it is really capable of handling...and most importantly, what it is not capable of handling and what you must avoid.

Concatenation is the other problem—when you use different types of compression on the same piece of video (DV and then MPEG, for example). Each compression scheme handles data differently, so compression artifacts (known as macroblocks because they look like blocks in the picture) and loss of video resolution are more apparent. Even staying within the same type of compression can cause problems, as the same brand and model of encoder may encode the same signal in a different manner.

While concatenation may not show up until generations later (if at all), you might want to know what compression will be used in post production as well as in the duplication master and distribution copies. Limiting the times the video gets re-compressed and the number of different types of compression that the video will be subjected to will only benefit you in the end.

HOW DIFFERENT PRODUCTION FORMATS CAN BE USED

While people, stations, facilities and networks begin to position themselves with their production format or formats of choice, there is some agreement as to how these formats will be used.

Film will continue to be used as the ultimate high definition imaging format. Currently, more than 80 percent of primetime programming (not including news programs) is shot in

Off-screen photograph from an ATSC HDTV broadcast. The scene consisted of random lightning flashes that lit the woman and the background. Notice the macroblock encoder errors caused by the random nature of the lightning on the image. Photo: CBS.

figure 2. Macroblock encoder errors.

film. Telecines can output the film image in any number of formats or even as a data file.

While looking at the information below, keep in mind what each format offers as well as the complexities of each type of production. You'll soon realize that all of these are natural fits. Also, the 704x480 format stretches pixels either horizontally for 16:9 or vertically for 4:3, so most people feel that it won't see that much use. It should be noted that equipment is just being introduced for many of these formats, such as the 1080p/24 video format introduced in 1999.

Movies (produced at 24 frames per second)
• Film as the ultimate originating format, telecine transferred to (or originating in):
• 1920x1080, 16H:9V, square pixel, 24 frames per second, progressive scan
• 1280x720, 16H:9V, square pixel, 24 frames per second, progressive scan
• 704x480, 4H:3V, non-square pixel, 24 frames per second, progressive scan
• 704x480, 16H:9V, non-square pixel, 24 frames per second, progressive scan
• 640x480, 4H:3V, square pixel, 24 frames per second, progressive scan

Sports (fast action)
• 1920x1080, 16H:9V, square pixel, 30 frames per second, progressive scan
• 1920x1080, 16H:9V, square pixel, 60 fields per second, interlace scan
• 1280x720, 16H:9V, square pixel, 60 frames per second, progressive scan
• 704x480, 4H:3V, non-square pixel, 60 frames per second, progressive scan
• 704x480, 16H:9V, non-square pixel, 60 frames per second, progressive scan
• 640x480, 4H:3V, square pixel, 60 frames per second, progressive scan

High Definition Episodic (big beautiful pictures)
• Film, like that found in more than 80 percent of current non-news primetime, telecine transferred to (or originating in):
• 1920x1080, 16H:9V, square pixel, 24 frames per second, progressive scan
• 1920x1080, 16H:9V, square pixel, 60 fields per second, interlace scan
• 1280x720, 16H:9V, square pixel, 24 frames per second, progressive scan
• 1280x720, 16H:9V, square pixel, 60 frames per second, progressive scan
• 1920x1080, 16H:9V, square pixel, 30 frames per second, progressive scan
• 1920x1080, 16H:9V, square pixel, 60 fields per second, interlace scan
• 1280x720, 16H:9V, square pixel, 60 frames per second, progressive scan

Regular Episodic (average television)
• Film, like that found in more than 70 percent of current non-news primetime, telecine transferred to (or originating in):
• 1280x720, 16H:9V, square pixel, 24 frames per second, progressive scan
• 1280x720, 16H:9V, square pixel, 30 frames per second, progressive scan
• 704x480, 4H:3V, non-square pixel, 24 frames per second, progressive scan
• 704x480, 4H:3V, non-square pixel, 30 frames per second, progressive scan
• 704x480, 4H:3V, non-square pixel, 60 fields per second, interlace scan
• 704x480, 16H:9V, non-square pixel, 24 frames per second, progressive scan
• 704x480, 16H:9V, non-square pixel, 30 frames per second, progressive scan
• 704x480, 16H:9V, non-square pixel, 60 fields per second, interlace scan
• 640x480, 4H:3V, square pixel, 24 frames per second, progressive scan
• 640x480, 4H:3V, square pixel, 30 frames per second, progressive scan

DTV IN THE REAL WORLD

UNDERSTANDING DIGITAL

PRE-PRODUCTION

PRODUCTION

AUDIO

GRAPHIC & COMPOSITING

POST PRODUCTION

DELIVERY & DUPLICATION

ENGINEERING & TRANSMISSION

APPENDIX

GLOSSARY

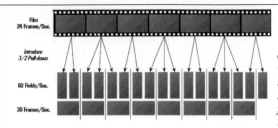

figure 3. 3/2 pulldown.

Film 24 Frames/Sec.

Introduce 3/2 Pull-down

60 Fields/Sec.

30 Frames/Sec.

When film is transferred to 60 frames or fields per second video, a 3/2 pulldown is used so that the 24 frames of film per second equates to 60 frames (or fields) per second of video. In interlace at 60 fields per second, two video fields are derived from the first film frame, three from the second, two from the third, and so on. It is the same with progressive at 60; two video frames are derived from the first film frame, three from the second, two from the third, and so on. This creates visible stagnated motion that Americans have become accustomed to.

In transmission, the ATSC encoder recognizes these duplicated frames and transmits a signal that basically says "same frame again" instead of transmitting the full frame. The ATSC decoder then sees this "same frame again" signal and outputs the same frame again from a frame buffer memory to the television or display. This is known as 3/2 pullup.

The new 1080/24p video format eliminates the need for 3/2 pulldown.

- 640x480, 4H:3V, square pixel, 60 frames per second, progressive scan
- 640x480, 4H:3V, square pixel, 60 fields per second, interlace scan
- 1280x720, 16H:9V, square pixel, 30 frames per second, progressive scan
- 704x480, 4H:3V, non-square pixel, 30 frames per second, progressive scan
- 704x480, 4H:3V, non-square pixel, 60 frames per second, progressive scan
- 704x480, 4H:3V, non-square pixel, 60 fields per second, interlace scan
- 704x480, 16H:9V, non-square pixel, 30 frames per second, progressive scan
- 704x480, 16H:9V, non-square pixel, 60 frames per second, progressive scan
- 704x480, 16H:9V, non-square pixel, 60 fields per second, interlace scan
- 640x480, 4H:3V, square pixel, 30 frames per second, progressive scan
- 640x480, 4H:3V, square pixel, 60 frames per second, progressive scan
- 640x480, 4H:3V, square pixel, 60 fields per second, interlace scan

A UNIVERSAL STANDARD: THE CIF

The world now has a Common Image Format (CIF) to allow producers the world over to trade and distribute content. Ratified by the International Telecommunications Union (ITU) in June 1999, the 1920x1080 digital sampling structure is a world format. All supporting technical parameters relating to scanning, colorimetry, transfer characteristics, etc., are the same worldwide. The CIF can be used with a variety of picture capture rates: 60p, 50p, 30p, 25p, 24p, as well as 60i and 50i. The standard is identified as ITU-R BT 709-3.

CONCLUSION

Producing in digital, and especially widescreen, comes with its own set of problems and concerns. The same way you have honed your craft as an analog and 4:3 professional, is how you will strive in the digital world—through practice. You've spent your career watching the work of others and critiquing your own work to become better at your craft. In the digital age, this skill may be your most valuable.

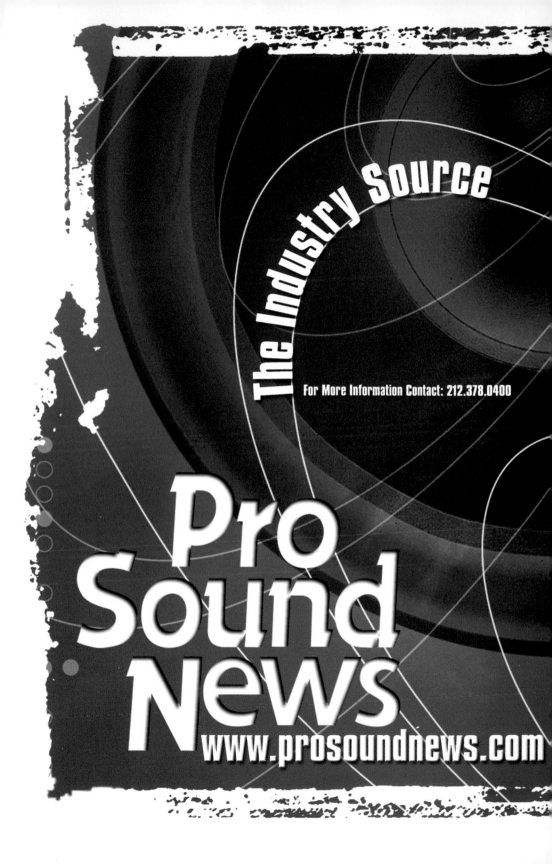

In the world of digital television, audio is no longer the bastard child of video. The ATSC transmission standard uses audio surround-sound compressed with Dolby Digital (AC-3). Six discrete audio channels are used: Left, Center, Right, Left Rear (or side) Surround, Right Rear (or side) Surround, and a subwoofer (considered the ".1" as it is limited in bandwidth), that are all encoded into one audio signal (whether one or six discrete channels are encoded). But that's just the presentation side. Audio when teamed with digital video must be as clean and crystal clear as the viewer expects. If you're producing for 5.1 surround sound, you'll need six discrete audio channels. Add two more channels for a second language stereo mix and you're post producing eight discrete channels. But even with a lonely single channel monophonic mix, digital audio will have to be the best that it can be. What follows are sections on digital audio production, post, DAWs (Digital Audio Workstations), how to build your own surround sound studio and the pros and cons of embedding audio in "601," Dolby Digital and Dolby E.

DIGITAL AUDIO PRODUCTION

GARY ESKOW

Analog recording continues to recede into the past as digital formats make capturing audio easier, more accurate and efficient. What are these formats, and what do you need to know about them?

In many ways digital audio is handled exactly as its analog counterpart was, whether recorded separately on a dedicated audio recorder or with video on videotape. Consideration number one is your budget. If pristine sound is critical to your project and you have the dollars to assign to this area, securing the services of a location sound recordist with dedicated gear is the way to go. These folks know how to "shoot" sound (the term comes directly from its visual counterpart), and you can pretty much forget about the quality aspect of your audio once you have a professional on board.

IT STILL STARTS AS ANALOG

Microphones are still analog devices, transferring sound waves into electrical energy. Even the new digital microphones still start with analog and do the analog-to-digital conversion within the microphone body. As the first link of the audio chain, microphones play a key role in the quality of the end product. In the past, videographers did not have to be overly concerned with providing the "very best" microphone quality. Analog recording and transmission degradation would eliminate any improvements they might experience from using higher-quality gear. With the advent of digital recording, post and transmission, this will no longer be the case. Keep in mind that digital offers videographers CD-quality sound that viewers will be expecting. Microphones should be of the highest quality available with wide frequency response and extremely low inherent self-noise to help ensure highly accurate sound reproduction.

DEDICATED SOUND

A sound recordist will ask you some questions. The answers will depend on the nature of your project, the importance of sound, and your budget. He or she will need to know how many microphones to bring on the shoot, and whether you will be using a mixing console, sending stereo pairs of your entire audio out to the inputs on a camcorder, or to tape recorders. This sending function, called bussing, is quite important. If your audio budget is limited, you may not have the luxury of sending your individual microphone outputs to multitrack tape recorders where it can be mixed at leisure in the post process. In this case, your sound recordist will execute an on-site mix and buss a stereo pair to a camcorder, two track recorder or DAT. Many mixing functions will be executed in the post process, but having a trained sound recordist working on location with a multiple mic set up and mixing console can be critical in insuring that the sound which makes it to post is clean and well balanced.

VIDEOGRAPHER AS AUDIOGRAPHER

Many documentaries, news shoots, and even some low-budget features use more modest audio set ups. You may decide to forego the services of an audio professional altogether and rely on the sound you get from the microphone on your camera. If you're shooting with a digital format camcorder, you're getting digital audio as well as picture. What do you need to know about recording digital sound in this case?

Actually very little, but one concern is of paramount importance: audio levels. Analog recording handles tape saturation or overmodulation—"hitting" tape at louder than desirable levels, in a relatively forgiving manner. Going too far into the red on your VU meter (recording at levels higher than 0 dB) will ultimately result in distortion, but the price you pay for not paying proper attention to the levels of your signal comes by degree. You'll almost have to be trying to end up with audio that is unusable because of distortion caused by improper levels on a shoot that uses analog tape. Automatic gain control and limiters help to keep analog audio levels where they should be.

Not so with any of the digital media, which include digital quarter-inch tape (found on the Nagra D—a very expensive machine used on most major film shoots), RDAT and digital mini disc recorders, and the digital audio portion of the tape you pop into your digital camcorder or VTR. Add to this list of digital recording devices the hard disk audio recorders that recently entered the market, and expect others to follow. All of the digital recording media offer clarity and an accuracy that far surpass analog technology. But watch out. There is danger lurking in the digital stream as well.

DIGITAL DANGER

Digital audio—this point cannot be underscored too heavily—distorts **immediately** when the 0 dB level is passed. This distortion is hideous and no recording that has it is usable. If you're familiar with audio terminology and want to impress the audiophiles on your crew, throw them a question like, "What is headroom and should you handle it differently when recording digitally instead of in the analog realm?"

Headroom refers to the difference, measured in decibels, between the sound recorded and the 0 dB mark. Analog tape has a hiss associated with it. As you get closer to the 0 dB point this unpleasant sound gets less noticeable, masked in effect by the signal being recorded. Consequently, engineers have made it their business to monitor the level of the incoming signal and make sure that the signal-to-noise ratio is as high as possible, always being careful to leave a little headroom, or extra decibel room, for the unexpected level burst that generally comes when you least expect it. Knowing how much headroom to leave is part of an engineer's skills.

Here's the good news. You can leave lots more headroom when you record audio digitally, thus minimizing the chance that you'll pass the dreaded 0 dB point. Why? Signal-to-noise is still a factor, especially considering the fact that your location sound will most certainly have to pass through analog to digital converters (microphones are still analog devices) which color the sound to one degree or another. Theoretically, then, you'd still want to get as close to the 0 dB point as possible, wouldn't you?

No, for several reasons. One is the lack of tape hiss associated with any of the digital media. Another point to consider: When your digital audio is taken to post it can be normalized. Sounds good, you say, especially when you know what it means.

NORMALIZATION

In a nutshell, normalization lets you take signals recorded at low levels and boost them until they come to within a fraction of the 0 dB mark. And there is absolutely no generational loss associated with this process, only zeros and ones rewritten so that they peak out just where you want them. This means that on your shoot you can give extra headroom to your sound recordings without worrying about the signal-to-noise ratio.

SPECS

Perhaps you've heard of the debate within the record industry that surrounds digital recording. Many record producers still favor recording to analog multitrack tape claiming that it's "warmer" and has more of a "live" feel to it. The hoopla that attached to CDs when they first appeared was met with disdain by many within the recording business. Is the quality of digital recordings fixed or is it an evolving medium? Is it "better" than analog recording? What specs should the videographer be aware of?

CDs recorded today sound better than the early ones, although the frequency range is the same now as it was in the late 1980s for most recordings and all of the playback devices. The formula to remember here is that digital sound must be recorded, or sampled, at twice the frequency of the highest pitch you wish to capture. Leaving aside the issue of the uppermost harmonics—the highest elements of a ringing cymbal for example—that you perceive more than hear, human beings distinguish sounds up to about 20 kHz. The CDs you have are generally recorded at 44.1 kHz, giving an accurate representation of most all of the frequency spectrum that we can hear. Most field recorders record at 44.1 kHz, or even 48 kHz, but it doesn't hurt to ask about the unit you'll be working with.

As we speak a debate is taking place within the recording industry. Some audiophiles insist that sampling at 96 kHz—double the current specs—is necessary to achieve the full sound that humans can perceive. At this high sampling frequency, many contend that the "warmth" advantage of analog recording will disappear. In other words, these people feel that the slightly harsh sound that is sometimes associated with digital recordings results from our not getting an accurate representation of the full audio spectrum when sampling at 44.1 kHz or 48 kHz.

Others argue that such a spec, while desirable in theory, does not have the practical value that would justify the memory requirements that would be required in the recording studio and in the field. Television and video professionals shooting digital sound will be one of the constituent groups that ultimately help decide, with their pocketbooks, whether a 96 kHz specification is adopted.

A second spec that you will hear about is bit rate. It is not synonymous with "volume." The word volume is ubiquitous in the recording industry, but in fact it is neither an engineering nor an electrical term. Rather, the word has been borrowed as a measuring term, but unlike a quart or gallon it has no specific definition when used to describe sound.

What you need to know is that more bits in a digital medium mean greater detail in representing amplitude variation in your recording. If all we had, for example, were recordings that divided signals into two levels, **VERY LOUD** and *really soft*, the sound would be unrealistic and quite disturbing to our highly refined and cultured ears. This is not the case, of course, with any of the digital media. The lowest bit rate you'll find is 8, and the mathematical relationship we're dealing with in this area is always two to the power of n. In this case that means 2 to the 8th power, which yields the number 256. You might think that having 256 amplitude steps for every sample that you record would be sufficient, but our ears are quite sensitive, and 8-bit recordings actually sound rough and unrealistic to us.

Sixteen-bit is the current standard for recording and mastering records and films.

That means that every sample in a 16-bit recording may be resolved, or rounded off, to one of 65,536 discrete amplitude steps. 16-bit recordings sound quite good to most of us. Still, purists within the industry argue that 20-bit, or ultimately even 24-bit, technology needs to become standard before we have recordings that match the sensitivity of human hearing. As with high frequency sampling, purists argue that anything less than 20-bit or 24-bit recording yields results that are unsatisfactory when compared to analog recordings made under optimal conditions.

RECORDING SOUND

Now that you know a little bit about the basics of recording digital sound, you'll be able to approach recording digital sound with some intelligence. If hiring a sound recordist is not in the cards for your current project, you'll probably be using a camcorder that has built-in digital audio. What makes and models are there for you to choose from?

Several years ago, some of the main players in the video industry agreed on a standard for their units. These manufacturers, which include Sony, Panasonic and Philips, have digital video recorders that offer digital audio as well. Typically, the specs on your digital audio channels on your professional digital camcorder are 48 kHz/16-bit. But beware, consumer formats, such as DV have lower specs or specs that are user selectable.

Regardless of your budget, there is certainly a digital recorder out there for you. It may be part of a digital camcorder, or it could be a separate digital audio recorder—a Nagra D, RDAT or mini disk recorder, or a digital multitrack unit such as the Tascam D-88 or Alesis ADAT. At some point your shoot will be over. If you've watched levels and not passed the 0 dB mark, you're in good shape. It's now time to for you to post audio.

DIGITAL AUDIO POST

GARY ESKOW

Now that your shoot is over, it's time to post audio. Here's where you'll take the sound you've recorded on location—whether analog or digital, clean it up, add music and sound effects where necessary and make sure that your final audio matches picture perfectly.

Before we examine the audio post process, there's one last element of location recording you need to know about—how the sound recorded during your shoot is referenced to timecode. As we mentioned in *Digital Audio Production* you may be working in a variety of ways. Budget is generally the factor that determines whether sound is recorded independently from picture. You may, in fact, be shooting audio directly onto a digital camcorder. In this case, both sound and picture will likely be cut together in post, and the audio that you've recorded on location will carry through the entire post procedure with no alterations. It is possible to separate digital sound from picture later on, but the cost is high, and if your budget allows, you'd be much better off recording audio to one of the other digital media formats discussed earlier.

SYNC TIMING

What do you need to know about timecode and how audio is synced to video in post? If you're shooting on film (a very viable HDTV acquisition format) your camera's internal crystal provides the locking mechanism. Timecode is added only when you have your dailies transferred to tape for editing purposes. Audio, on the other hand, is referenced to SMPTE timecode on location.

By the late 1960s videotape had replaced film in many broadcast applications. Tape has advantages over film—cost being one—but it posed a sync problem. Positional information is printed visibly along the edge of film stock, but videotape frames are recorded magnetically, and this information is not detectable. The Society of Motion Picture and Television Engineers devised a method of identifying frames and subframes that is commonly referred to as SMPTE. Practically speaking, how does SMPTE affect your audio work?

On a film shoot, each take will be slated with a clap stick. In video, a timecode generator sends out a SMPTE number stream to your digital tape recorder. The numbers that correspond to the beginning of each take can be determined by stopping the film at the clap and noting the SMPTE location. Later, when a new SMPTE stripe is laid against your dailies, an offset will be computed that allows for an exact match of picture and audio.

Let's assume that you're shooting on film and using a Nagra D to record digital audio. A SMPTE generator feeds timecode to the Nagra, and a clap stick marks the exact starting point of each take. Dailies are then transferred to 3/4-inch tape for editing with fresh SMPTE laid onto them. What happens if the first several takes of Scene One are duds and you don't bother to transfer them? In this case the first of your dailies, take three for example, will start with a SMPTE location of 01:01:00:00 (SMPTE is generally laid down with a starting point of one hour and one minute). The audio that goes with that picture will have entirely different numbers, say 01:04:22:11 as determined by checking the clap stick number for that take. Those numbers are part of an edit decision list (EDL) that the transfer house uses. They will compute the offset needed to start the audio at the exact point where the corresponding picture begins and transfer both elements so that they are in sync with each other.

If the transfer house does its job properly, the dailies that you view will have temporary audio that is locked to picture (sync sound). In the real world, transfer houses are sometimes less careful with audio than picture, so make sure that the sound you get is clean. Once you've determined which takes are keepers, it's time to get down to the business of posting audio.

POSTING

Following the example that has you recording digital audio onto a Nagra D machine in the field, we now need to ask ourselves whether those original tracks will be used in post. Not likely. In general, when a transfer house ports over the sound from the master tape to a work print video (remember, we're only using the Nagra D as an example; timecoded RDAT machines are often used, and complicated shoots may require a multitrack format such as the Tascam DA-88), it will make a digital copy for the audio house, leaving the originals as safety masters. If a two-track format has been used, the digital clone will most often be a SMPTE encoded RDAT. The SMPTE on this tape will reference the numbers that are on the work print, not those found on the original audio tape. From here on out the EDL associated with picture is all that counts.

How has the digital revolution changed the way audio post is conducted? Radically, in a word. Digital Audio Workstations (see To DAW Or Not To DAW?) have made it possible to work faster and more efficiently than ever before. In general though, don't count on spending less time in audio post than you might have a decade ago. DAWs also let you experiment with sound in exciting ways, and when you start playing around with sound effects, foley and music, you may find it hard to stop.

What work stations are out there, and what do you need to know about them? The first work station adopted by the audio post community was built by a company called New England Digital. The Post Pro was sophisticated for its time, but by today's standards the power it possesses is relatively tame, and the hefty price associated with this work station relegated it to museum status when a music company decided to get into the game.

DigiDesign founder Peter Gotcher originally made chips for samplers—devices that play back digital recordings of sounds—that the music industry found quite appealing. Several years ago, DigiDesign came out with its first ProTools system. ProTools, which synchronizes multiple tracks of digital audio to picture using Macintosh hardware, took the audio post market by storm.

ProTools is currently the work station of choice for many high-end audio post professionals around the world. Work stations built around the PC platform have also made great inroads, and systems based on proprietary hardware and software continue to be used to post audio as well. What do these systems offer to you, and what should you know about them as you prepare to post your audio?

Digital work stations combine the flexibility of computer functionality—the copy, cut and paste features that you're aware of—with digital signal processing (DSP) power that previously was found only on standalone processing devices. Much of this power comes from software plug-ins that augment the functionality of the core DAW system. Work stations can be configured in a variety of ways, and the amount of money spent on a system will determine how complex a set of tasks can be executed at one time.

Don't go to a studio that has more power than you need. Here's where a little knowledge can help save you a lot of money. If your project has a stereo mix of location sound, and all you need to add is some stock music and end up with a stereo master, why pay for a house that has three or four rooms with expensive DAWs? Cheaper facilities can be found with operators who can execute a four-track mix and buss to a stereo master at a fraction of the price. So what if you have to work in an apartment or basement studio?

You don't need a prestigious location to get good, quality work, and often the lower overhead of a project studio can mean bigger savings to you in the long run.

If, on the other hand, you need to record foley (recording footsteps against picture, for example), replace unusable dialogue with clean speech recorded after the fact (automatic dialogue replacement, or ADR), create effects that involve extensive sound design and add music, you're better off going to a larger facility.

What should you expect in terms of digital power when you're paying several hundred dollars or more an hour?

To start, at least 16 tracks of digital recording, more likely 32. Remember, the DAW acts like a tape recorder. Your location audio is digitally transferred to two or more of these tracks, and subsequent tracks are built around them. Who will you be working with, and what exactly does he or she do?

More often than not the person assigned to help you with audio will carry the title *sound designer*. You don't need a degree to hold this title. What does a sound designer do, and how much of what can be done do you really need?

DESIGNING SOUND

Once again, a little preparation can save you a lot of money. Don't rely on a sound designer to tell you what you need to do with your tracks. Sound designers can take bits of sound from a variety of sources and create wonderful effects, but you might not need all of their creative skills. They like to experiment. It's fun to add robotic DSP to the voice of that mean old man down the street in your film, but did you really want anything other than the level of this character's main monologue pulled up? Be careful.

A good DAW operator can clean up poorly recorded audio to a remarkable extent. Let's say you didn't notice that an air conditioning unit was humming away in the background while you shot an interview. Some software, like DigiDesign's DINR plug-in, let you "teach" the system the contour of the unwanted sound and reduce it to a nearly inaudible level. After-the-fact remedies are never a substitute for careful field recording, but removing unwanted noise is an area in which sound designers specialize. If your tracks can not be cleaned up with the noise-removing software that comes with a system like ProTools, you may have to go to a very expensive work station like Sonic Solutions. That will add additional dollars to your budget. Clean audio captured in the field should make this step unnecessary.

Are you incorporating music into your project? Whether you've commissioned an original score or are licensing stock music, a good sound designer can be of great assistance in this area. Cutting and pasting cues, taking bits from several musical cues and cross fading them (making smooth transitions from one to the other), even changing the pitch or duration of a cue are things that can add emotional depth to your project, and a good sound designer is well experienced in this area.

Whereas analog track recording continues to have adherents, no one questions the superiority of posting audio in the digital realm. For one thing, the fact that your original audio can be copied and pasted, processed and reprocessed with no generational loss means that you can experiment to the full extent of your budget with no degradation of your original material.

The flexibility of disk-based file management also means that you can move from any point in your audio to any other without waiting for tape to rewind or fast forward.

Your last concern involves format. Will the post house that is completing your project require a simple stereo master from the audio post house? In this case they'll probably want you to deliver an RDAT master with SMPTE. If you've executed a more complicated mix, with dialogue, effects and music broken out as separate stereo pairs, they'll require a multitrack tape from you.

These days the Tascam DA-88 is the machine of choice for many, but check before you complete your post work and save yourself a possible hassle.

Be aware that there is a move in the studio away from tape towards central storage and digital dubbers using hard drives and MO disks, due to their high quality and random access ability.

Getting the most out of your budget and maximizing your creative options during the audio post process are your two fundamental goals. Thinking one step ahead while recording in the field and during post means that you won't be caught short anywhere. Remember, there are three critical phases in your audio work. First comes location recording, next audio post, and the peak of the triangle arrives when you hand off completed audio tracks to the company you've hired to execute your final mix. Know where you are throughout the journey, and the path that your audio takes you down will be interesting and fun.

TO DAW OR NOT TO DAW?

Matt Charles

While the advantages of nonlinear editing may seem obvious to most of you, there are probably still a few "die-hards" out there utilizing tape-based editing systems that don't take advantage of the power of computer-based editing. There are probably even more of you who view the audio portion of video editing as a necessary evil, that is best taken care of as quickly and painlessly as possible. However, with the emergence of 5.1 surround sound, DVD and HDTV broadcasts, the need to ensure a better sounding finished product becomes more critical. Enter the next generation of the Digital Audio Workstation (DAW).

Although DAWs have been around for many years, the ever-increasing "bang for the buck" ratio of personal computers has elevated the level of performance of the PC- and Mac-based DAWs from a non-professional audio "sketch pad" to a serious, professional audio recording and editing tool. In the recent past, such features as non-destructive editing, snapshot recall, waveform editing and mild effects processing were common in almost all DAWs. However, the lack of timecode synchronization, latency issues and non-intuitive user interfaces limited the effectiveness of some DAWs as a professional video tool. Today, timecode sync is available on almost all DAWs, latency problems have been reduced to a point where they're not really an issue, and products like the Mackie HUI and CM Automation's Motor Mix provide a easy to use, familiar work-surface and interface.

Some of the latest DAWs derive their increased horsepower from having processor chips built onto the plug-in card itself. This design allows the plug-in card to handle the audio signal processing and frees up the computer's CPU, allowing it to focus on screen graphics and other normal computer functions. This design approach allows for a higher number of discrete channels of audio per card and ensures smoother and quicker operation of the system.

Some DAWs, like Mark of the Unicorn's 2408 systems, take this concept even further by connecting an external "Breakout Box" to the sound card via a special computer cable. By moving the input and output jacks to an external box, they facilitate the patching of audio cables and help reduce the "rat's nest" of wires often found in the back of most computers. This design makes using outboard signal processors and external A/D and D/A converters much easier, which ultimately should help improve the overall sound of the audio. Since most of these types of systems are modular, they can be "stacked" to add more discrete channels of audio, depending on the availability of bus slots on your computer.

Many DAWs, like Digidesign's ProTools system, incorporate various digital input and output jacks (Lightpipe, AES/EBU and SP/DIF) that allow for direct transfer of digital data from DAT machines, Modular Digital Multitracks, and other digital recording devices. This feature not only makes the transfer of data quicker and easier, it also bypasses the converter circuitry that can add distortion and degrade the quality of your signal.

Another contributing factor to the power of these new DAWs is the quality and availability of software "plug-ins" that offer features like time-based effects (delay, reverb, pitch shifting, flanging, chorusing, etc.) and dynamics processing (compression, EQ, limiting and noise gating). Sonic Foundry and Waves are just two manufacturers that offer software plug-ins that actually become part of the DAW by placing the buttons and menus for the effects right on the DAWs interface screen. These features allow you to make use of the processing power of the computer without having to toggle back and forth between the workstation and the effects processors, which saves you time by keeping you in your creative working environment.

Of course there are companies that sell complete "turnkey" systems that incorporate a computer, breakout boxes and software into a perfectly matched package that is dedicated solely to recording, editing and processing audio and video. Avid offers a complete editing system that utilizes Digidesign's ProTools as its DAW. This is a particularly powerful combination, because both video and audio workstations are designed from the ground up to work together and offer enhanced functionality that can only be found in integrated systems. Some features include realtime, simultaneous "scrubbing" of video and audio and 5.1 surround sound functions incorporated right into the workscreen.

Obviously, the type of DAW you buy depends on your needs and budget, but the capabilities and affordability of the current crop of workstations is unparalleled. It's hard to imagine an excuse for not taking advantage of the power and ease of use they offer for video and audio editing.

One warning: the file format used in DAWs differs from manufacturer to manufacturer. If you know that you may be going from one brand of DAW to another, make sure they either support each other's file formats or use a third intermediate format for exchange, such as Open Media Framework Interchange (OMFI), Direct File Exchange Initiative or Advanced Authoring Format (AAF).

TO EMBED OR NOT TO EMBED?
THE PROS AND CONS OF EMBEDDED AUDIO
Nigel Spratling

The SMPTE 272M standard specifies the formatting method for digital audio to allow a maximum of 16 audio channels to be carried in the ancillary data space of the SMPTE 259M serial digital video standard. Further, SMPTE 299M also specifies the architecture of up to 16 audio channels that can be incorporated within the SMPTE292M standard for the high definition television serial digital interface.

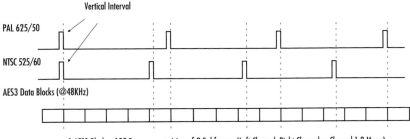

Vertical Interval

PAL 625/50

NTSC 525/60

AES3 Data Blocks (@48KHz)

1 AES3 Block = 192 Frames, comprising of 2 Subframes (Left Channel, Right Channel or Channel 1,2 Mono)

figure 1

Embedding audio within the video signal offers tremendous advantages over traditional methods of running separate audio/video systems, particularly in broadcast facilities where limited audio breakaway is required. Utilizing embedded audio offers some very attractive benefits; simplified system design, reduced cable requirements and distribution amplifier count, a single routing system and, of course, excellent cost savings.

In the past there have been problems that the industry has been forced to accept within embedding and disembedding. One of these is switching errors. When a switch is made between two video sources that contain embedded audio data, it is difficult to resolve a clean audio transition at the receiving end. Figure 1 shows the timing relationships between PAL, NTSC, and AES. At 48 kHz, there are five AES blocks during each PAL video field and 4.170833 AES blocks for an NTSC field. Therefore if a video signal is used as a genlock source for AES signals, the frame alignment and phase relationship between audio signals is arbitrary. In this circumstance, regardless of whether a signal is embedded or not, clean audio transitions are difficult to achieve.

Some manufacturers have provided solutions to the switch error problem by including audio sample rate converters in the embedder design. This has the potential of minimizing the problem, but removes any possibility of controlling audio phase.

Then there are the multi-channel difficulties. When more than four channels are required, the normal technique has been to cascade embedders and disembedders (see figure 2). Cascading is expensive and relies on the ability of the embedder to determine if current ancillary data content exists and where to allocate new data. The more channels inserted, the more difficult it becomes to determine channel location at the receiving end. Plus, with the advent of surround sound in general usage, phase alignment becomes all

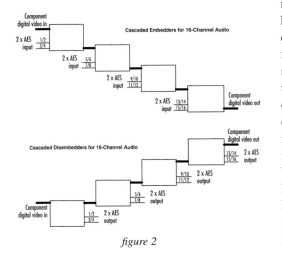

figure 2

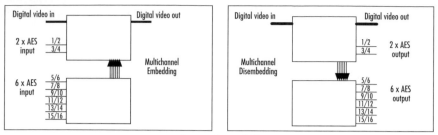

figures 3a and 3b

but impossible with cascading. Multi-channel embedding and disembedding creates indeterminate phasing across channel groups, possibly destroying the effect of surround sound.

A few manufacturers are now offering innovative embedder and disembedder modules that solve these problems. All audio inputs are accurately timed to the house AES reference (which is locked to the master video clock), to create error-free switching if the NTSC video path lengths are the same (PAL is not a problem). Should NTSC path lengths differ, a re-framing (re-timing) ASIC in the disembedder comes to the rescue. If the AES framing is disturbed by a video switch, this ASIC will continue to provide a constant AES output, thus eliminating the possibilities of receivers losing lock and requiring a finite (and audible) recovery period.

With these new designs, cascading of modules is no longer required to support multi-channel expansion. An expansion module can add an additional 12 audio channels (for a total of 16) to these novel embedding and disembedding products (see figures 3a and 3b). Not only does this save money it also solves the previous problems of identifying channel location when utilizing cascaded modules.

All data allocation difficulties are resolved by selectable group assignment. Further, the proprietary AES re-framing on all inputs accurate sample alignment across all four groups. Transport for uncompressed multi-channel audio and surround sound mixes is now reliable with total phase control.

There are still many things that need to be considered when designing a system that utilizes audio embedding. Once audio and video are combined, audio and/or video insertion and mixing may no longer be possible without first de-embedding the

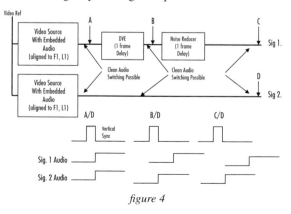

figure 4

audio. Even inserting a station logo on video via a master control switcher might disturb the embedded audio data, therefore limiting your ability to manipulate any signal without first routing it to the appropriate disembedding and re-embedding devices.

Another point of consideration is that any video equipment in the signal path might introduce possible delays. As audio data is embedded in almost every line of video, realignment of video data can be detrimental to the audio information. It may still be recoverable, but it will certainly not be synchronous with other signals and it will no longer be possible to provide error-free switching with another signal that did not take the exact same path (see figure 4).

Embedded audio has its place; it can be a valuable cost-saver in new systems and it's a great way to distribute multi-channel. Serious consideration should be placed on how to utilize the new features and functionality provided by embedders and disembedders during system design and any product that is under consideration should be thoroughly tested for the specific application. It's probably no surprise to hear that there are good products and not-so-good ones available, however the errors that can occur are often very subtle. So please, if you decide to embed, choose carefully.

GET A FEEL FOR SURROUND

STEVE "WOODY" LA CERRA

Five-point-one audio is here, and it's no joke. So what's the point of mixing in 5.1? Visceral impact. If you really want to *experience* audio, park yourself in the center of a 5.1 system and let it rip. You'll hear an emotional intensity that's sorely lacking in most recorded music. And as artists and engineers, that's supposed to be the point of our exercise—to touch people. In talking with producers and engineers, the one thing that was mentioned time and again was that 5.1 makes the listener a participant in the experience, not just an observer. And studios don't have to panic over equipment considerations for 5.1 mixing, because it can be done using any console from a Yamaha 03D to a Euphonix CS2000 to an AMS Neve Capricorn.

If you're set to take the 5.1 plunge, here are some quick tips:

- Use the same brand and model speaker to monitor each of the five full-range channels.
- Drive those speakers with identical power amps.
- Make sure that monitor levels are accurately calibrated.
- Don't clutter the center channel with too much information.
- Use compression conservatively.
- Think three dimensionally and don't be afraid to place instruments discretely to a single channel.
- Don't go for the whiz-bang effect. It quickly becomes tiring to the listener.
- Edit reverb programs with respect to the environment in which the recording took place.
- Confirm that all of your mix busses are providing equal audio quality.
- Always remember that there are no rules.

For the first time since the development of stereo, our industry is being offered a new tool with which to deliver our message. Distinct creative opportunities are opened up in the 5.1 mix platform, not only for recording and mixing, but for composing as well. The possibilities are virtually endless.

SETTING UP FOR SURROUND SOUND:
HOW TO EQUIP AND DESIGN
YOUR STUDIO'S CONTROL ROOM

BOBBY OWSINSKI

S urround Sound. Everybody wants to hear it. Everybody wants to do it. But while setting up a normal stereo studio is pretty straightforward because there's lots of experience to draw from, setting up a surround system can be quite a different challenge. Well, we're here to cut through some of the mystery, explain just how to do it and, most importantly, make it fit into almost any budget.

We're talking about six-channel "5.1" surround setup in this article (see figure 5), which means three speakers across the front (Left, Center, Right), stereo rear (or side) surround speakers, and a subwoofer (the ".1" of the system). Unless you're specifically planning on doing some work in the four-channel Dolby Pro Logic (popular in broadcast and home theater, but quickly being overtaken by 5.1) or the eight-channel (7.1) Sony SDDS film format, there's little reason to go to these formats, since there's an additional cost of equipment (encoder/decoders and speaker/amplifiers) that's not required in 5.1. So by and large, 5.1 seems to be the most popular surround configuration now and in the future so that's what we'll refer to. When we're setting up a surround system, we have to address the issues of monitors, level control, panning, outboard gear, and acoustics. Let's examine each one.

MONITORS

More so than with stereo monitors, all surround monitors are not created equally, which means there's a fair amount of things to consider before installing speaker components for a system.

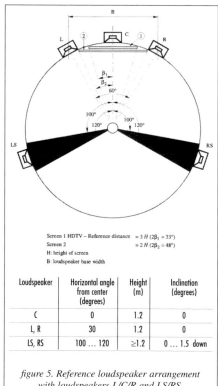

Screen 1 HDTV – Reference distance = 3 H ($2\beta_1$ =33°)
Screen 2 = 2 H ($2\beta_2$ = 48°)
H: height of screen
B: loudspeaker base width

Loudspeaker	Horizontal angle from center (degrees)	Height (m)	Inclination (degrees)
C	0	1.2	0
L, R	30	1.2	0
LS, RS	100 ... 120	≥1.2	0 ... 1.5 down

figure 5. Reference loudspeaker arrangement with loudspeakers L/C/R and LS/RS. Image: International Telecommunications Union/RECOMMENDATION ITU-R BS.775-1

TYPES OF SURROUND SPEAKERS

There are three distinct types of speakers available to be used as the rear surround monitors and great care should be used in choosing the one best suited for your needs.

Direct Radiator—This is a speaker where the sound shoots directly from the front of the cabinet, as in the majority of stereo monitors (see figure 6). The advantages in using these as surround speakers is that you get a fair amount of efficiency and level, which is necessary if you're going to be sending a lot of source material to the rear speakers. In many cases, these speakers are smaller than the front speakers, but in a perfect world, these should be identical to your front speakers since you may be sending some full-range source material there.

Bipoles:—In this case, the sound emanates from the sides of the monitors (see figure. 6 again). You get the advantage of additional coverage area here, which works well for ambiance material, but not so well for source material.

Tripoles—This is a trademark held by M&K which incorporates the best of both worlds, combining direct radiators and bipoles in the same cabinet (see figure. 6).

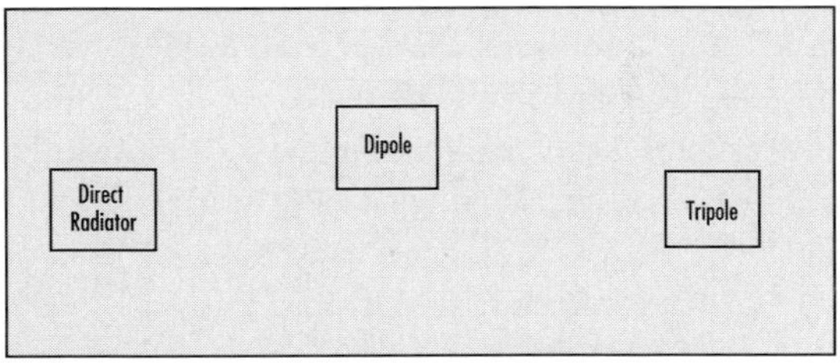

figure 6. 5.1 Surround using dipoles.

SPEAKERS

For anything other than jazz or classical (meaning rock, techno, R&B, etc.), I like all speakers to be identical and of the direct radiator variety. Classical and jazz come from a different place where mostly ambiance is panned to the surrounds with very little source material. The same applies to film or television sound, with only ambiance and effects in the rears. With most other music, however, the mixers I've known have liked to use the surrounds for some heavy-hitting source material—and with very good results, I might add. I had good luck the one time I used Tripoles, and this seems to be the best of both worlds, especially if you do a wide variety of music. Although I've seen some people just slap into use whatever extra speakers they had laying around in order to get a poor man's surround system, just as in stereo, it probably won't translate well to the consumer.

CENTER CHANNEL

The center channel is important in that it anchors the sound and decreases the "phantom images" that we have with two-channel stereo. It's most important that the center channel be identical to the left and right front speakers in order to get smooth panning across the front. That being said, many home theater systems actually use a center speaker different from the front right and left that sit horizontally on top of the television. Theaters, however, have identical center speakers. Play it safe and make it identical.

SUBWOOFER

The subwoofer in a 5.1 system receives a special audio channel called an LFE (for Low Frequency Effects) channel. The LFE, as the name implies, was originally designed specifically for special effects like earthquakes and explosions in the movies and has an additional 10 dB of headroom built in. Although some of the low-frequency information from the main system can be automatically folded into the LFE, most engineers take advantage of the channel and use it for additional kick and bass information.

During playback of a 5.1 program, a special "bass management" circuit is employed to route the proper frequencies to the subwoofer. This is part of the hardware that comes after the Dolby Digital (AC-3) decoder in a consumer receiver that will do one of three things:

1. Send the LFE channel only to the subwoofer.
2. Sum the low end (from 80 Hz down) from the five main channels and send it to the subwoofer.
3. Both of the above at the same time.

There is only one box on the market designed for bass management in a professional environment: the M&K HP80LFE, which is rack mountable and retails for $300. It is possible to use a consumer receiver to do the job, but then you must put up with all of the attendant hassles that come with using a semi-pro device such as RCA connectors and lack of rack mounting. This means that you have three choices when it comes to bass management:

1. Do nothing. Just send your LFE info to the subwoofer.
2. Use the M&K box.
3. Adapt a consumer receiver.

This is a tough call because the consumer ultimately decides what signal will be sent to the subwoofer. The majority of the projects I've done have used the LFE to sub-only method with good results, but only because the M&K box was not available at the time. I'd personally get a bass-management box if only to be able to check the low end in all situations.

PANNING AND LEVEL CONTROL

The biggest problems with surround sound is controlling the level and panning, which go hand-in-hand. In stereo, when we want to change the volume, we're used to just grabbing the control room level control, but when we're dealing with six channels instead of just two, it's just not that easy. The same goes for panning, which is taken for granted in stereo but becomes far more complicated in any surround scenario. As in most aspects of life, things can be done cheaply—level and panning is no exception. I've broken this down into four financial categories.

HIGH PRICED

Buy a new console with surround panning and monitoring built-in. Although a few years ago that would have meant a film-dubbing console, there's now a proliferation of consoles on the market in a very wide variety of prices ranges (from

$6,000 to more than $600,000) that come equipped with surround panning/monitoring as standard. These include consoles by Neve, SSL, Euphonix, D&R, LaFont, Otari, and more, right down to the relatively inexpensive Yamaha 03D. This is the fastest and easiest way to get surround panning and monitoring, although you've got to lay out some cash to do so.

MEDIUM-HIGH PRICED

But let's say that you just can't afford a new console and you just want to add on a product to your existing console to give you surround panning/monitoring capabilities. Otari has a brilliant two-piece add-on called the PicMix that will give you both monitoring and panning in any of the previously mentioned surround formats. The Monitor Controller gives you multichannel monitoring in any of the popular formats as well as preset and calibrated level control for $5,225. The PicMix Panner gives you four channels of panning control (two on joysticks) for $3,600.

LOW PRICED

An even cheaper alternative is the TMH Panner: a true 5.1 add-on panner available for less than $500 per channel designed by the father of the format, Tom Holman.

NO PRICED

Okay, so you're poor or you just don't want to commit to any investment until there's a ready market for your efforts, but you still want to play around with surround. There is a poor man's way to do surround panning and monitoring utilizing the busses on your current desk, only in an unusual way. This requires an English-style split desk with the input channels on one side and the subgroups and monitor section on the other to do it well.

Here's how to do it. First, set up busses 1 and 4 to go to the front left and right speakers and busses 2 and 3 to go to the left and right rear (see figure 7). As you pan from 1 to 4 you will be panning from left to right. When you pan from 1 to 2, you'll be panning from left front to back and 4 to 3 from right front to back. Now set up an aux send to your center channel and another aux to your subwoofer (LFE). Although not perfect, this method allows you to do at least some limited surround panning. Now take the output of bus 1 into track 1 of your DA-88, aux 1 (or center channel) into track 2, bus 4 into track 3, bus 2 into track 4, bus 3 into track 5, and aux 2 into track 6 (see figure 7). This is the *de facto* standard track configuration (but not the only one—DTS uses LF, RF, LR, RR, C, S). Now take the six outputs of the DA-88 into the insert returns of six subgroups and the outputs of those groups into your amps/speakers. Your busses and auxes control the level to tape, and the groups control the control room level. It's complicated, but it works.

OTHER GEAR

Mixdown Machine—The *de facto* standard mixdown machine is the DA-88, although any format with six channels will do. In many cases, the addition of a Rane PacRat allows for 20-bit recording (while taking up the additional two channels), and additional outboard A/D and D/A converters would be nice, depending on the budget.

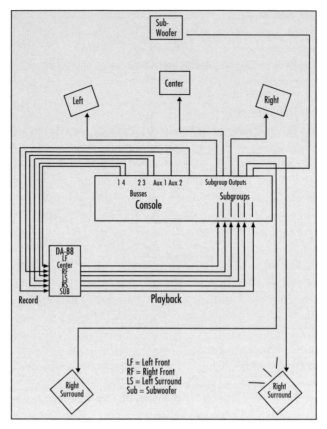

figure 7. 5.1 Surround control room flow chart.

Effects Processors—Since a great deal of the material that you mix may be encoded in Dolby Digital (AC-3) (in which 5.1 is standard but even a single mono channel may be encoded), the question always comes up about listening through an encoder/ decoder.

Surprisingly enough, it's not necessary, or even practical to do so (due to the high cost) since you can't actually change anything on the encoder anyway, and Dolby Digital is already pretty benevolent with the mix. This is not true with Pro Logic (a four-channel playback format encoded on two channels), which does some pretty serious signal steering and absolutely requires a codec on hand through which to listen.

Surround mixing will also require a new generation of multichannel effects processors. Unfortunately, none are available yet, but they may be on the way soon. I've heard the value of such a device. In some of the surround mixes that I've done, I used three Lexicons (two PCM90s and an 80) for the five channels (utilizing a custom program for a decorrolated center channel), and the results were far deeper, wider, and much more usable in the surround format than a normal stereo reverb.

ACOUSTICS

No discussion of surround sound setup would be complete without presenting at least a couple of acoustic considerations. Without getting too deeply into a subject that's worth a chapter all it's own, here are a couple of things to think about.

In stereo, you can have an asymmetrical room with asymmetrical diffusion (such as Live End Dead End), but in surround, diffusion must be used symmetrically. In other words, once you start to spread speakers around the room, then some traditional stereo acoustic concepts (like LEDE) might be rendered not only ineffective, but counterproductive.

Also, in surround you must keep in mind the old Inverse Square Law. Since your level changes by 6 dB (four times less) as you double the distance, it doesn't take much of a position change to change your system balance. This is why side speakers sometimes work better than rear ones because the level doesn't change as much as you move backwards.

Surround sound is a brave new world, and many of the concepts that we've lived with for so many years must now be rethought. The only way forward is to get in there and do it, make some mistakes and some discoveries, and be sure to tell the rest of us.

DOLBY DIGITAL—THE MISSING PIECES

Nigel Spratling

Dolby Digital (AC-3) is the chosen audio compression scheme for the new digital television transmission system. This technology allows up to 5.1 channels of discrete digital audio to be compressed into a single 640 Kbps data stream. The system is quite flexible in that it allows an AC-3 surround sound signal to be decoded as mono, stereo and Pro Logic, as well as the full 5.1 channels.

This scheme was chosen because it provides decoding flexibility as well as a very high compression ratio with excellent quality retention. However, it does have a few drawbacks to those considering production, distribution and re-transmission.

In production, the movie industry has been producing multichannel surround sound for a considerable time with movie theaters now routinely being equipped with 5.1 or 7.1 channel systems. Consumers have added Pro Logic Surround Sound systems to try to achieve a movie theater atmosphere in their homes, and recent technology has begun to make AC-3 5.1 available through laserdiscs, DVD and special amplifiers and receivers. For television broadcasters it has been a struggle to introduce stereo production and transmission, and in fact, many of the smaller stations are still only capable of transmitting a monaural audio signal. To date, almost one-half of all cable headends still do not pass whatever stereo signal they receive from broadcasters.

By FCC edict, it is now necessary for broadcasters to get on the fast track to an all digital transmission of standard definition TV, high definition TV and Dolby

Digital sound. So what new problems will face designers attempting to build new systems for this application?

AC-3 is a perceptual coding scheme that breaks the original signals into spectral components and, in simple terms, realigns the audio data to maximize the use of the 'gaps' and 'imperceptible' information found in the original audio recording spectrum. This spectral 'realignment' allows for significant bit rate reduction, while retaining sufficient data to allow very high quality playback once decoded.

However, this scheme does not come without a price. AC-3 was never designed to be anything but a distribution technique. It is not meant to be decoded then re-encoded.

In broadcasting, it is normal practice for a television station to receive programming material via satellite feed, landline, or videotape. This programming material is then inserted into the station playout schedule, more often than not this received material is edited to allow station identification, announcements and local commercial insertion. If the received material has audio coded as AC-3 data, it can be decoded to allow audio editing. However, once decoded it is almost impossible to re-encode to AC-3 properly due to the spectral realignment that took place during the first encoding. Double encoding AC-3 will at best, result in poor quality audio and, at worst, no discernible audio signal at all.

Due to this fact all audio signals, prior to the final transmission, must be received as either baseband data or via some mezzanine compression scheme that does not interfere with the Dolby technique. Of course, if the signals are mono or stereo (possibly with Pro Logic coding), then they can be distributed via a single AES audio connection and delivered to the AC-3 encoder at the transmitter.

TODAY'S PROBLEMS

If true surround sound is to be transmitted, some problems appear. They are:
- Most current DVCRs have only four audio channels.
- Most existing routing and distribution systems have been constructed for two or four audio channels.
- True surround sound requires 5.1 (five, plus one band-limited subwoofer) channels, meaning six discrete audio channels (add a SAP or separate audio program such as a second language or description stereo track, and you're up to eight discrete audio channels).
- AES audio maintains perfect stereo phase, but correct phasing between AES signals is difficult to achieve.

Here's what will be required to overcome these issues:
- DVCRs with six to 10 discrete channels.
- Eight (four AES) channel distribution and switching systems.
- A system where AES inter-signal phase integrity can be guaranteed.

If you're designing or considering the design of a new facility, be aware that the audio systems may need to be much more complex, and designed with much more care and upward expandability, than you had previously considered.

What you decide to do in audio post today will affect the value of your product tomorrow. You may post in mono, stereo, Pro Logic (with a left total and right total audio track), or true 5.1 surround sound depending on the project and its anticipated value in the future.

For further information on digital audio referencing and timing issues, read *THE BOOK, An Engineers Guide To The Digital Transition* (and its sequal *THE BOOK II*) freely available from ADC/NVISION (1-800-719-1900) or at www.nvision1.com.

DOLBY DIGITAL (AC-3) AND DOLBY E
CRAIG TODD

Television audio has successfully made one major transition—from mono to two-channel stereo. That transition required changes in the broadcast infrastructure and stimulated a number of new technical developments in distribution and emission technology.

While the new digital TV systems now being put into place for emission are inherently capable of delivering Dolby Digital (AC-3) 5.1 channel audio to the home, the infrastructure required to convey multichannel audio from the post production studio to the emission transmitter is not yet in place.

Also missing is the infrastructure to carry important audio metadata. Many new technical developments are required in order to make the delivery of multichannel audio routine and practical.

The Dolby Digital coding system allows very high quality audio to be delivered to the listener at a very low bit rate. Also, a number of important user features are provided by the use of a number of elements of "metadata" (data about the audio essence), including dialog normalization, which is a form of level uniformity based on matching the level of speech across all programs, and dynamic range control, which allows the simultaneous delivery of both wide and narrow dynamic range audio with the choice made by the listener.

Fundamental to the design of the Dolby Digital system are the concepts that:

• the audio essence is delivered without any alteration such as level shifts or dynamic range compression or limiting;

  • metadata is generated by those doing the creative work in the sound studio; and

  • some metadata usage is under the control of the listener.

The listener can choose, for instance, whether to listen to a typical narrow dynamic range presentation, or to listen to a very wide dynamic range presentation equivalent to what would be obtained in the cinema—or something in between. It is critical to the proper usage that both multichannel audio and metadata pathways exist between the output of the post production studio and the input to the Dolby Digital encoder which feeds into the DTV transmitter.

The use of low bit rate coded audio within a new infrastructure is attractive, as it can allow much of the current equipment (VTRs, AES/EBU distribution, etc.) to carry both multichannel audio and metadata. A new architecture employing audio coding should add multichannel capability without removing any important functionality which currently exists.

Unfortunately, existing audio coding systems are simply not designed to be video friendly. In the chain of video contribution, production, post production and distribution, a number of cascades of coding will be required. Any coder employed must be capable of multiple generations of concatenation without significant audible degradation, and must have a time delay which can be managed so that A/V sync can be maintained.

In order to avoid unnecessary concatenations, it is also important to be able to perform video synchronous switching between coded audio streams without affecting A/V sync and to edit encoded audio streams on existing VTRs, both without introducing audible glitches.

Currently available audio coding technologies can achieve good performance at reasonable bit rates and with reasonable equipment cost. However, when trying to apply these existing coders to the task of increasing audio channel capacity in existing video and broadcast facilities, the problems described above become apparent.

A major problem is that there is no alignment between video and encoded audio frames. When switches or edits are performed on an A/V signal, the edit points will occur at video frame boundaries but will not, in general, occur on audio frame boundaries. This will lead to damaged audio frames, or a need to move the audio edit point relative to the video edit point in order to find a suitable edit point for encoded audio.

A search for a workable solution has led this author to the conclusion that an entirely new coding system with a number of desirable properties is required. These properties include manageable coding delays, editability on video frame boundaries, metadata carriage, and satisfactory quality when a number of generations are concatenated.

A new coding system designed specifically for use with video is available from Dolby Laboratories. First demonstrated privately at the NAB '97 convention, the system is referred to as "Dolby E." With the Dolby E coder, the audio framing is matched to the video framing, which allows synchronous and seamless switching or editing of audio and video without the introduction of gaps or A/V sync slips. All of the common video frame rates, including 30/29.97, 25, and 24/23.976, can be supported with matched Dolby E audio frame sizes.

The Dolby E coding technology is intended to provide approximately 4:1 reduction in bit rate. The reduction ratio is intentionally limited so that the quality of the audio may be kept very high even after a number of encode-decode generations. The fact that operations such as editing and switching can be performed seamlessly in the coded domain allows many coding generations to be avoided, further increasing quality.

A primary carrier for the Dolby E data will be the AES/EBU signal. The Dolby E coding will allow the two PCM audio channels to be replaced with eight encoded audio channels. A VTR PCM track pair will become capable of carrying eight independent audio channels, plus the accompanying metadata. The system is also intended to be applied on servers and satellite links.

A time delay when encoding or decoding Dolby E is unavoidable. In order to facilitate the provision of a compensating video delay, the audio encoding and decoding delay have been fixed at exactly one frame. When applied with video recording formats which incorporate frame based video encoding, it can be relatively easy to provide for equal video and audio coding delays. When applied with uncoded video, it may be necessary to provide a compensating one-frame video delay.

There are two philosophies as to where Dolby E encoders and decoders should be placed: the point of constriction versus point of use. The first is to place the coding equipment at the points where bandwidth is limited, such as around VTRs or satellite links.

The second, and perhaps preferred, philosophy is to place the coding equipment at only those points where the audio signal is created, processed, or consumed. This point of use method places encoders and decoders in studios, and not at tape machines or satellite terminals (except for lower-cost confidence monitoring decoders), and requires routing of encoded audio. The benefits are that fewer coding units may be required (a cost savings), metadata carriage is assured, routing costs are reduced and unnecessary decode/re-encode generations can be avoided.

More information on Dolby Digital and Dolby E can be found on the Dolby Laboratories TV Audio Web Page at www.dolby.com/tvaudio/.

Editors' Note: Other manufacturers, including Techniche and ADC/NVISION, provide compressed multichannel audio options as well.

The Studio System
Movie Magic Scheduling
Movie Magic Budgeting
InHollywood.com
Planetpoint.com
AnimationWorldNetwork.com
CinematographyWorld.com
MediaTechnology.com
DesignInMotion.com
DirectorsWorld.com
PostIndustry.com
TVIndustry.com
EditorsNet.com
DVDArtist.com
VFXPro.com
2-pop.com

APPLICATIONS

RESEARCH

DEVELOPMENT

SCHEDULING

BUDGETING

PROCUREMENT

MANAGEMENT

Creative Planet.com
The Network for Creative Professionals

COMMUNITY

DIRECTORIES

NEWS

EDITORIAL

AND MORE...

Computer-graphic imaging (CGI) systems configured for television and film production comprise several different areas. Common to these applications is that they are at the heart of today's digital television revolution and increasingly encompass every area of teleproduction. This chapter is intended only as a basic introduction to the subject's history, current state, and future possibilities.

THE ART OF DIGITAL

BRIAN MCKERNAN

Slightly more than a decade ago, computer-generated imaging (CGI) was the domain of university and military research labs and the design departments of the aerospace and automotive industries. Today CGI is used to generate such mainstream entertainment as the *Toy Story* films, photorealistic digital effects for TV and movies, and interactive content for the Internet and video games. In a relatively short time span, CGI went from being a difficult and expensive discipline dominated by scientists to an increasingly powerful—and inexpensive—creative tool for generating whatever moving image the mind can conceive. And CGI continues to advance, with each new Titanic-sized project adding additional capabilities to the field's repertoire of software capabilities.

figure1. Toy Story 2 *exemplifies how far CGI has evolved since 1962.*

As remarkable as the hardware and software of modern CGI is, it remains at its core basically a very sophisticated replacement for pencil and paper. What it does best is remove many of the barriers standing between the human inspiration to create moving images and the actual creation of them. As such, CGI greatly extends the human ability to communicate visually. Although it may—in some circumstances—involve the automation of certain repetitive tasks that are otherwise labor-intensive, CGI is not the roboticization of moving-image production but a powerful means of advancing it to new levels of sophistication.

As high-profile as its relatively recent uses in entertainment have been, CGI's applications in industrial design, medical imaging, and scientific visualization have been even more profound. In such areas CGI has been an effective tool in visualizing advanced geometrical objects too complex to render in any other fashion. One excellent example is the work by IBM researcher Benoit Mandelbrot in fractal geometry. His "Mandelbrot set" includes a computer-generated pattern that has been described as one of the most remarkable discoveries in the history of mathematics. Or, put another way, as "the thumbprint of God."

CGI, in this sense, augments the mind's visual abilities. And while it should be no surprise that CGI—a product of advanced mathematics—should prove such a boon to science and high-tech entertainment, it also can communicate data effectively in its simplest forms: static business graphics of pie charts and bar graphs. In television, CGI-based systems are used to generate sports scores and animate weather maps on the nightly news, and make arresting, dynamic images of animated logos or photorealistic aliens. CGI images can be produced at NTSC's 525-line 4:3 rectangle or at 2,000 (or more) lines in a 16:9 shape suitable for HDTV or motion pictures.

CGI systems are at the leading edge of digital teleproduction, increasingly offering not only multiple graphics applications but also editing functions for images and sound. The ability of computers to seamlessly process and manipulate digital data representing different kinds of visual and aural content means that the same computer can run multiple software packages, passing moving-image and audio files back and forth among them. The Softimage Digital Studio is a leading-edge example of the increasing trend toward all-in-one systems.

HISTORY

It is generally agreed that the field of CGI began in 1962 with a young graduate student at the Massachusetts Institute of Technology named Ivan Sutherland. His doctoral thesis (titled "Sketchpad: A Man-Machine Graphics Communication System") included a way for people who weren't programmers to "draw" simple shapes on a picture tube connected to a computer. Previous to Sketchpad, "computer graphics" entailed writing lines of programming code that dictated paper print-outs of crude patterns of X's and O's that might look like something from several feet away.

Sketchpad made history by enabling anyone to use a light pen and a row of buttons to create basic images. According to the late Robert Rivlin's book *The Algorithmic Image* (Microsoft Press, 1986), "except for the addition of color and a few minor details concerning how the graphics processing is accomplished, the 1963 version of Sketchpad has remained virtually unchanged in 95 percent of the graphics programs available today, including those that run on home computers."

In 1964 Sutherland teamed up with Dr. David Evans at the University of Utah to develop the first academic computer graphics department. CGI advanced through the years as a part of computer science, evolving in the labs of universities, corporations, and governments. A long series of innovations gradually improved the technology, including: the display processor unit, for converting computer commands and relaying them to the picture tube; the frame buffer, a form of digital memory that improved upon that principle; and the storage-refresh raster display, which made computer-graphic screens practical and affordable. These screens use CRTs (cathode-ray tubes) that divide images into picture elements, or "pixels," the basic unit of computer graphics and digital television. Digital, random access memory (RAM) determines the number of pixels on the screen, their location, color, etc. Each pixel is assigned a particular number of memory "bits" in a process known as bit-mapping. The more bits the greater each pixel's potential color combinations. "Bit depth" is a term that refers to the number of these bits. The greater the bit depth, the more color levels possible. In a 24-bit system, the computer provides for eight bits each of red, green, and blue. It is from these basic colors that all other hues are cre-

DTV IN THE REAL WORLD

UNDERSTANDING DIGITAL

PRE-PRODUCTION

PRODUCTION

AUDIO

GRAPHIC & COMPOSITING

POST PRODUCTION

DELIVERY & DUPLICATION

ENGINEERING & TRANSMISSION

APPENDIX

GLOSSARY

ated in CGI. A 30-bit system provides for 10 bits per basic color; a 36-bit system, 12. More color means more shading, detail, and-in the hands of a skilled artist-realism.

Hand-in-hand with CGI technology improvements came ever-increasing advances in writing the programming code necessary to make graphic objects and present them with three-dimensional perspective. This long process of discovery went from inventing ways of drawing wire-frame "skeletons" of objects, to developing algorithms for what's known as polygon rendering to give them surfaces, to animating them in ways the human eye finds appealing (see figure 2). As with every field of human endeavor, CGI researchers built upon past accomplishments and knowledge to continually refine the technology in a process ongoing to this very day. Drawing upon mathematics, physics, and other fields that measure and describe the physical world, the science of CGI continually improves the ways that images can be synthesized and achieve the "look and feel" of matter and energy responding to the universe's natural laws.

figure 2. 1-Wireframe, 2-Polygons, 3-Completed Image. © Ray Tracy™

Early applications of CGI included flight simulation and CAD/CAM (computer aided design/computer aided manufacturing), but it wasn't until the late 1970s that it began to be applied to the mass media. Richard Shoup was a young computer science Ph.D. at Xerox's Palo Alto Research Center (PARC) when he developed not only one of the first digital frame buffers but also the first sophisticated video painting software. NASA used the technology to create television news animations of its Pioneer space missions. Known as SuperPaint, it was the first computer graphics ever broadcast. In 1979, Shoup left Xerox PARC to found Aurora Systems, an early manufacturer of digital video paint and animation systems.

Alvy Ray Smith, another Xerox PARC researcher, made significant software-design contributions to Shoup's paint program. Smith went on to work at the New York Institute of Technology and NASA's Jet Propulsion Laboratory, two hotbeds of CGI research in the 1970s. In 1980 Smith and fellow CGI pioneer Ed Catmull were hircd by *Star Wars* producer George Lucas to run what later became Pixar, a company formed to advance the art and science of CGI in motion picture production. While these and many other pioneers worked to improve the ways in which computers could make pictures, they were also finding applications for the use of such pictures, and writing the necessary software to generate them. At the same time, computer technology itself was undergoing a revolution. Processing power continued to rise and costs dropped, an ongoing situation described in 1965 in what's become known as Moore's Law, named after Gordon E. Moore, physicist, co-founder, and now chairman emeritus of Intel Corp.

Moore noticed that manufacturers had been able to double the number of circuits on a chip every year, causing exponential leaps in power over time. That leap in power meant the cost per circuit was cut in half each time. Experts say that microprocessor power is now quadrupling every three years.

Each new software application, meanwhile, built upon and improved what had gone before. The year 1974 saw the birth of the Association of Computing Machinery (ACM)'s Special Interest Group on Computer Graphics (SIG-GRAPH), which went on to play an instrumental role in providing support for this new science. SIGGRAPH also organized conferences and provided a valuable information-sharing environment. This is even more true today.

In the past 10 years, the computers necessary to create CGI have evolved from large mainframes to large workstations to custom-built PCs to off-the-shelf Macintoshes and Windows computers optimized for video. The high end of CGI technology is still a place where millions of dollars are easily spent, and although high-end capabilities invariably gravitate down toward affordable systems, the high end is continually developing its own special capabilities. Similar technological forces are at work across the range of CGI systems: ever-faster and more powerful microprocessors, increasing storage-system capacities, and advances in software. CGI systems run the gamut from turnkey systems that package software with a particular brand of computer to shrink-wrapped programs intended for personal computers.

In addition to a computer, monitors, keyboard, and some form of data storage, nearly all CGI systems also employ a mouse, graphics tablet, and pen. The tablets usually work by means of an embedded wire grid, which senses the location of the pen and relays it to the computer; the "drawing" is displayed on a computer monitor. CGI systems typically use some sort of graphical user interface, usually running under the UNIX, Macintosh, or Windows operating systems. Quantel, a leading maker of CGI systems, is an exception, still employing its own proprietary computer and operating system optimized for CGI tasks-and doing so with great success.

CGI software exists today to produce everything from animations that look like classic hand-drawn cartoons to photorealistic images nearly indistinguishable from reality. CGI is frequently combined with live action to create convincing special effects and fantastic eye-catching environments in movies. Major applications of CGI technology include character generation, two-dimensional electronic paint and animation, three-dimensional modeling and animation, and even virtual sets and actors.

DTV IN THE REAL WORLD

UNDERSTANDING DIGITAL

PRE-PRODUCTION

PRODUCTION

AUDIO

GRAPHIC & COMPOSITING

POST PRODUCTION

DELIVERY & DUPLICATION

ENGINEERING & TRANSMISSION

APPENDIX

GLOSSARY

CHARACTER GENERATORS

Although character generators perform a relatively basic task in the hierarchy of CGI systems, they represent advanced technology essential to news and live television production. Character generators connect a keyboard to a frame buffer, the output of which can be displayed as letters and numbers that can be colored, sized, and keyed over another video source. A process known as antialiasing keeps curved characters from getting a "sawtooth" edge as they cross video scanlines.

The most common use of a character generator is to superimpose a name under a talking head or to add a credit roll to the end of a program. Character generator systems can offer limited digital effects capabilities, including the ability to rotate, spin, extrude or otherwise manipulate type. (Like CGI systems, digital video effects equipment employs a digital memory to store video. In this case, however, the video is input from a live or recorded source and then manipulated and output by the DVE's computer according to whatever capabilities the system's operator decides to use-a page turn, a mirror-smash, etc.)

Depending on the brand and model, some character generators also offer limited paint and animation functions (see below), as well as a host of other features that can include multiple fonts, spell checking, storage of multiple pages, "canned" background textures, variable-speed movement of characters, networkability with other video-production devices, and more. Chyron, a leading maker of character generators, is often used inappropriately as the generic term for this kind of equipment. Chyron character generators are designed to provide speedy operation and generous storage capacity so text can be created or updated quickly onscreen in news and sports applications, and many "pages" of text can be called up in an instant. Character generation is but one aspect of CGI, the bulk of which is performed not in on-air applications but in post production.

PAINT SYSTEMS

A picture is worth 100,000 words, said Confucius, which is why paint systems are essential to communicating news. Devices such as Quantel's Paintbox are used to take still images from a type of computer memory known as a video still store and provide a graphics designer with the tools to color, size, add type, and otherwise configure graphics for display behind news readers. Over-the-shoulder graphics are a familiar part of television news, enhancing reports with imagery and often text (rape, robbery or murder). A limited form of animation known as color-cycling can be applied to give the appearance of flickering flames and other repetitive motion.

Paint systems are typically used for more elaborate tasks in post production than in broadcast news. These tasks can include such processes as rotoscoping (frame-by-frame drawing on top of video or film footage to alter the preexisting image), wire removal, matting, and other techniques. Such work can be performed manually or in automated fashion.

The art of wire removal has changed dramatically with the use of digital technology. Years ago, wires to support or fly actors or props were made as invisible to the camera as possible to help the illusion of flight. Today, wires are colored bright noticeable colors so that the computer artist can easily see them and remove them.

3D

Three-dimensional modeling and animation in video refers to the display on a two-dimensional computer screen of objects that—when rotated or otherwise manipulated—give the appearance of being 3D. Stereo-optical 3D, which often requires viewers to wear special glasses, can be created with 3D CGI (as it can with probably any other kind of image-creation technique), but beyond that the two kinds of "3D" refer to two different types of imaging.

Three-dimensional programs create objects with x, y and z coordinates to correspond to what their real position would be in three-dimensional space. They begin as wire-frame objects composed of vectors, or lines of specific length connected to other lines. The more numerous and complex these lines get, the more variety and detail there is in the polygons they enclose. Creating

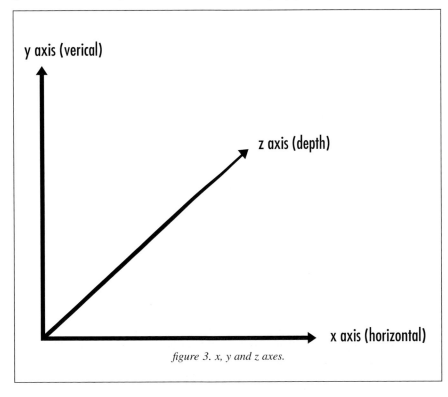

figure 3. x, y and z axes.

objects with the kinds of random, multiple curves found in nature requires ever-greater detail than even complex polygons can describe. Drawing from the mathematics of irregular surfaces, CGI developers have turned to an ever-more exotic variety of surface elements—known as patches—to build their models. Metaballs, nurbs, and Bezier curves are among the advanced geometric descriptors that enable CGI designers to create objects of sophisticated complexity, including objects that are organic in appearance.

Animators use their keyboard, mouse, and pen-and-tablet interface tools to tell the computer the shape of these mathematical models, some of which may be chosen from a library of shapes, such as those offered by Viewpoint Data Labs. Sometimes an actual 3D object—a model, statue, or even a real person—is used, its topography and dimensions communicated to the computer via a special input device. These can include the Immersion Corp. MicroScribe-3D for small objects or the Cyberware laser-scanning system for large ones such as human beings.

Once all the contours of the object have been defined by whatever form of modeling is used (constructive, procedural and solids modeling are three different approaches), animation of the wire-frame object can begin. Animators typically storyboard the action of the scene they intend to create for effective planning. Motion paths can be determined and "camera" positions (the point of view that viewers of the finished animation will have) and movements specified. "Key frames" are specific, periodic points at which certain actions will occur; the computer can then interpolate and generate the "in-between" frames between key frames.

When the animation process is complete, the object or objects being animated can be given a surface via rendering, which assigns whatever color, shading and other surface attributes the animator desires (metallic, matte, textured, etc.). "Mapping" refers to the computationally intensive process by which the computer calculates and "draws" in the "skin" or surface of the object(s) in the animation. Again, it's not as if the computer is taking over from the human designer; the human designer has instructed the computer on what the animation should look like. The human designer has determined where the "light" source is coming from in the scene, what the surface should look like, what the motion path should be, the colors, the quality of the "camera's" lens, etc. The computer then relies upon its rendering program to carry out these directions, mathematically calculating and drawing the finished action for each successive frame of the animation. The final animation can be output to videotape, motion picture film, or other storage media, such as a digital data recorder.

COMPOSITING AND CONVERGENCE

One of the most important applications of CGI today is in compositing, where graphic elements can be seamlessly merged with live-action imagery or with other computer-generated footage. Movies featuring photorealistic dinosaurs, ocean liners and monster insects are all examples of high-end compositing work. Images from live-action footage—most often shot on film—are scanned and turned into digital data then imported into a high-end digital re-touch system such as Quantel's Domino or Discreet's Inferno. That film imagery—now existing as zeros and ones—can be manipulated and combined with CGI to complement it in whatever fashion the script calls for. When the sequence is completed to the director's satisfaction, this data is output to a 35mm film recorder for incorporation into the final motion picture negative.

Even more common is the use of compositing technology in television commercials, where the end product goes out to D1 or D5 videotape, and the end result may or may not be used to make fantastic images. This CGI may just as often consist of pleasing designs or pictures that would have been too difficult to create using any other means. Examples can be as different as a simple promo showing multiple, moving layers of 2D type choreographed against geometric shapes and film clips, to a gasoline commercial showing a filmed image of a car with a superimposed computer-generated 3D "x-ray" of its engine running. Specific effects may be applied via software in the edit room or compositing suite.

The production of a composited scene may employ any number of other CGI functions, some of which are familiar—such as paint—and others that are the result of new, leading-edge software capable of innovative effects. Increasingly, compositing, effects and other CGI functions are being integrated within editing systems. Any graphics manufacturer, for instance, can interface their graphics, paint or animation system into any of the Avid Media Composer nonlinear editing systems. Such systems offer pull-down menus for these functions right inside the edit menu. An editor can access 3D animations while in an edit program or take a clip or series of clips and send it out as a graphics file.

Nonlinear edit systems employ multiple "tracks" of imagery as a means of organizing the sequence of clips. Many such tracks are for computer graphics. Even a simple logo is seldom simple anymore. It's not uncommon to composite many different paint or character-generator segments, with each character existing as its own computer-graphic layer complete with shadows, different light sources and other visual attributes. Designers can, for instance, "fly-in" a word, object or other element so that it has multiple shadow layers. Avid Technology's Media Composers can import garbage mattes, which is a graphics function. The idea is to make edit systems more efficient so that if an editor imported a paint-system graphic and the keyhole wasn't perfect, the editor could touch it up. Discreet's Fire system has a paint package called Retouch.

Conversely, more and more CGI systems are offering editing functions. In many instances the computer on which the editing and CGI functions are performed is the same, and clips can be easily moved back and forth among applications. This convergence is ongoing and is tending to blur the distinction between CGI and editing, instead combining the two as co-equal functions of post production. Although very specific skills are necessary to cut moving images so as to maintain pace and rhythm, editors today are also able—if they choose— to perform paint and other CGI tasks as part of their work. Likewise, graphic design is its own discipline, requiring special talents and experience. There are, however, instances where graphics designers need access to editing tools to make them more efficient. High-end graphics systems makers such as Quantel and Discreet have introduced CGI systems with editing capabilities to address these creatives.

Much of today's CGI work is done on personal computers and small work-stations that outperform the largest mainframes of a decade ago. As mentioned earlier, the three principal types of computers—or "platforms"—used are the Apple Macintosh, IBM-compatible PCs and the line of workstations made by SGI. Key to these platforms are their respective operating systems, specialized software that manages the computer's hardware components and the onscreen commands (the "interface") by which the computer is used. Operating systems provide and manage access to different kinds of software "applications" (edit-ing, paint, character generation and compositing) and to the files created with-in them. Most importantly, operating systems provide a uniform environment that programmers can write to, and thus create different kinds of software appli-cations that can all be used by the same computer. Leading operating systems include that used by Macintosh; IBM-compatible PCs used for CGI usually employ either Microsoft's Windows 95 or Windows NT operating systems; SGI computers use a form of the UNIX operating system known as IRIX.

Although opinions vary, the Macintosh is regarded by many as the leading image-processing platform and the one whose operating system's foundation code has been best exploited by software developers. Many interface com-mands are the same from program to program, and a Macintosh user can have multiple programs open simultaneously. Users can pass images or "film strips" from program to program. For instance, someone using the Media 100 non-linear video editing application can simultaneously open Adobe Photoshop for paint, Adobe After Effects for effects, Electric Image for 3D, and Puffin Software's Commotion for rotoscoping, and move files seamlessly among these applications. Whether or not the Macintosh will continue to play a leading role in CGI and other video functions will depend on how successfully Apple Computer and its technology partners fend off competition from Windows NT computers, which are less expensive and increasingly able to do anything a Macintosh can.

SGI workstations, meanwhile, tend to lack homogenous interfaces and the ability to move files across applications as effectively as on the Macintosh. On the other hand, software for SGI computers typically offers greater bit-depth (up to 12 bits per color) and computational power. This increased bit depth pro-vides greater color spectrum than the eight bits per color afforded by Macintosh software (although the computer itself can handle much more bit-depth); greater bit-depth enhances realism when generating the kind of high-resolution CGI necessary for motion picture production. The computational and data-storage capacities of SGIs' Octane and Origin computer/server combinations and the power of the big Onyx2 workstations makes these systems favored tools for high-resolution motion picture CGI and effects work.

Although the barriers between editing and CGI are becoming increasingly blurry, having one person do all the work on one system is not necessarily desirable for all video facilities. A small "project studio" business may find it expedient to have one or two people performing all tasks on a single computer, but high-end studios typically use the kinds of talent who prefer to specialize in their own particular area. And on top of that there's no system today that does everything really well. Why have an editor do graphics when you can have a graphics designer doing it faster and better on a less-expensive system? In such environments, workgroups speed efficiency.

Workgroups use Ethernet or other high-speed computer networking systems to link editing, graphics and other functions in such a way that different people can work on the same body of material simultaneously. In a workgroup, editing, graphics compositing, 3D animation, paint and audio talent can all access the same footage and work in a timely manner. Workgroup editing enables users to expedite the adjustments between, say, a paint workstation, an animation workstation, and an edit system.

VIRTUAL SETS AND ACTORS

Everyone is familiar with the use of chromakeys in television: weathermen superimposed over maps, local used-car dealers keyed over a comical background. A new technology know as the virtual set, however, expands on chromakeying by adding the dimension of foreground/background–related movement. Virtual sets place actors in some sort of environment and allow them to walk around that environment in realistic fashion. In reality, however, the entire set is really a photorealistic 3D CGI model. This very high-end technology is being promoted as a way to turn any blue- (or green-) screen stage into any kind of environment you can create with CGI-from the Old West to outer space. In any case, a virtual set is—ideally—cheaper than building a real one.

Virtual set installations start with a CGI model of the set created using such 3D software as Alias|Wavefront, or Softimage. That model is then stored in a powerful computer (such as a SGI Onyx) capable of rendering it in realtime. A moveable video camera (or cameras) then captures images of the actors' performance on the blue-screen set. Using either motion sensors, a motion-control head, or pattern-recognition technology, the camera's position is fed into the computer, which then "draws" (renders) the background as it should be seen from that particular point of view. The actor(s), and the CGI are then combined, and a virtual environment is created—hopefully one that convinces viewers that there's no trick involved.

CGI objects can also be introduced into the scene; with proper rehearsal and blocking it can be made to look as if the actor is interacting with these objects (a computer-generated bird, for instance, flying through the scene). Camera movement is what makes a virtual set seem real; the computer generates a background image that corresponds to what the camera's (audience's) point of view should look like from any given position. And the computer is powerful enough to re-draw the scene in realtime as the actor(s) move within the "set."

Although several companies sell virtual set systems, this is still a technology in development and virtual sets tend to be extremely expensive and balky to operate. But as the technology matures it's entirely possible that Hollywood carpenters may have something to fear from CGI artists.

Similar technology is used to electronically replace advertisements on stadium billboards in televised sporting events and to place sponsor logos on the playing field but not over the players.

Virtual actors may scare Hollywood actors even more. As each new CGI software revision further advances mankind's ability to synthesize images, we come one step closer to being able to create photorealistic images that will be indistinguishable from real human beings. Each year, the SIGGRAPH film and video show spotlights the best CGI clips, and synthetic humans are inevitably among the featured attractions; each year these images are just a tad more convincing.

A decade ago critics contended that CGI actors could never display sufficiently convincing facial expressions or physical movement to pass for real or even earn an audience's empathy. Total realism is still to be achieved, but it comes closer every year (as we've seen recently in *Toy Story 2* and *Stuart Little*). As it does, software engineers learn more and more about the complexity of human movement and facial expression. Humans are conditioned from birth to "read" faces; the better computer-generated faces get, the more bizarre they seem to us. Unless and until total realism is achieved, the brain will know that something is amiss, so central to our psyche is the perception and interpretation of facial expressions. CGI seems, however, to be gradually closing-in on the goal of total realism. This could be bad news for movie and TV actors but good news for producers.

Assuming totally convincing virtual actors (also called "synthespians," for "synthetic thespians") can be created, their advantages will be many: They don't age, don't get sick or need vacations, aren't potential subjects of personal scandal, and they don't demand raises. A synthespian can be crafted to please a selected demographic profile and combine all the best traits of the most beloved movie actors. Digital compositing technology's cut-and-paste capabilities have already brought forth synthespians from the past—sort of. Deceased stars such as John Wayne,

Marilyn Monroe and Fred Astaire have been digitally lifted from various film performances and composited into new live-action commercials hawking everything from vacuum cleaners to beer. Perhaps it's just a matter of time before Moore's Law brings forth computers so advanced that Hollywood sound stages will be sold off for valuable real estate and major studios will operate in small rooms in whatever locations creative CGI talent wishes to reside.

BUYING A CGI SYSTEM

As with every other area of digital teleproduction, consideration of which CGI system is most appropriate for a given facility's needs depends upon the tasks that will be performed on it. The word system is a bit of a misnomer; software and hardware typically come from separate vendors, although some software companies also sell off-the-shelf computers they've optimized for the task. In an age when processing power, software sophistication and operating systems are continually being revised, it's a given that CGI systems need updating on a regular basis. Good arguments exist for both the so-called "open-platform" systems (those based on personal computers or workstations) and for the "dedicated" systems that use a custom-configured computer (these "open" versus "closed" debates appear frequently in television and video trade magazines such as *Television Broadcast* and *Videography*). Ultimately, the best course of action in choosing a system is to clearly understand the tasks you wish to perform, obtain as much information as possible (talking to other facilities to learn of their experience is a good place to start), and then make sure you investigate all the products on the market. In a technology arena as dynamic as this one, it's not impossible that a lower-priced system will outperform a more expensive one. Also, compromises in speed can yield savings; a less expensive system may offer all that its more costly counterpart provides—if you're willing to tolerate getting your work done more slowly, typically through increased rendering time. Whatever you choose, rest assured that CGI technology continues to offer more functionality at ever-improving price-performance ratios. Moore's Law is on your side.

THE FUTURE OF CGI

As mentioned earlier, CGI technology continues to evolve at a rapid pace and get cheaper as well. In addition to recent consolidations among software and hardware companies is the trend toward very small groups of developers creating advanced—yet inexpensively marketed—software to generate ever-more complex simulations of such natural forms as smoke, hair and liquids. An increasing quantity of this code is sold as "plug-ins," which add to the capabilities of existing graphics software. Adobe's popular After Effects software package now has hundreds of sophisticated and inexpensive third-party plug-ins available to increase its digital effects-generating capabilities.

DTV IN THE REAL WORLD

UNDERSTANDING DIGITAL

PRE-PRODUCTION

PRODUCTION

AUDIO

GRAPHIC & COMPOSITING

POST PRODUCTION

DELIVERY & DUPLICATION

ENGINEERING & TRANSMISSION

APPENDIX

GLOSSARY

On the hardware side, Apple's Macintosh operating system has enjoyed a resurgence of developer interest now that the company's original co-founder Steve Jobs has returned and reinvigorated the company with innovative and powerful products. These include the G4 workstation, so powerful the U.S. government originally classified this IBM/Motorola-processor powered machine as a supercomputer too sophisticated for export. Intel-based PC's running the Microsoft Windows operating system also continue to improve in computational horsepower. Sun Microsystems' UNIX and Java-based technologies also add power to CGI for applications as diverse as engineering visualization and Web design.

The operating system wild card is Linux. This public-domain operating system is free of charge, has attracted tens of millions of users, and runs efficiently on a wide variety of machines, including both PCs and Macs. Many consider it to be a serious contender to displace the aging and expensive operating systems that now dominate the market.

The Internet's booming increase in usage continues to spur demand for all kinds of CGI for business and enterprise. DVD, on the verge of becoming the next major home entertainment format, is a major vehicle for CGI. Virtually all DVDs require some original graphic work and the trend will increase as the format becomes more pervasive. DTV and HDTV will similarly create many new channels for all kinds of animated CGI content.

Besides the enhanced distribution of the Internet, advanced telecommunications are also making new production paradigms possible. High-bandwidth networking and connectivity are making virtual production "studios" more and more practical, allowing artists and producers to work remotely. This will enable new business and creative models to evolve in the industry. Such networking enables video and audio editors, CGI designers and animators to locate their own boutique production studios wherever they choose. The ability for such professionals to log into large commercial render servers for compute-intensive operations will become increasingly feasible, both technically and commercially.

This kind of industry expansion requires management, both in terms of the networks themselves and the CGI, video and other data they carry. The stakes are high and there are a host of relatively new companies vying to define a new industry segment known as "media asset management" (see Appendix B: Storage & Archiving/Asset Management). Such systems, as the name implies, are used to catalog, search, retrieve and distribute large databases of all kinds of media. Without question, the eventual impact of this technology will fundamentally affect the creative uses of CGI.

Despite the rapid evolution, advancing capabilities and increasing affordability of CGI technology, however, certain factors don't change. Chief among these is the value of a good story. CGI in entertainment, in the final analysis, is simply a new means of making moving images. And, as the success and failure of various recent Hollywood movies have shown, if you don't have a compelling story to tell, using the latest picture-making technology won't make any difference. Of course, that might change if computers get really good at writing scripts as well.

DTV IN THE REAL WORLD

UNDERSTANDING DIGITAL

PRE-PRODUCTION

PRODUCTION

AUDIO

GRAPHIC & COMPOSITING

POST PRODUCTION

DELIVERY & DUPLICATION

ENGINEERING & TRANSMISSION

APPENDIX

GLOSSARY

>Digital Television The Future of Television Is Here!

>www.digitaltelevision.com

>For More Information: 212.378.0400

DIGITALTELEVISION.com

It's your image.

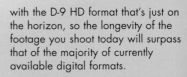

D-9 is a high-quality video tape solution that's proven to be an exceptional value for production and broadcast facilities every-where—and an outstanding choice for migration to HDTV.

It's your money.

QUALITY EQUAL TO DIGITAL BETACAM* AT A FRACTION OF THE COST

A SMPTE/EBU task force found the quality of D-9 equivalent to Digital Betacam and superior to both 18Mbps and 50Mbps MPEG-2 systems. The task force actually *recommends* the 50Mbps data rate and 4:2:2 sampling of D-9 for today's network television productions. D-9's 4:2:2 signal is ideal for converting to MPEG-2 for digital television *distribution*. But, unlike even the newest MPEG-based tape formats, there's no generation loss with D-9 on the *production* end—assuring the highest quality images. With that in mind, is it any wonder that more broadcast and production facilities have chosen D-9 over any other 50Mbps system?

HIGH-RELIABILITY, LOW COST OF OPERATION

D-9 utilizes robust 1/2-inch tape, providing high data capacity and superior reliability (consistently outperforming its 200-pass specification). D-9 is also the only 50Mbps format that allows for a full two hours of recording time. This reliability and versatility, combined with surprisingly affordable equipment and low-maintenance costs, makes D-9 ownership extremely practical.

ACQUISITION & STUDIO PRODUCTS POISED FOR THE DIGITAL FUTURE

D-9 offers a lineup that's DTV-ready and compatible with virtually all the equipment in your editing suite. And, because it *already* provides an acceptable data rate for high-quality HDTV upconversion, you're assured that your investment in D-9 won't become quickly obsolete. In fact, D-9 will also be compatible

with the D-9 HD format that's just on the horizon, so the longevity of the footage you shoot today will surpass that of the majority of currently available digital formats.

JVC INNOVATION AND VALUE

Think about it—the combination of exceptional quality and economy... *and* a logical solution for transitioning to HDTV. You simply can't make a better investment in your image than D-9.

DIGITAL BROADCAST & PROFESSIONAL SYSTEMS DIVISION.

www.jvc.com/pro

1-800-JVC-5825

COMPONENT DIGITAL

POST PRODUCTION 7

QTV IN THE REAL WORLD

UNDERSTANDING DIGITAL

PRE-PRODUCTION

PRODUCTION

AUDIO

GRAPHIC & COMPOSITING

POST PRODUCTION

DELIVERY & DUPLICATION

ENGINEERING & TRANSMISSION

APPENDIX

GLOSSARY

"Fix it in post" has never been easier now that editors are armed with a variety of digital tools. However, as the industry moves towards digital post production, editors must remember that digital means both tape (linear) and disk (nonlinear). While digital tape offers relief from generational loss and faster-than-realtime transfers, it is disk-based nonlinear editing that has transformed post production.

Moving from analog tape machine editing to nonlinear computer editing invites a variety of questions and concerns for an editor—not just "how does it work?" But only you can answer these questions based on your unique situation.

NONLINEAR EDITING: GOING TAPELESS
MARK J. PESCATORE AND MICHAEL SILBERGLEID

The move from a linear, tape-based system to a nonlinear, disk-based system is like trading in your old reliable car for a new model. Both vehicles will still get you from point A to point B, but your new car doesn't handle the same as your old one. Once you've adjusted to your new vehicle, though, you'll see all its advantages—and you'll appreciate the new engine that has a lot more kick.

Put simply, nonlinear editing (NLE) is the future. It's a sneak preview to the tapeless environment of tomorrow. And it's safe to predict that eventually, acquiring footage on disk, rather than tape, will be the norm.

Like it or not, fellow tape editors, change is coming; in fact, for many, it's already here. In a recent survey of news directors by *Television Broadcast* magazine, slightly more than half of all news departments (51 percent) reported having at least one NLE (with the number increasing every year since the introduction of NLE systems). In this case, though, change is good. Nonlinear editing is more than the latest gadget; it's a time-saving tool that makes your options as an editor significantly more flexible without sacrificing quality.

Remember, nonlinear editing systems are a tool to help you edit more efficiently. The basic principles of editing remain the same—except now you can think in a nonlinear fashion, free of concern if something has to be moved or changed in the middle of the program in the final edit, since it's just a few mouse clicks away. You're still trying to tell a story. You can still edit on the fly or select precise editing points. And you can still edit video and audio separately or together. In fact, you often have more tracks/channels at your disposal than even the best tape-based linear editing systems. It's not the task that's changing—only the equipment. As an editor in a nonlinear world, you'll use a keyboard and mouse as your edit controller—some of the same tools you use in the tape world. The flexibility of the computer, however, will allow you to make changes instantly—changes that are non-destructive to the original digitized footage in the computer, as what you are really editing is a set of directions for how the audio and video are manipulated.

How many times have you had to run the gamut of wipes for a client who is just not sure what is going to look best? With nonlinear editing, preroll is eliminated. Video, audio and effects are accessed instantly in realtime systems, although some systems must render effects and transitions. When you don't need to preroll or postroll, you save time, as well as wear and tear on tapes, machine transports and heads. Maybe a savings of 10 seconds doesn't seem like a great deal of time by itself, but when you save that much time with every cut and every effect, it adds up quickly.

Of course, a significant time disadvantage to nonlinear editing is the process of digitizing media. There is no high speed method of transferring analog footage to the computer's hard drive, although four-times normal play speed transfer systems exist for digital tape formats. For most of us, digitizing takes place in realtime.

Comparison will naturally be made for years about the positive and negative aspects of each method of editing, but the new technology is very promising. Put simply, nonlinear editing is a new way to do your job. It's a better way to do your job. And, provided that you receive plenty of training, it's an easier, faster and more creative way to do your job.

NLE PRACTICAL CONSIDERATIONS

The following makes a good checklist for systems under consideration:

✓ If the system compresses video, does the system offer compression rates that are considered "online" quality?

✓ What types of compression does the system offer, and how does that compare with compression types used in acquisition and delivery of final product?

✓ What types of video inputs and outputs does the system have—analog (component, composite, s-video), digital, faster-than-realtime?

✓ What types of audio inputs and outputs does the system have—analog (RCA or quarter-inch), AES/EBU (XLR or BNC), fiber-optic digital?

✓ Does the system include software updates and how are they delivered?

✓ What is the cost of a maintenance agreement and what does it specifically cover (hardware repair, technical support, upgrades; when and where—24/7 and toll-free, fax, email)?

✓ Who is the first line of technical support—the manufacturer, the dealer, or someone else?

✓ What is the storage capacity of the base system and maximum expansion possibilities?

✓ How many video formats and aspect ratios can the system handle and will there be upgrades (including high definition)?

✓ Is the system composed of dedicated components or are there limited manufacturer-approved configurations regarding third party hardware and software?

✓ How effective is the system in a networking environment?

✓ If the system renders, is the render time acceptable to you and your potential clients, especially if you have to re-render to fix something?

✓ Does the rendering software recognize multi-processor configurations?

✓ How many video layers is the system capable of handling without rendering to a single layer?

✓ Does the system support EDL importing/exporting?

✓ Does the system have a good built-in character generator?

✓ Does the system offer audio editing capabilities?

✓ How do you back up files?

✓ During editing, can audio files be on a separate drive than video files, like other hard drives or a Jaz drive?

✓ Can the system export QuickTime files for use on the web, in CD-ROMs or in third party software? Does it support different frame sizes, compression rates, color depth and frame rates?

✓ What is the minimum size for a clip on the timeline—one frame, three frames?

DTV IN THE REAL WORLD

UNDERSTANDING DIGITAL

PRE-PRODUCTION

PRODUCTION

AUDIO

GRAPHIC & COMPOSITING

POST PRODUCTION

DELIVERY & DUPLICATION

ENGINEERING & TRANSMISSION

APPENDIX

GLOSSARY

✓ What is the maximum size for a clip on the timeline and/or in a bin?

✓ Does the system offer audio VU meters and/or audio waveforms that are accurate and functional?

✓ How many audio channels are there? Are they discrete channels or locked into stereo pairs? How can they be panned or faded?

✓ What is the resolution of the system, is it changeable or media-dependent, and does it include an alpha key channel?

✓ How will the system's compression engine handle video noise?

✓ Does the system offer multiple compression types (such as DV and MPEG)?

✓ Can the system do both compressed and uncompressed video? Are projects restricted to compressed or uncompressed, or can the system mix compressed and uncompressed in the same project?

DIGITAL POST: THE PARADIGM WARS

BOB TURNER

Digital is changing all the rules in post production. But, how can you play the game if you don't know the rules? Convergence, Paltex, Ampex Ace and CMX are all gone. Editware is now supporting the former GVG SuperEdit system and Sony still offers a high-end linear system, but both Sony and Editware are "pushing" the system's hybrid capabilities.

Processes are changing. The models on which we base our planning decisions may not be valid any longer. I am not sure what video will look like in the next three years. How will I know which editing system makes sense? (No wonder NAB is always in Las Vegas.)

When the first edition of this book was written there was a dilemma between linear editing and nonlinear editing. Today, it seems that there is a larger conflict between traditional nonlinear techniques versus system-wide workgroup models. Do you want traditional two video stream nonlinear editing, or more modern systems that will allow many layers of audio and video without the need to layer two streams at a time? Or should you go with a "state-of-the-art", metadata-based post production facility where all creative workstations are integrated with servers, library and/or your scheduling and newsroom software?

CONFLICTS ABOUND

Time versus cost? Quality versus cost? Innovation versus a wrong choice? System-wide networked solutions or starting application-specific post production solutions? Workgroup post production with application-specific workstations versus all-in-one workstation? Open systems versus closed systems? Peer-to-peer networking versus "essence media" (what we old-timers used to know as audio, video and graphics) accessed from a server? Or does it make more sense to continue with independent workstation storage (and "sneaker-net" until the networking decision becomes more obvious)?

"Click and drag" mouse, trackball or pen and tablet versus traditional keyboard editing? How many audio and video tracks are needed on a timeline? Should there be interaction between journalist workstations, the edit system and the newsroom and scheduling systems and servers? Will you have union or job description problems? Will employee skills match the tools they are given or will they be frustrated with either the lack of editing tools or with post production tools that are too complex (which may cause those employees, subsequent departure from the company)? How much will the training period cost and how long will it be before the operators can at least achieve the performance output that existed prior to the change in technology? Are there economic benefits to certain systems—will they require fewer operators/technicians? Will there be maintenance and/or supply expense reductions or are you committing to high annual maintenance fees? And with all this to decide, there is the most important question: what will my competitors be offering to my clients or perspective clients? Let's take a look at some of these conflicts and what they will mean for post production.

TIME VERSUS COST

Can you save money by choosing a more expensive system that is more efficient? Do you have enough work to maximize the benefits of those efficiencies? Can you deal with increased rendering time for a system that costs less? Will "essence media" networking be more efficient and stable—ending days of "sneakernet?" Are video and audio digitization/transfer delays a thing of the past? Who will be making the creative decisions, the logs and the rough-cuts? Are there faster processes that will save time and money? Today, there are both optical disk and hard disk-based video camcorders, so you can plug in the disks or HD storage units and start editing without any transfer delays. There are digital tape cameras that log clips with picture-icons or thumbnails of those clips that can later be fed into the editing system or logging package (with designations for good takes). There are PIM (personal information managers) devices that can do the logging and clip evaluations with in-points and out-points that greatly decrease the times for digitization or digital video transfer/transcoding. There are digital tape formats that allow transfers at four-times normal play transfer rates. There are journalist workstations that can let a journalist do logging and rough cuts, so the editor can work more efficiently and finish more programs or segments on a given work shift.

When the editor finishes a segment, that segment can be zapped to the news server or even accessed by master control from the edit workstation, if necessary. With workgroup models, you can have several editors, graphic/effects artists and audio specialists working together from a central server to get the job done faster and better. The typical problem with all this is that generally, the more efficient you make the operation, the greater the initial cost. Another of the "time versus cost" variations is the "greater-than-realtime" concept. These are technologies that appear very attractive. Time is money, and if you can stream video around at four-times realtime speed, why not? Well, perhaps there are reasons why not. Will edit points remain accurate when streaming the edited program at four-times or greater? In addition to this concern, you will probably have to limit operations to a specific compression algorithm or a more expensive transport technology. Perhaps this speed may only be available from a very limited selection of hardware, which require equipment selection compromises to be made.

QUALITY VERSUS COST

You can spend $700,000 and up for an uncompressed video editing system or under $40,000 for a slightly compressed video editing system that may have better editing tools. The worst part about this fact is that both the client paying the bills and the video program viewer may not notice the difference. Will the uncompressed video editing system prevent client and viewer complaints? If you are a post production facility, will the client be willing to pay for the higher capitalization costs if it keeps them from worrying about any compression difficulties? Do most clients even know the right things to worry about with regard to compression, or is it just a bad word?

Most in our industry believe that DTV will bring image quality issues to a new high-point in the decision-making process. Some industry researchers theorize that consumers will begin to notice image quality differences as soon as they purchase digital TV sets in a manner similar to the way audio CDs changed the recording industry. Will the system you are considering protect your investment from future quality improvements or even the possible transition to HDTV? Today, you may see some cascaded compression errors on graphics-oriented or heavily composited programming. Experts appear to agree that if you cannot work with uncompressed video, the next best solution would be to remain in the same compression (e.g. DVCAM/DVCPRO or 4:2:2 MPEG-2 ML@MP) throughout the production/post production process from camcorder to newsroom/program server. There is no loss when doing newsroom-style cuts-only editing and remaining consistent in one of these digitally compressed formats. But even with remaining consistent with such a format, you can suffer digital generational loss with each composite, key, transition and effect. The compromise that some editors and compositors suggest is to uncompress and do all your compositing, graphics and effects before recompressing. What will you choose: HDTV-capable post production, uncompressed video post production, compressed digital post production, or to put off a decision? And if you decide to go the uncompressed route, there remains the question: will the high-cost system you select be competing against a low-cost uncompressed system in six months to a year, and if so, will that put you at an economic disadvantage? And will the system work with higher-resolution video when the need arises?

INNOVATION VERSUS MAKING A POOR CHOICE

There have been several exciting innovations in the field of video post production within the last few years: workgroup integration, working with multiple aspect ratios and image qualities, new recording/storage solutions, and even new profit models including interactive broadcasting.

Will standard definition, digital television production get you through the life of the equipment you are purchasing? If you select a format, will this lock you into a long-term commitment that goes further than the life of the system you are purchasing? Will it allow you the flexibility to do interactive programming? Will the physical and electronic infrastructure need to be rebuilt, and will that lock you into something more permanent than you intend? For example, will you be able to work in both of today's aspect ratios? How do you "up-rez" when needs demand? Will you be able to switch to a progressive scan video image if and when the need arises? Is there flexibility inherent in your decisions?

Another concern is the "Rule of Three Versions." Some call this rule an old wives' tale. It states that no post production software is truly usable before its third version. The problem is that new paradigms mean all new processes and new software. Can you wait five years until version 3 of the software you are considering is available? If not, is the alternative a gamble that puts your personal security at risk?

MPEG-2 post production development may be behind the DV production alternatives: DVCPRO and DVCAM. But these 25 Mbps formats appear to be evolving and 50 Mbps per second (interlace and progressive) and 100 Mbps format choices for this digital video standard set are emerging this year. Which do you choose? Or would a more expensive uncompressed video method be the best post production solution? If you choose incorrectly, what do you do about the choice you have committed to? (Will you be able to find another job?)

OPEN SYSTEMS VERSUS CLOSED SYSTEMS

"Open Systems," "OpenDTV" and "Open Studio" are attractive concepts, but do they represent reality? Are these viable solutions? If you purchase an "Open System" will it offer compatibility with other "Open System" components? Will it offer the "economies of scale" that the concept implies? Will the platform or computer operating system that the "Open System" is based upon stand the test of time? Today, leaders in "Open System" editing software packages frequently mandate specific hardware requirements. Different configurations could provide different levels of storage, accessibility and performance while allowing the user to scale the system to better fit their requirements and budget.

One of the most popular "Open System" manufacturers will not allow you to put other "non-approved" software on their high-end workstation or upgrade the workstation's operating system software (when such upgrades become available) without their approval. If you do, you will invalidate their technical support commitment and warrantee. This results in a facility that may have two or more versions of an operating system on identical computer systems—a maintenance headache to be sure. And requiring a facility to limit the software that can be installed on an expensive computer system prevents the facility from maximizing this hardware investment.

Competitive "Closed System" manufacturers may be more expensive, but may offer performance benefits due to the closed nature of the design. In addition, "Closed System" manufacturers may offer programming possibilities such as Java Application Program Interfaces or scripting languages, which may provide advantages you hope to find with an "Open System."

TRADITIONAL PURCHASE AND MAINTENANCE VERSUS SOFTWARE MAINTENANCE

In the traditional linear realm, every year you would budget for the purchase of "black boxes" that would keep your customers happy. These customers demanded the latest "wizbangs," and "wizbangs" meant expensive hardware. This hardware was maintained by a team of hardware engineers and kept working only with constant cleaning and routine maintenance. It usually became obsolete by someone else's wizbang box within a year of purchase (which kept the antacid companies in business). The boxes were proprietary but the software was provided for free.

With our paradigm shift, the annual hardware purchasing is—for the most part—being replaced by software acquisition. Both the software and the hardware platform it works with can usually be easily upgraded. This usually means a long-term commitment to the hardware decision you make. Furthermore, this "new way" generally means much less expensive hardware and less hardware maintenance. It also means purchasing things that you are not used to budgeting for: software and software maintenance/technical support.

Once again, when the first edition of this book went to press, the norm for this new technology was the purchase of maintenance contracts. Now there is a conflicting trend that may or may not be to your liking. Because many large purchasers (who often have software support personnel on staff) objected to the high fee for software maintenance—without any guarantee of the number or quality of new versions in a given year—began pushing a "pay-as-you-go" alternative. You see what the new version of software offers and decide whether or not it is worth purchasing.

While this sounds reasonable, the people who budget for the next year no longer have the ability to plan for this expense—a major disadvantage with institutional purchasers. In addition, this new model means that the manufacturer will need to provide technical support for several different versions at a given point in time, and someone will have to pay for that additional expense (guess who?). On top of that, the manufacturer can no longer use the expected maintenance contract revenues to pay for the research and development, so the manufacturers loose their budget-planning abilities. Generally, the smaller facilities, while objecting to the high cost of software maintenance and technical support contracts, were better off than the uncertain world they now find themselves in without those contracts.

The technical support is also getting much more complex, both in the purchasing and the methodology. Some limit technical support to telephone support at specific times. Some offer the ability to remotely diagnose problems via a modem or even provide routine remote maintenance. Some offer Web technical support forums. What is the board replacement policy? Is "on-site" support available? Does whatever is available work for you? Another change may be the discovery that supplies that had been routinely budgeted for are no longer necessary, but others such as digital storage devices are always in urgent demand. Is digital storage a supply item or a capital purchase? Lines blur.

WORKGROUP POST PRODUCTION VERSUS ALL-IN-ONE WORKSTATION

Two conflicting trends continue at the National Association of Broadcasters convention:

1) Workgroup editing networks where audio workstations, editing systems, graphics workstations, digitizing stations, assistant editor/logging stations, character generation systems, compositing/effects systems and 3D animation

workstations all interconnect and frequently access the same "raw" images simultaneously; and

2) All-in-one workstations that could facilitate all those previously mentioned capabilities in one system.

The question then arises: Is this actually conflicting? Does it make sense to purchase several identical systems and make one an animation station, one a compositing/effects station, one an audio station, one a video editing station, etc., and have them all networked together instead of tying together different types of workstations? Are there maintenance and purchasing advantages with this concept? Would it not be better to be able to select the best workstation and software for each area? If you go the latter route, are the systems metadata compatible and is the network able to transfer the metadata that the workgroup members need to access? Would transcoding of essence media be required? Do operators exist with high levels of skill and expertise in all these categories so that they can expertly edit, design graphics/effects composites, create 3D animations and sweeten audio on a single workstation? Does it make economic sense for that operator to have an All-in-One system? (What would keep him, once he masters the system, from going off on his own with his own "project studio?") Could this combination of talent and technology not promote a more focused "autour" type of production that has the potential for exciting stylistic programming? Will the communications and resource sharing problems found with workgroups be eliminated? Wouldn't this be a much less expensive option from both staffing and a capital expense point-of-view? Again, do such "prodigies" exist?

ESSENCE MEDIA STORAGE

Central storage versus peer-to-peer networking? These may be two very different models, but are they completely independent of one another? Can't workstations have both networked storage at the workstation as well as access to the audio/video data stored on the central server? Of course they can. And it gets much more complicated as you add multiple servers to serve different purposes, such as programming, news and commercial servers; daily, weekly and archive server solutions; or servers for multiple formats and resolutions. This complicated storage dilemma is discussed elsewhere in the volume, but here are a few of the issues:

THE CENTRAL STORAGE VERSUS PEER-TO-PEER

The Central Storage model allows multiple users to access the same footage simultaneously and, with wide enough bandwidth, can allow real-time, high-quality editing/compositing at multiple workstations from moving images stored on this server. This model allows for engineering specialists

---

to supervise sound/image input into the server system from a central VTR/equipment room with proper test and monitoring gear. This model also keeps equipment and fan noise problems out of the post production suites. It may prove to be extremely efficient and cost-effective. On the other hand, it may offer a single point of failure that can be inauspicious at best. Peer-to-peer models usually allow sound and images to be transferred from one system to another—frequently at high transfer speeds. Each workstation has its own storage to be manipulated as the operator wishes without affecting the operators at other workstations, unless the operator has to pause when their sound or images are being accessed by another workstation. This may be a more expensive solution in the short term since no one wants to run out of storage, but the cost of additional capacity is generally becoming progressively less expensive. There are no hassles fighting for space on a central server. There are no communication problems with controlling the storage available or accidentally deleting something a different operator at another workstation needs. This redundancy does increase cost and it is more inefficient when multiple workstations need access to the same essence media.

For either model, is it easy to find and access the sound or images you need? If you are sharing images or sequences, does the required metadata follow? Just how easy is it to access a composite from an effects/compositing workstation to the editing system? How long does it take? Is it in a truly compatible form and is there any image loss caused by the transfer? Can the audio engineer easily access the video for mix-to-pix? Are there security access controls, communications capabilities and other administration issues that are addressed and does this "control data" flow over the same network with the video, audio and metadata?

And how much bandwidth do you need? There are now realtime, broadcast-quality long haul 270 Mbps video transport networks that have proven track records. A few of these systems allow you to double throughput by doubling the cable connections and offers the hardware/software capabilities to marry the signals flawlessly at the workstation. Today, Gigabit Ethernet and other high-bandwidth solutions are being installed in facilities.

How many systems require access through the same network simultaneously, and what does this do to bandwidth capabilities? Can the network data bandwidth be "throttled back" on specific systems based upon specific workstation needs? Can this "throttling back" be a dynamic process, based upon the temporal needs of the "networked workstation community?" Does the administration software allow you to grow and work with any type of network (SCSI, Fibre Channel, SSA, ATM, etc.)? What are the risks of an individual workstation bringing all other workstations connected to it down? Can the network interface with other systems such as scheduling, library management or newsroom software?

TAPE LIBRARIES VERSUS ARCHIVING SYSTEMS

Traditionally, everything could be stored in a tape library for later access. With digital, however, there may not be source tapes. Today, images go to digital storage from satellite, telecine, networking or directly from a camera. When and how can you archive the original sound and images now that this "tape recording" process is gone? Do you need to save this information for future use, and if so, in what format? Should you save it as uncompressed video, compressed video or digital data?

What metadata information (labeling data, logs, EDLs, color correction, enhancement processes, audio level settings, DVE programming, source media identification, etc.) gets stored with this essence media? What type of database/media asset management is required? Is this metadata compatible with all your various workstations that would desire access to the information? Can all systems (library database, creative workstations, billing systems, scheduling, etc.) access this metadata? We are now at a point, technologically, when this digital information can be stored practically on data tapes, hard disks or optical technology for ease in archiving. Which will you choose? Will the format chosen for archival purposes have a life as long as the need for the images stored on the format? How fast can this archived data be accessed? What degradation problems will arise from long-term archiving, how will they differ from format to format and can they be corrected—can the damaged digital data be reconstructed? Does it make sense to invest in a robotic "nearline" archive system or levels of archiving? Or does it make more sense to simply output it to videotape and store it in a tape library? (See Appendix B: Storage & Archiving/Asset Management.)

IS THE HYBRID EDITING CONCEPT DYING?

Today, one digital post model is called "hybrid post production." Rather than scrap your traditional equipment (DVEs, VCRs, DDRs, switchers, mixers, character generators, graphic systems, etc.) and convert to an entirely new model that is difficult for some to even comprehend, a number of manufacturers have tried to create hybrid technologies incorporating the best of both models. They do this by modifying processes to allow you access to the greatest benefits of the new technology while continuing to utilize some of the expensive, previously-purchased technology, adapting it to a random-access style of operations.

This concept appears to be rapidly withering on the vine. The phrase, "A hybrid system cannot do either linear or nonlinear well" may be partly responsible, but it has been based upon the experiences of several such systems. Sony ES-3 edit system was hybrid, but it is no longer. Fast Electronics manufactured one of the more popular hybrid systems, but now focuses all R&D on nonlinear-only technology. Other leading hybrids have bitten the dust or the manufacturers have eliminated the linear capabilities. Sony BE-9100, Accom Axial (note: Accom recently purchased Scitex Digital Video, owners of the Sphere NLE line), ETC Multilinear Ensemble Gold and SuperEdit (now owned by Editware) still offer hybrid capabilities, but all come from a linear background.

As storage technology solutions continue to expand in capacity while the price plummets, the trend away from "hybrid" and toward "total" nonlinear editing will probably continue. But this does not rule out all the advantages of the hybrid editor. One of the highest-end nonlinear editing systems available today is clearly nonlinear in concept and execution, but offers an I/O port for external machines such as a DVE, a downstream character generator, and even has the ability to control external VCR to external VCR recordings. Most owners do not access these capabilities because the system offers excellent DVE, titling and hard disk-based editing capabilities, but still they are available for "hybrid use."

One of the biggest missing ingredients to "hybrid editing" technology as well as first-generation nonlinear editing systems is the inability to edit "vertically" (creatively arranging layers of clips on multiple video or audio tracks on a nonlinear timeline) in addition to the ability to edit "horizontally" (ordering clips in time).

VERTICAL LINEARITY

The concept of "vertical linearity"—the ability to edit multiple video tracks (layers)—is an important new model that warrants strong consideration. It allows close integration and modification at any point of the multiple-layer building process. Early nonlinear and hybrid systems allowed complete random access and clip manipulation of two video layers (and a limited number of audio layers). But to add additional video (or audio) tracks/layers required rendering the existing tracks into a new combined track and then adding an additional layer to that. For a composited video segment, you may have to render and combine several times. Unfortunately, if you want to change one of the earlier layers, you had to start this process all over. This then becomes a clearly linear process that does not allow for creative manipulation or organization of the various layers. Many of today's nonlinear systems allow multiple tracks, but often only two can be combined in realtime—the rest require rendering. In other systems there may be more tracks, transitions or processes that can be combined in realtime. The number of layers/tracks can vary dramatically from system to system.

Some multiprocessor systems allow you to assign one or more of the available processors to dedicated rendering. This may allow you to play back a composited sequence soon after you complete it, especially if the more intense layering was built early in the sequence. And rendering times for multiple tracks or layers can vary widely, depending upon the workstation, the software, the resolution required and the complexity of the composite.

TRADITIONAL OPERATIONS VERSUS THE NEW WAY

Can the editors, compositors, graphics designers and other operators or staff members in traditional post production environments adapt to the new digital models? How easy is it for a keyboard editor to adapt to the "click and drag" of a mouse, trackball, or pen and tablet? How easy is it for these people to think in nonlinear fashion? Can those who have depended upon engineers to maintain equipment and are unused to computer crashes or even the standard operations of the operating system that their new workstations use, adapt? In the transition from film to tape, there were many talented and skilled personnel that could not adapt and were lost to our industry.

Assuming that those remaining can adapt, how long will it take, and how much re-training is required? After they learn the basics, how long will it be until they are as productive as before the switch? This can be an expensive and time-consuming jump from the traditional to the new. After this "jump," how soon will it be before new versions or technological improvements require additional training and downtime. (The development is evolving rapidly.) How do you estimate the time and expense? With all the rules thrown out, how do you predict the chaos? How do you budget time to ramp-up, training expenses, staff loss, morale problems, etc.? Do your job classifications need to be changed? Do you have union concerns? Will the "new way" improve productivity, which will result in staff reductions or re-assignments? Would it be better to start anew with new staff for the new technology, and continue to use the old investments until they are no longer demanded or viable and then dump both the equipment and the staff that operates it?

WHAT ARE THE BENEFITS?

By now you may be screaming, "Why are we doing this?" Actually there are several reasons—improved quality and federally mandated digital broadcast transmission are two, just for starters. Post production has been evolving with new digital tools since the beginning of electronic video editing. The TBC, the DVE and the character generator are obvious examples. But the time and expense required for post production, the capitalization of post facilities and the clear limitations of traditional methodologies have created this revolution to occur. The continuing evolution of editing, audio mixing, graphics, compositing, and animation systems and techniques all pressing against the edge of the technological envelope can also be "blamed." Viewers, and those that provide the programs for those viewers, crave the new and exciting, and the artists that create for those viewers have demanded new, more efficient and powerful tools. Viewers are now demanding more from both the post production crafts (the middleman in the production/distribution process) and the delivery mechanisms. You have little choice but to adapt to these changes. The problem is, there are few rules to provide guidance. In fact, the problem may be that you have too many choices. The game is changing. And if you want one additional reason to enter the paradigm wars, check out what the competition is doing.

DTV IN THE REAL WORLD

UNDERSTANDING DIGITAL

PRE-PRODUCTION

PRODUCTION

AUDIO

GRAPHIC & COMPOSITING

POST PRODUCTION

DELIVERY & DUPLICATION

ENGINEERING & TRANSMISSION

APPENDIX

GLOSSARY

GOVERNMENTVIDEO

For

Video

Professionals

in the

Public

Service

www.gvmag.com

DUPLICATION & DELIVERY 8

DTV IN THE REAL WORLD

UNDERSTANDING DIGITAL

PRE-PRODUCTION

PRODUCTION

AUDIO

GRAPHIC & COMPOSITING

POST PRODUCTION

DELIVERY & DUPLICATION

ENGINEERING & TRANSMISSION

APPENDIX

GLOSSARY

It's done. Now you have to deliver the program—either to the individual client or to tens, hundreds, thousands or even millions of people. And although your master might well be a masterpiece, the delivery and duplication process can play havoc with your work.

Analog comes back into the process with VHS as the 800-pound gorilla and BetaSP as the number-one professional format (with one-inch and U-matic still showing up here and there). Digital is also here, but that can mean QuickTime Movies, streaming Web video, CD-ROM and the newest entry vying for the hearts and wallets of consumers—DVD.

What you want for a master is a tape, disk or file of the highest quality, which might be a different format than the submaster used for duplication. Talking to your client and communicating with your duplicating facility will ensure that everyone gets exactly what they need for today and in the future.

MASS DUPLICATION
DIGITAL BE DAMNED:
CONSUMERS STILL LOVE VHS
Mark J. Pescatore

We can produce programming with the latest digital technologies, but for now, our final product for most consumers remains analog.

Plenty have tried, but no one seems to be able to knock off the king of the consumer format mountain, VHS. Betamax was better, the engineers said so, but the home audience would not listen. Then came clearly superior recording formats, more compact formats, prerecorded laser-accessed formats. And the general public responded with varying degrees of shrugging their shoulders. Sure, some of us have 8mm or even Hi8 camcorders at home, and more than a few have recently invested in DVD players. But generally speaking, when we're watching at home, we're watching VHS.

No matter what new format attempts to win the hearts of consumers, they will find a formidable foe in VHS, which has been the format of choice since its inception in the late 1970s. According to the Consumer Electronics Association (CEA), VCRs are in an estimated 91 percent of U.S. households and VCR sales continue to increase. The CEA reported record VCR sales of 18.1 million in 1998, more than an eight percent increase over 1997 sales. Lower unit prices and improved features (including improved resolution at extended play speeds) will no doubt help VHS continue its dominance of the home video market.

Although unit sales and market penetration pale in comparison to VCRs, DVD players are enjoying outstanding sales growth. More than one million DVD units were sold in 1998, up more than 200 percent over 1997 sales, and the CEA expects sales of 6.5 million units in 2000. Meanwhile, laserdisc (LD) continues to falter in the wake of DVD. Sales dropped from 49,000 units in 1997 to 20,000 in 1998—and most of those sales were DVD/LD combination players. Through the third quarter of 1999, VHS tapes also continued to outsell all compact tape formats (including VHS-C, DV and 8mm) by a margin of more than 5:1.

Digital VHS (D-VHS) from Hitachi, JVC and Panasonic is the latest attempt to convince consumers to change formats. In this process, the VCR records the MPEG-2 bit stream directly to the D-VHS videotape from a digital satellite system (DSS) receiver and plays it back through an integrated receiver decoder (IRD). The IRD decodes the MPEG-2 signal and provides playback with high-quality audio and video (more than 500 lines of resolution). D-VHS is able to record and playback high definition programs and even multiple program streams by recording the ATSC MPEG-2 digital television bit stream. And for today's consumer, the system can play and record standard VHS, so current tape libraries are not rendered obsolete.

Selectable data rates allow consumers to record up to 49 hours on a single DF-420 cassette (at the lowest record quality). Standard mode allows for seven hours of record time, while high speed (HS) mode, at 28.2 Mbps, will record up to 3.5 hours of high definition digital broadcasts on one cassette.

Sounds promising, even more promising than Super VHS (S-VHS) did when JVC introduced it in 1987 (though admittedly, S-VHS has carved itself a niche in some small market ENG and educational applications). However, there are some problems. First, the consumer has to purchase both a D-VHS VCR and the compatible DSS receiver to complete the system, which alienates cable customers. The second issue is price, as the JVC HM-DSR100DU D-VHS VCR has a suggested retail price of $999.95. (Panasonic's PV-HD1000 digital VCR designed for HDTV has a similar price tag.)

How likely is the average consumer to change tape formats? History tells us that home viewers are quite content with their VHS, thank you very much. And now, with many VCRs priced at less than $100 and many prerecorded VHS titles available for $10 or less, not to mention an extensive library of titles available for rental, it seems unlikely that consumers will abandon VHS anytime soon. If anything, consumers might supplement their VHS decks with DVD players, as prices continue to fall and more titles are released on that format. But the big selling point today is that consumers and professionals can easily record VHS at a very low cost, while affordable, recordable DVD is years away.

FROM CAMERA TO DESKTOP: THE DISTRIBUTION AND HANDLING OF VIDEO AS FILES

ROBERT R. GERHART

S how me...
In this digital age, audio and video have replaced static forms of communication, and the computer is no exception to this rule. Lifeless text has given way to sound and motion. The problem has come in finding ways to translate information from traditional analog platforms into digital media that can be readily distributed in formats serviceable and sophisticated enough for the professional data handler, yet understandable enough to be usable by the average consumer.

DIGITAL VERSUS DIGITIZED VIDEO

Today's modern studios use a mixture of digital, digitized and analog media for content creation. Most people in the video field, however, commonly refer to just about any computer-based moving picture as "digital video," regardless of its true origin and nature. While this definition is not entirely wrong, it is certainly less than accurate. To better understand the handling of video as files, a common frame of reference needs to be established.

True digital video is, quite literally, a digital version of analog video. It is defined by its signal characteristics under the guidelines set by SMPTE, which dictates the legal values, gamma, colorimetry and amplitude of the digital signal. These guidelines, like those of traditional analog video, provide a standard for the handling of digital media across a variety of equipment types and from different manufacturers. In contrast, digitized video is a product of the computer age. It can exist in a number of different formats, many of which are not necessarily compatible, and on a variety of computer platforms, most of which are also incompatible. And, unlike true digital video which is defined by its signal characteristics, digitized video is classified by the method used to store the media in the computer.

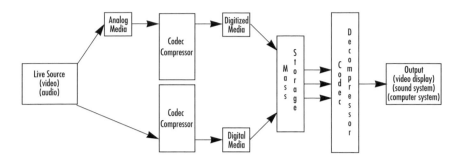

figure 1. Digital media versus digitized media.

UNDERSTANDING VIDEO AND THE COMPUTER

Digitized video (or media, as it often includes audio and other information) is probably the most common format in use today and, as such, is the focus of this article. It is the backbone of every nonlinear editing system, makes media transfer over the Internet possible and functions as the core technology behind every major communication media in use today. In order for computers to work with digitized media, however, the programs in question must be able to handle a variety of contingencies inherent with this technology. At the most basic level, they must first be capable of reading and, in some cases, writing the particular format or formats used for media storage. These reading/writing devices, known as **codecs**, are usually chosen by a vendor with a specific purpose in mind, such as the handling of video, audio, animation, MIDI or some other dynamic media type or combination.

For most broadcasters' and videographers' purposes in handling digitized media, specialized codecs have been written that give a system the ability to reach beyond the normal computer-based parameters of file size, data rates, window size and compression scheme to manipulate the variables internal to a media file's content. These can include video parameters such as line structures, aspect ratios, colorimetry and gamma, as well as audio parameters like sample rate, bit depth, stereo pairing and volume controls. With so many media types available, careful selection of the codecs supported by a program reduces the probability of error or confusion by the user and helps to produce a higher quality end product, with lower system operating overhead and a more affordable price. Taking this idea a step further, many manufacturers have either modified established codecs or created their own proprietary versions, ensuring maximum compatibility with their programs at the expense of inter-program or cross-platform file sharing.

Also note, digitized media seldom remains in one place for very long. A program designed to handle this media must be able to work across the different platforms used to capture, store, manipulate, transfer and view it. The program must be able to recognize both the media type and content, as well as the file type the media is stored in and its platform of origin. Though some would argue that this is more an aspect of computer networking than of digitized video, it is still important to the overall procedure of handling video as files and therefore necessitates consideration.

CODECS AND COMPRESSION THEORY

Codecs are the functional part of a program or operating system that contain both compression and decompression algorithms. They are an integral part to the creation of both digital and digitized video, as well as a variety of other media. These algorithms determine with which formats of digitized media a program can work. Fast-compressing codecs increase the efficiency with which digitized media can be created, while fast-decompressing codecs increase the speed at which the user can open and manipulate the finished file. Obviously, the faster that both of these processes can be performed, the better. Decompression, however, is usually most important—especially for CD-ROM, network and Internet-based delivery applications.

Compression and decompression times are often not equal given the same data stream; codecs that provide higher compression ratios tend to require substantially longer times to compress than decompress—these are known as asynchronous codecs. Two main factors will determine which codec is best suited for a particular type of media: the speed of the codec's compression algorithm and the reproduction quality of the images being compressed. Each codec takes advantage of different properties of a file to achieve compression, so the type of material being compressed and how it was produced significantly affects both how much compression can be applied and how well the codec can reproduce the compressed material. Compression quality can be adjusted at two levels during the creation of a digital or digitized video file, spatially or temporally, depending on the codec involved.

Spatial Compression is the process of applying compression to individual frames. It eliminates the redundant information within each frame but does not affect the frame relative to the image sequence of which it is part. The best example of this type of compression is found in JPEG images, where the tradeoff between the quality of an image can be easily compared to its file size. In most codecs, key frames are usually only spatially compressed.

Temporal Compression is the process of applying compression to a sequence of images such as video and multimedia. The individual images themselves can also have spatial compression applied to them, either before or during the temporal compression process, but this is not always the case. Temporal compression is applied to the different frames of an image sequence—those frames that are not designated as keyframes. This compression technique takes advantage of the fact that, in general, a given frame has much in common with the frame that preceded it, therefore the codec only needs to recognize the differences between the frames and store the changes that have occurred from one frame to the next. Keyframes function as the reference frame for the image sequence that follows, and therefore need to be complete images. It is for this reason that they are not able to be temporally compressed.

IT'S A CODEC MOMENT: THE WORKING CODEC

There are many different codecs available to the computer user today. More than a few have been created or modified to work with specific application programs or hardware systems. Designed to compress a wide variety of media including video, animation, audio, MIDI, time code and more, most offer more than just spatial and temporal controls. The setting of these controls will play an integral part in determining the nature of the media file being created and can influence both reproduction quality and file size dramatically. The following list will examine a number of these parameters and how they affect the media file.

Keyframes are the designated frames in an image sequence that provide a point from which a temporally compressed sequence may be decompressed. The use of more keyframes in a sequence will increase the overall file size of the finished media file, but will benefit the enduser by permitting more effective random access to any part of the sequence and improving a sequence's reverse playability. If these features are not deemed important, the number of keyframes can be reduced accordingly. However, sufficient keyframes must be present to allow the media player to keep video, audio or other data synchronized during playback. The creation of keyframes can be either natural or forced. A natural keyframe is the first frame of a cut in the image sequence, while a forced keyframe is one that is created arbitrarily by the application program itself, or the codec being utilized by the program for compression. Many applications and codecs will automatically create a forced key frame when they detect a certain percentage or greater difference between the current frame and the previous frame in an image sequence.

Frame Rate—Most applications allow you to select the desired frame rate for playback. This number can be set to any amount, however, for smoothness of playback, it is strongly recommended that a frame rate which is a sub-multiple of the source rate be utilized (from a digitized NTSC source of 30 fps, you should use 30, 15 or 10 fps; from a digitized PAL source of 25 fps, use 25, 12.5 or 6.25 fps). Reducing the frame rate of the media file will obviously reduce the file's size and increase playback stability accordingly, but an excessively low-frame rate will create jerky movement in the action and erratic or unfinished looking transitions.

Frame Size—Most traditional analog broadcast professionals recognize television frame size as being either 640x480 pixels for NTSC or 720x576 pixels for PAL. Many media-handling programs in use today come with a variety of commonly-used frame sizes preset, including these, and often allow for the manual creation of custom aspect ratios for alternate applications. Programs that support the use of custom frame sizes can often be set by the user to either crop or distort an original image to fit different frame dimensions. For draft purposes or non-broadcast applications, some programs offer the option of outputting reduced frame sizes without changing the working resolution, usually featuring settings from full to half, third or quarter of the original size, depending on the software being used. Smaller frame sizes not only create smaller file sizes for the finished media file, but provide easier playback on older or less-sophisticated systems. When full-size resolution is not critical to the final product, reducing the frame size is an easy way to create significant increases in media playback performance.

Pixel Shape—Once upon a time, the only answer was "square." With the advent of digital video and HDTV, that is no longer the case. Modern media handling, especially for broadcast applications, requires software to have the ability to either set or select a pixel shape compatible with the aspect ratio of the media's final output. This range often spans from traditional NTSC square pixels to those necessitated by the numerous aspect ratios and line configurations of digital video formats and HDTV standards, with many programs offering user-selectable or custom settings.

Color Depth—Many programs and codecs also allow you to select the number of possible colors, or color depth, of the media file being created. Though most computers today are capable of delivering a color palette into the millions of colors, only a small portion of this is ever needed or utilized. As human vision is limited to a only small fraction of that possible spectrum, it makes sense to eliminate those frequencies that are beyond or below our range of perception. Limiting a media file to the lowest possible number of colors can make for substantial reductions in file size, as well as increase its playback stability on older or less sophisticated systems. Eliminating color altogether, of course, takes this efficiency a step further, though this is usually not a feasible option. Care needs to be exercised when reducing color depth in addition to applying video compression. Too much compression used in conjunction with an overly limited color palette can cause posterization, solarization and a generally overall poor image quality, especially when applied to an intricate or dithered source.

Data Rate—This setting designates the amount of data provided or required at a specific moment in time to play a particular media file. Control of this number (measured in Kbps) is an important factor, not only in regulating the final file size of the finished file, but in determining the minimum system configuration required to decompress and play the media without problems or interruptions. Higher data rate settings will create a media file with better overall quality, but too high of a setting can cause problems with playback on less powerful machines or those with slower peripherals (when playing back through a network, over the Internet or from a CD-ROM). Lower data rate settings will reduce overall file size and increase playability on older machines, but will make the media look unclear and "primitive," especially on more technologically advanced systems. It should be noted that in codecs where you can set a limit to a file's playback data rate (for example, Cinepak), the spatial and temporal quality settings are adjusted dynamically during compression, so the specified data rate is not exceeded as the finished media is decompressed.

HARDWARE- AND SOFTWARE-BASED CODECS

Codecs, for all their numbers and diversity, essentially come in two varieties: hardware-based and software-based. Usually tied in with specific program packages or operating systems, they often constitute a primary part of the host system's functionality.

Hardware-Based Codecs, as the name implies, require a hardware component, usually in the form of a peripheral board or sub-processor module, to function at their optimum efficiency. Though most hardware-based codecs can operate without this component, their efficiency is usually greatly reduced and some, designed to run within specific applications, are unable to function at all. The benefit of working with hardware-based codecs is recognized in their superior performance. The hardware element allows the codec to handle markedly higher data rates without dropping frames or losing synchronization with related media, thus enabling the user to work in greater resolution, with larger aspect ratios and at higher frame rates than software-based solutions.

This performance is not without its drawbacks, however. Hardware-based codecs are considerably more expensive than their counterparts, largely due to the cost of the hardware component. Their usefulness in some situations is also limited because of their connection to the hardware—media files created with these kinds of codecs usually are only able to be viewed on computers containing similar hardware. Also, the flexibility and features of the codec are often dictated by this symbiosis—if it isn't supported on the hardware, the codec is probably incapable of doing it, now or in future revisions, without modifying or replacing the hardware element. Finally, updates, if available, are usually hardware- or firmware-based, and may necessitate a trip to an authorized service center to complete.

Software-Based Codecs, on the other hand, rely on the computer's own CPU for their computational power and, therefore, can be installed on any system with sufficient processing ability. Available in greater numbers and for more diversified applications than their hardware-based counterparts, software-based codecs are considerably less expensive and usually offer more available features, sacrificing top-end performance for enhanced functionality. Their effectiveness is dictated solely by the host system's processing capability. Many systems that rely on hardware-based codecs for their main functionality will often incorporate software-based codecs for inter-program or cross-platform media exchanges.

GETTING THERE IS HALF THE FUN

The world is analog and, as we've seen, computers (and therefore the future of media content creation and distribution) are not. At some point, content will have to be converted to a digital format of some nature so that it can be edited, manipulated, integrated and distributed. That process can take place at the time the media is acquired or at some point in the future, but it will happen. Codecs will define the media's parameters as it is captured and stored, but it is the hardware and related software that will dictate when and how the media will enter the digital realm.

To get the most out of your media, "digital in" is obviously the best place to start. This means getting the A/D conversion process as close to your source as possible. This will ensure the clearest possible recording while, at the same time, reduce the chance for degradation to a minimum. Starting with a clean source will make any future digital manipulation easier and faster, as errors and artifacts require more processing time and storage space to address. Computers, as a rule, do not know the difference between an error, artifact or element, and will treat them all with equal enthusiasm, expending valuable processing resources in doing so. Failing "digital in," the next best alternative is to digitize from the cleanest possible source material using the highest quality equipment, cabling and connectors available. A wide variety of possible alternatives is presented at this stage, ranging from simple pieces of software that utilize a computer's stock input ports and system CPU, to elaborate and exotic nonlinear editing workstations with specialized hardware and custom software and codecs. Obviously, at this level, some sort of determination needs to be made based on the media, its origin, its intended use and its final destination as to what sort of equipment will be employed to digitize, store and otherwise manipulate it.

Once digitized, source media often changes form several times before reaching the output and distribution stages. Editing and other content manipulation usually takes place at the highest possible quality level, during which time the primary media is often combined with additional material such as audio, data tracks or other information. The resulting program is then output as a self-contained file. It is usually at this stage where preparation for distribution takes place. This can be done either by the software that created the file, or by another, more specialized media manipulation program. Preparations can include repackaging the media with a new codec, reductions to the data rate, color palette, frame size or frame rate. Equal attention must also be given to available audio tracks, which can be eliminated or combined, have their sample rate or bit depth reduced or any one of a number of codecs applied. All of these factors and more are reliant upon the media's final destination and playback methodology.

GENTLY DOWN THE STREAM

With the number of personal computers on the rise, and the future of broadcasting going digital, it is not hard to envision the eventual nirvana that will be streaming content over the Internet. Though increasingly more common, streaming video is still in its infancy; it has a long way to go before even beginning to approach broadcast quality as we know it today. Several companies and numerous technologies continue to make headway in this area, but the core process remains the same—content must be digitized, prepared and then distributed. The venue is the Internet and the limitations are numerous and ever-changing. Bandwidth constrictions and modem limitations make realtime streaming problematic at best. To overcome this, a technique called Progressive Downloading is most frequently used, whereby media is downloaded onto a computer's hard drive and played back from there, instead of being processed in realtime directly from the data stream. Transferring and viewing media in this way has numerous benefits, including reduced bandwidth demands and improved media quality and playback reliability. Files can be created with the more space-efficient, if time-consuming, codecs instead of those designed to move quickly at the expense of quality.

The popularity of streaming media will continue to increase in the coming years and, with it, so will the technology to make better files faster and move them more efficiently. Streaming media is no longer reserved almost solely for professional Web masters or large corporations, but is now available to virtually anyone with a good personal computer and a reliable Internet connection.

PLAYING WITH YOUR MEDIA

Players are a computer's software architecture for allowing users to access video, audio, animation, text and other dynamic information. Available in a variety of formats, from stand-alone programs to system software components and plug-in drivers, a multitude of players are available for each of the different computer architectures commonly in use today—Macintosh, Windows and SGI. Some players, such as QuickTime, have versions for more than a single operating system (including Java), providing comparable features as well as a standard of compatibility for exchanging files between programs and computers. Players are usually self-contained packages which work in a stand-alone capacity to view, and sometimes manipulate, media files. They can be as simple as a small shareware program that will allow you to play files downloaded from the Internet, or as complicated as a high-end nonlinear editing or compositing workstation costing tens or hundreds of thousands of dollars. More sophisticated players are often able to access any additional codecs that might be available on the host system and incorporate their functionality into its own. In some cases, especially when working with hardware-based codecs, special players are provided by the vendor which are designed to interface with the non-system hardware for enhanced performance.

Like codecs, players vary in form and function. Even the most basic may look simple from the user's perspective, but underneath they often have to handle a variety of rather complicated functions. QuickTime, for instance, probably the most commonly installed player available, is composed of over 200 separate software components divided into more than 20 different categories. This component architecture not only includes system software, but also compression facilities, human interface standards and standardized file format recognition. Its modular design allows for timely updates that support new technologies and enhancements to existing ones without necessitating costly or lengthy revisions. These components combine to create a cross-platform architecture that allows developers to create multimedia content once, then distribute it across multiple platforms with virtually no additional work.

As with video, audio media can be played and edited in much the same way. Again, a variety of players are available ranging in price and sophistication, from small shareware programs to sophisticated digital audio workstation systems. Most of the time, however, the same player used for accessing video media functions works quite well with files containing only audio information. Like their video counterparts, audio players are available which are not only able to play audio media, but edit the audio content as well. These usually incorporate a selection of built-in codecs, and may be able to access additional ones available on the host system.

PICKING A PLAYER FOR YOUR TEAM

A good player, or application that incorporates its own built-in player, is one that does not have to rely on extensive driver libraries for support of other platforms, applications or configurations. It will natively support the relevant codecs and give the digital content creator the ability to easily view or manipulate media from a variety of sources without concern for file or format compatibility. Whether your application for digitized media is as involved as nonlinear film compositing or as simple as the creation of a few basic animated files for the Internet, a general understanding of the codecs and principles involved will go a long way to helping you create better, more effective content for your viewing audience.

DELIVERING VIDEO OVER THE INTERNET

SHELDON LIEBMAN

The past few years have seen a great deal of activity in the area of delivering video content over wide area networks (WANs). Previously, this process involved expensive, high-speed private networks. More recently, steps

DTV IN THE REAL WORLD

UNDERSTANDING DIGITAL

PRE-PRODUCTION

PRODUCTION

AUDIO

GRAPHIC & COMPOSITING

POST PRODUCTION

DELIVERY & DUPLICATION

ENGINEERING & TRANSMISSION

APPENDIX

GLOSSARY

have been taken to use the Internet and its global connectivity as a conduit for video delivery.

One of the reasons private networks have made sense in the past is that many companies were trying to deliver realtime video across a WAN. The use of private networks ensures that both parties can achieve a connection speed and quality of service that supports the sharing of video content, which requires a tremendous amount of bandwidth. One second of uncompressed ITU-R 601 video is over 30 megabytes (MB) in size, which is very difficult to transmit in realtime. For this reason, compression technology is usually applied to the source material. With MPEG-2 compression, the bandwidth requirements can be reduced significantly, but high-speed links are still required for realtime sharing of video.

However, there are problems with this approach. The first is that both locations need to be available at the same time in order for it to work. The second is that both locations need to be connected at the proper speed. Even if one location can send realtime video, can the other receive it in realtime? Finally, there is the issue of network reliability. In a realtime environment, it can be annoying if there is a hiccup in the network and the stream is interrupted.

INCREASING THE OPTIONS

For many applications, however, the use of realtime video is a bonus rather than a requirement. After all, most video applications today are based on sending videotapes from one location to another. Even broadcast programming is often received at one time and broadcast at another. Unless the sender and the receiver need to view the material both immediately and together, realtime delivery is optional.

If the realtime requirement is removed, a store and forward process can be used. With this technique, the transmission process is completely separated from the creation and playback process. Instead, video clips are stored at the source and at the destination, increasing the options for transmitting the information.

By choosing this approach, television stations and production facilities can transmit material to remote locations whenever they choose. They can also control the quality of the material, which determines the size of the video file that is created and the amount of time it will take to transmit at a given bandwidth. For approval video, lower resolution settings can be used; for final copy, broadcast quality material can be transmitted that is full-resolution, full-motion and full-screen.

A PUBLIC SOLUTION

In early approaches to this problem, lower-speed private networks were used. More recently, companies have developed ways to use the IP protocol and IP addressing to move material from one station to another. With video over IP, the world's largest public network, the Internet, is now available for transmitting video.

This process is based on standard FTP transmission and allows any device with an IP address to transfer a digital video file to any other device that has an IP address. This technique offers many advantages.

The most obvious advantage to using the Internet for video transmission is that connection speed requirements disappear. The initial connection is simply a gateway to the very high-speed Internet backbone. In this way, companies using low-speed connections (like traditional modems) can send information to companies using medium-speed (DSL or cable modems) or high-speed (T1 or higher) Internet connections. In fact, with the development of satellite-based Internet connectivity, even the need for a physical connection is removed, with the advantage being that only the intended recipient(s) can actually receive the information being transmitted.

Using IP and the Internet also makes it easier to distribute video information to more than one location. In a multicasting environment, many locations connect with a single server to access the same (video) file at the same time. This is similar to current video streaming technology over the Internet, although the result is a digital file containing broadcast quality video instead of a realtime display. Or, if the server mimics the functionality of a traditional e-mail server, the same file can be sent to multiple recipients over a period of time. The difference between these two approaches is which party controls the process.

Another advantage to using the public Internet is that both sides are insulated from network problems. If a packet of data doesn't get through correctly the first time, it can be sent again and the process is completely transparent to the user. In the end, the resulting video is the same, whether or not the network is operating at peak efficiency.

Non realtime systems transmit over the Internet every day. Home PC users capture video onto their hard disks, transmit those videos as e-mail attachments to anyone they choose, and the recipients can watch the video on their computer screens. In a broadcast video environment, the biggest change is the quality of the captured video.

This illustrates one of the biggest advantages of transmitting video over IP— it can go from virtually anywhere to virtually anywhere. If an Internet connection is available, you can send and receive video simply by knowing the recipient's IP address. Also, since many companies are already paying for full-time Internet connections, there may be no additional connection cost associated with transmitting clips using this process—it just piggybacks the connection you already have. Size and distance are no longer factors.

Of course, transmitting large files with FTP is not always a smooth process, especially if the receiving station doesn't have enough room to store the entire

DTV IN THE REAL WORLD

UNDERSTANDING DIGITAL

PRE-PRODUCTION

PRODUCTION

AUDIO

GRAPHIC & COMPOSITING

POST PRODUCTION

DELIVERY & DUPLICATION

ENGINEERING & TRANSMISSION

APPENDIX

GLOSSARY

clip being sent. This is one of the problems faced by companies who want to transmit video files over IP, but solutions have already begun to appear.

Another issue that needs to be addressed is bi-directional communication. If a very large video file is being transmitted from point A to point B, how can we verify that it arrived?

In the same area, methods must be developed to deal with errors and glitches in the process. If an error occurs in the middle of transmitting a 1 GigaByte (GB) file, does the entire file need to be transmitted again or is there a way to pick up from where the error occurs? Ultimately, if a transmission is unsuccessful, can a way be found to automatically retry until it can succeed?

The research being done in the area of video over IP suggests that solutions to these and other related problems are just around the corner. Once they become available to everyone, the method by which we transmit video from one location to another may never be the same.

INTERNET VIDEO: BANDWIDTH, BUZZ AND INTERACTIVITY DELIVER A NEW MEDIUM

JON LELAND

Only in the astounding world of the Internet could a technology that is barely five years old inspire (at least in part) the biggest merger in entertainment history. As many journalists have already explained, perhaps the biggest factor in AOL's decision to acquire Time-Warner was access to the latter company's cable modem (and future cable modem) customers. Of course, the most commonly mentioned use of the broadening of Internet bandwidth (as delivered by cable modems among other technologies) is video. Video on the Internet is still only an emerging marketplace, though video programming on the Internet is already being pioneered and delivered. While the future convergence of Internet programming and DTV channels is one dimension of the future, the emergence of video on the World Wide Web has already taken on a life of its own.

In fact, the Web is not one thing. It is many. And the world of Internet video also has many faces. For example, there are entertainment sites including extensions of existing broadcast channels, sites that are ramping up to deliver pay-per-view movies (such as MeTV.com) and creators of original Web video content. This later rapidly expanding market includes such major players as Pop.com, a co-venture of Dreamworks SKG and Imagine Entertainment, and Macromedia's Shockwave.com, which has signed deals with *South Park* creators Matt Stone and Trey Parker, as well as film director/animator Tim Burton, among others. In addition, there are many other kinds of video being distributed on the Web. These include training, corporate communications and distance learning, as well as personal/amateur productions of all kinds. Likewise, there are also a variety of technologies in use while others are still being developed.

Essentially, the technology that supports the realtime delivery of both live and on-demand video programs has evolved rapidly; at the same time, audiences have enjoyed increased access to faster modems and higher performance (broader bandwidth) Internet connections. When combined with the Web's own unique forms of interactivity, a completely new media platform is being created.

In fact, on-line video created a "buzz" for being one of the next "big things" (i.e. an important, emerging Internet technology). However, its unique character and grass roots beginnings may lead one to believe that traditional broadcasters may not have the necessary new media experience to compete with more Web-savvy start ups. Just as many "bricks and mortar" retailers have suffered at the hands of their more virtualized e-commerce competitors, broadcasters are certain to be challenged over the next few years by a new medium being built on completely new technologies and with a whole new variety of viewer relationships.

TECH PERSPECTIVE

Never before has a video distribution platform been so easily accessible to so many, and when combined with cost performance breakthroughs like DV production and desktop post production, video on the Internet represents the possibility for a grass roots revolution. In its start-up years, video on the Internet was limited by bandwidth. While that's still true to a large extent, it is changing rapidly. As the cost of computers drops radically while PC performance continues to accelerate, some experts think the cost of higher bandwidth is dropping even faster. One Internet video executive told me, "The cost of Internet bandwidth [bits per second] is dropping even faster than computing power [MIPS]."

Innovations like DSL and cable modems, combined with the increasing accessibility of corporate and educational networks, are creating an on-line world that is increasingly rich in video quality-enhancing bandwidth. This ever-expanding pipeline is certain to enable more and more "VHS-quality" Internet video viewing experiences in the very near future.

STREAMING COMPLEMENTS DOWNLOADING

Historically, in the "old days," (which in "Internet time" means just a few years ago), all video on the Internet consisted of digital files that had to be downloaded. At the time, this was a time consuming process. The first significant Internet application to break the "downloading barrier" was Progressive Network's Real Audio. (That company is now the streaming industry leader and has changed its name to RealNetworks.) For relatively early Web browsers, RealAudio introduced the concept of "streaming" media. By utilizing compression and a RAM buffer, Real Audio enabled the immediacy of virtually realtime audio playback. RealVideo followed in less than two years. However, while streaming is the standard for realtime, live Webcasts, the improved quality of the media files that are now available for download via higher bandwidth connections has lead to a resurgence of downloaded digital video. The significant popularity of the MP3 audio format is the most prominent example of this trend, and downloading continues to be important as an ongoing component of the on-line video environment. This was underscored in the summer of 1999, when Apple reported 23 million downloads of the QuickTime version of the trailer for the movie *Star Wars Episode 1: The Phantom Menace*.

MULTIPLE STREAMING STANDARDS

Despite the lesser quality, streaming has become the most popular way to view video over the Internet because of its immediacy. Clips are available for viewing much more quickly. Technologically, streaming utilizes a client-server software system to load the first part of a media clip into a memory buffer on the user's PC. Then, while that segment begins playing on the viewer's screen, the software streams the next segment into the buffer so that it is ready to begin playing as soon as the first segment is finished. Thus, streaming provides audio and video-on-demand (VOD), including access to live events, over the Internet. Now, with all new computers shipping with at least a 56K modem, and with many users getting even faster connections, the quality is improving quickly.

While there were initially almost a dozen companies battling for the Internet streaming video standard, three remain as viable leaders. The current leaders in terms of streaming and other multimedia architectures for the delivery of video via the Internet are RealNetworks with its RealPlayer, Microsoft with its Windows Media Player and Apple with its QuickTime platform. At the time of this writing, the most popular Internet video sites most commonly offer RealPlayer, with Windows Media Player a close second (and frequently offered as well as RealPlayer). QuickTime is more frequently found on smaller Web sites where files are offered for download (or "progressive download," explained below). Apple launched the streaming version of QuickTime during 1999 and it is yet to enjoy widespread use.

Regardless of the streaming platform, video on the Web offers a new kind of viewer control over video material. This is the first generation of truly interactive video on a network; and Web enthusiasts appreciate the power to view whatever video clips they want whenever they want them. (As an aside, the streaming market also includes other "microcast" audiences and applications. These include, for example, SitePath and Cisco IP/TV, which are targeted to corporate Intranets, as well as other forms of hybrid distribution including satellite services, video conferencing systems, WebTV and other so-called Internet appliances.)

TYPES OF STREAMING

Even with the partial shake-out in delivery software options, Internet video is still a complex medium to comprehend because it continues to support a variety of delivery formats. These include live events and on-demand programs, single streams, multiple streams and multicasting. In fact, the competition is heating up to deliver the massive server and distributed networks necessary to Webcast to larger audiences.

Network services companies like Akamai (which has an offer pending to buy Web video service provider InterVU), Digital Island and others are competing with streaming video hosts like the Real Broadcast Network (RBN) and Yahoo Broadcast.com to deliver these services. However, few of these vendors agree on a specific technological approach. Each one claims to know the market better and brags about its proprietary systems and technologies. (For more on this please see my article, "The Pomp and Promise of QuickTime TV" at www.mediamall.com/promedia/videoWeb/QT_TV1.html.) There are also different kinds of Webcasts, including live and on-demand. Live Webcasts have less flexibility and must be delivered with lesser quality because the compression of their footage must take place in realtime. On the other hand, live Webcasts can also use a technique called multicasting to reach larger audiences with far less server capacity than single stream events. On-demand programs are available whenever requested, 24 hours a day, seven days a week, and can feature high quality and the benefits of post production.

In order to face the challenge that I call "The Grand Canyon" Gap between people and technology, I have found it necessary to create some of my own terms for the various types of streaming video applications. I break these technologies into four general types:

Pseudo-Streaming: Also known as "progressive downloads," this approach is not true streaming because it uses hard drive space rather than a RAM cache or buffer. Pseudo-streaming is a file download that is enhanced to enable the viewer to "screen" part of the clip during the process of the download. QuickTime, which has pioneered this approach, uses a technique called FastStart that enables the video to start playing as soon as there is enough material transferred to the user's hard drive. However, once the viewer reaches the end of the what has been transferred (assuming that the playback is faster than the download), he must wait until more content has been transferred before continuing to watch. As a monitor for this experience, the QuickTime play bar, which is located below the digital video image, fills progressively with a black stripe in order to show the user how much of the video clip is currently available for viewing.

Since pseudo-streaming is, in fact, a standard TCP file transfer, it also introduces a copyright issue that is of concern to some producers but is not an issue with streaming. As streaming constantly caches and flushes the video stream from the user's computer memory, the user never receives a copy that can be saved or distributed. Downloading, on the other hand (as illustrated by the MP3 phenomenon), may provide a copy of the digital file with which the user can do as he or she pleases.

Mono-streaming: This is the basic approach to streaming. It delivers a single video or audio clip that's fed in realtime, and thus avoids downloads altogether. This approach is supported by a dedicated server such as a RealVideo, Windows

DTV IN THE REAL WORLD

UNDERSTANDING DIGITAL

PRE-PRODUCTION

PRODUCTION

AUDIO

GRAPHIC & COMPOSITING

POST PRODUCTION

DELIVERY & DUPLICATION

ENGINEERING & TRANSMISSION

APPENDIX

GLOSSARY

NT or Apple QuickTime server that utilizes the UDP (rather than the TCP) protocol. Streaming delivers the audio or video clip while it's being viewed or listened to, and for this reason there's no disk storage (which also inadvertently protects copyrights). Its most important feature is immediate, on-demand access over the network. It is applicable to either live events or to stored video programming.

As mentioned, Akamai and other providers are building networks of streaming servers on literally hundreds (and soon thousands) of servers around the country and the world to facilitate streaming delivery to thousands (if not millions) of simultaneous users. The essence of this kind of service is proprietary software that instantaneously finds the content you want on the best server on that network depending on your geographic location The selection of the most appropriate version of the requested clip is determined intelligently by specialized software depending on the content, various servers in various locations and a "weather map" of Internet traffic at that moment.

Multistreaming: This is a term I've invented. It is also referred to as "synchronized multimedia" and in some cases as "illustrated audio" or "illustrated video." Multistreaming combines the audio or video streaming process described above with other synchronized media content, such as scrolling text and data streams (like realtime stock quotes), HTML page flips, synchronized images, and MIDI sound. All of these media types are synchronized with the main video or audio stream to create a visual presentation composed of multiple simultaneous streams. The images and other media types are synched to timings in the audio/video track (think of Ken Burns' Baseball series on PBS), but they are displayed next to the clip (or elsewhere on the screen) rather than as part of the video clip.

The most dynamic use of these capabilities is currently demonstrated by the G2 versions of RealPlayer, which offers a window that can include multiple media types and a selection of streaming video channels. The multiple media types are displayed within the RealPlayer video window using the Synchronized Multimedia Integration Language (SMIL) for layout. In this context, streaming video clips are most frequently complemented with clickable links that offer immediate access to other clips, such as other news stories. QuickTime also supports integration of multiple media types within one window; however, these capabilities are not as widely used, certainly not in the streaming space. I believe multistreaming is a very important development and can help to differentiate the on-line video viewing experience. Yet, it is still largely underutilized.

Multicasting: This term has been misused, in my opinion, by broadcasters proposing to multiplex several compressed digital channels into their new DTV spectrum allocation instead of broadcasting HDTV. In Internet terms, multicasting has already been in use for years, as it was pioneered by the MBONE. Multicasting refers to using multiple servers to "spread the load" of streaming in order to multiply the number of available streams, and thus expand the potential audience significantly. However, it is important to note that multicasting can only be used for live events and live programs.

Here's how it achieves its distribution advantages. If one server delivers 100 streams to 100 other servers that, in turn, each deliver 100 streams to users, you quickly have 10,000 available streams originating from one server, but without any one server carrying an impossible load. MCI and RealNetworks, as well as perhaps the largest Internet Webcaster, Yahoo Broadcast.com, are building dedicated multicast "networks" or server systems.

In fact, Yahoo Broadcast.com founder and CEO Mark Cuban insists that multicasting is the only viable way to build a network of servers for large, *live* Webcast events. He told me, "When it's the bottom of the ninth [in a live baseball game] and the server on one of your ISP's network fails, what are you going to do? Page the ISP and ask them to fix it? It's easy to route around when there is just one thing going on. But when there are 30 or 40 or 1,000 [live] events like we have going on, then one server failing impacts tens or hundreds of events." For these reasons, Broadcast.com is building a multicast network which uses distributed routers instead of servers. Cuban claims that they already have 700,000 "multicast-enabled dial-up and broadband ports." Cuban immodestly claims that his network "blows away distributed servers for live [events] any day of the week." For more information on Yahoo Broadcast.com's multicast network, visit: www.broadcast.com/about/multicast/.

THE COMPONENTS: HOW STREAMING WORKS

The best available quality video streaming requires a combination of a UDP server, a compression codec and a client or browser player. Here's how these components work together to provide the virtual miracle of real-time video at dial-up bandwidths.

Servers: Perhaps the most fundamental component of most multimedia servers is the introduction of the more sophisticated UDP (User Datagram Protocol) networking protocol rather than the Internet-standard TCP (Transmission Control Protocol). TCP is a transport-oriented protocol that makes reliability its first priority. The downside is that it is inefficient for data-intensive applications like streaming media because it is "chatty" as a result of a continual process of data receipt confirmations. In the world of streaming media, where dropped packets are to be expected, the resulting attempts at data recovery take longer than they are worth because they hurt performance. However, the TCP protocol is simpler to configure because it runs on a net-standard HTTP server; thus, when video clips are being downloaded, it treats video or audio just like any other data type.

UDP, on the other hand, while delivering adequate reliability, is more efficient. Roughly speaking, the UDP software application tells the server, "I'll tell you if something important breaks down; otherwise just keep sending more data." However, because UDP is not the Net's standard protocol, it requires specialized server software. Beyond performance, UDP also enables important and more sophisticated streaming functionality, such as buffering, load balancing (to facilitate the efficient delivery of more streams from one server), live streaming, multistreaming, multicasting and random access play (so a streaming clip can have pause and rewind buttons).

According to one engineer, "The Internet is a dirty place where one out of 10 packets gets dropped. On a good day, delivering a video stream without a specialized server might work. But when you as a content provider have limited bandwidth or anticipate a big volume, you'll want a server that makes the best possible use of the available bandwidth." Clearly professional media companies require higher performance as well as interactivity-enhancing features.

For example, one chief technologist for a large video-oriented Web site told me that he assumes an audience of thousands of users. His broadcast orientation demands UDP performance and begins to define streaming on terms that go beyond most of today's applications. To this man, a single stream is just the beginning. He said, "Mono-streaming audiences that fill a T-3 (bandwidth for hundreds of viewers), that's a demo." In other words, hundreds of individual streams just won't create an audience big enough to support a commercial Webcast.

Codecs: Since the compression-decompression algorithm known as a codec is frequently bundled with a server-player platform, many people confuse the codec with the server-player. That is changing as the players attempt to become utilities. For example, RealPlayer, Media Player and QuickTime are now supporting as many different codecs as possible (i.e. AVI, MPEG, etc.), with the obvious exclusion of their direct competitors (i.e. Media Player does not support the RealVideo codec). For this reason, compression is increasingly becoming player and server independent; however, the codec "connection" to server-player systems continues because there are yet to be any real codec standards. Even MPEG, for example, has several different low-bandwidth versions. As a result, the relevant codecs that your system needs to play a particular streaming video clip are still most commonly downloaded and installed as part of the video player system set up on the user's PC.

Players: On the browser or user's system, a video player is required. Frequently these are integrated with the browser either as a plug-in or "Helper" application (Netscape Navigator) or as an Active-X controller (Microsoft Explorer). Like having a properly configured set-top box on a cable system, these software receivers are required for the integrated software delivery that streaming demands. Some solutions, such as Emblaze, use of the Java programming language to provide "playerless" video delivery, however, Java's quality compromises and the technical glitches are still too common to make this approach popular.

TECHNOLOGY TRENDS

The streaming "arena" continues to change rapidly. While there are certain to be unpredictable changes ahead, the following are three major trends that appear likely to continue, at least in the near future. These are important to keep in mind as you and your company plan your participation this new media "universe."

The Platform Wars: Although there have been (and still are) many competitors, RealNetworks claims that 75 to 80 percent of the streaming content on today's Web is in one of its formats. However, just as they did to Netscape in the browser wars, Microsoft is threatening to change this situation, and its market share in the streaming market is growing the most rapidly at the time of this writing. In addition, Apple's QuickTime is a familiar platform to many video producers, and QuickTime is already integrated into many video non-linear editing systems. While QuickTime made a late entry into the streaming market, there's still time to play catch up, and Apple's corporate resurgence underscores the fact that they should not be dismissed. In addition to evolving its own technology, Microsoft has an especially strong position among many corporate networks, and they are using their exceptionally strong cash position to make strategic investments (including $30 million in InterVU) to leverage an even stronger position in the Internet video market. Furthermore, many corporate networks are standardizing on Window NT servers, and Microsoft's media server is bundled free with the Windows NT server (recently upgraded to Windows 2000). Of course, the Windows Media Player, as well as the most recent release of Internet Explorer, is now standard with Windows 98, enabling Microsoft to conveniently extend its streaming player penetration. RealNetworks may be the current leader, but Microsoft is clearly taking aim at this market and we have not heard the last of Apple. In fact, Apple's interest in the digital video market is growing. This interest is underscored by Apple's acquisition and release of its Final Cut Pro digital video editing software and its release of special DV versions of the iMac.

These three players are clearly the streaming platform players to watch.

Better Bandwidth: As mentioned, the increasing accessibility of broader bandwidth connections and the emergence of additional technologies will further enhance the on-line video viewing experience. From DSL connections to corporate intranets and cable modems, from satellite systems to wireless systems and other forms of video network system offerings like SitePath, there's no question that higher quality video is on the way.

In fact, researcher Paul Kagan & Associates reports that there are 137 million homes which are "broadband ready," and they project an Internet broadcasting market just shy of $20 billion by 2008. The result is that broadband video providers like Excite@Home and some of the larger telecommunication companies have begun to experiment with special video programming designed especially for high bandwidth customers. This trend is certain to increase. As the availability of broader bandwidth increases, so will the variety of streaming video programming.

New Content Formats: Since Internet video is presented on the Web and is usually triggered from a Web page, its relationship to the Internet's vast quantity of print and graphics information naturally complements the video presentation. Internet video exists within the medium of the World Wide Web itself. This is an interactive relationship that not only changes audience dynamics, but also presents (for better or worse, depending on the skill of the producer/developer) whole new varieties of communication challenges. Furthermore, it presents a whole new generation of advertising/sponsorship applications that are also unfolding right before our eyes.

Announcements like the Reuters investment in Virage (the video indexing software company which demonstrated keyword-searchable on-line access to video footage during the Clinton-Lewinsky scandal) indicate increasingly broad search capabilities for video on the Web. Short form programming (for example, video clips up to 15 minutes long) also seems to be more appealing on the Web. In short, this new medium is still being invented; the only thing we can say for sure it that it is not TV. What it is remains to be seen. Watch for more innovative and varied on-line presentation environments as this on-line video space evolves.

CHALLENGES AND OBSTACLES

The leading edge wouldn't be referred to as the "bleeding" edge if it didn't have its share of challenges and obstacles. Here are four important challenges to consider:

Revenue: Large-scale Web sites seem to succeed more on the basis of market capitalization than on profitability. While there is broad agreement that the world of Web media is a huge opportunity, it also seems clear to me that developing profitable businesses will take time. Meanwhile, the Web will be used, as it is today, as a complementary medium both for promotion and as a new layer of interactivity to existing video channels. In other words, in many cases, video on the Web will live alongside (if not feed from) traditional broadcasting. The pioneers and innovators are most likely to be venture funded—in one form or another.

Firewalls: Streaming video that uses the UDP protocol described above has frequently run into a technical obstacle when confronted by firewalls designed to protect the security of corporate networks. While the streaming software companies are working with the firewall software companies to allow the video streams to get access to these corporate networks, this is a process that takes time. Also, the challenges of bandwidth management have also limited streaming videos accessibility on WebTV and on some cable modem systems. This is a potential stumbling block and also a Microsoft advantage, at least for companies using Microsoft networking solutions.

Communication Design: For my money, this is perhaps the most critical issue, but it is a creative, not a technical, challenge. Just because you make something interactive doesn't mean people will want to interact. I call this "The Participation Paradox." In essence, couch potatoes are more comfortable channel surfing—and it will take more compelling interactive programs and applications to get traditional video viewers more involved in the Internet. And it is especially challenging to attract viewers in sufficient numbers to create compelling business models.

User Configuration Hassles: The necessity and array of browser plug-ins and other forms of video players both confuses and complicates the life of the viewer/user. He is used to relatively simple operations like channel switching and pushing "play" and "rewind" on a VCR. Some computer users are early adopters, but to reach a wider audience, configuring a computer to play streaming video must become much simpler. While interim solutions like automatic network upgrades are being built into newer software like RealSystem G2, in the near term, browser software configuration is more of a hassle than it should be—and sophisticated video-enhanced Web sites all need to provide support to help users with their streaming setups.

HOW TO MAKE THE MOST OF STREAMING VIDEO

While the increase in available bandwidth is beginning to alleviate these problems, streaming video for consumer bandwidths still forces some producers to make distinctions between "high motion and low motion video" that just doesn't come up when using full motion video. Unfortunately, these considerations are the opposite of what's normally referred to as "high production values." As anyone who has worked with compressed video (for example, for CD-ROMs) knows, camera motion like pans, zooms and dollies which are normally used to enhance the visual interest of a production cause low-bandwidth codecs to "choke," thus causing image quality to suffer visibly.

As a result, streaming video producers who are concerned about the low-end dial-up user's experience need to tread lightly on the compression-decompression process by (wherever possible) limiting unnecessary movement in the video frame that will cause the compression process to be more computing intensive. Talking heads, for example, are the easiest to compress because so little of the image is moving. On the other hand, movement in the background, such as people walking across the frame, and camera movements, such as zooms or dollies, further reduce the quality of streaming video. Likewise, special effects such as wipes and DVE moves are difficult for codecs to handle. Producers should reduce or eliminate unnecessary transition effects from their productions before encoding for streaming.

These inherent limitations of low-bandwidth streaming video are what makes me think the use of additional components that can be displayed next to the video should be used more frequently to create a more compelling presentation. For example, consider a distance-learning computer science course at Stanford. In this application, the lecturer is shown and heard in a small streaming video clip while roughly two-thirds of the remaining video screen "real estate" is used to display bullet-point-style graphics that complement his talk. Referred to as multistreaming or with the wonderfully oxymoronic term "illustrated video," I believe this technique can go a long way toward making the most of the new on-line video medium. In addition, many producers will benefit from using a network of resources to deliver their streaming productions rather than attempting to do everything themselves. While the market is still emerging, I believe that many "content providers" will be effectively served by the on-line equivalent of desktop publishing "service bureaus," or what might be called post-post-production houses, who will provide encoding services and heavy-duty servers on a time share basis. CNN, for example, outsources its video hosting to InterVU and, in fact, made an investment in that company.

SOMETHING TO SAY

Given the glut of information already on the Internet, the good news for video professionals is that there is an increasing need for talented and knowledgeable interactive producers who can turn these new technologies into viable programs. In this new environment, I think we have to avoid what my friend from the Corporation for Public Broadcasting, Ted Coltman, calls the "channel mentality." You don't need a full-time channel's worth of content to say something worthwhile. On the contrary, I think it was G.K. Chesterton who said, "I would have written you a shorter letter, but I didn't have the time." The bottom line is that it's what we have to say that will make good use of these new channels, and perhaps that is the most important consideration of all. While broadcast DTV is attempting to build its technical infrastructure, Internet video is already coming to life. For video programmers, the "bad news" may be that the Web offers a more complex creative environment than any medium that we've ever faced. The "good news" is that the Web's wired interactivity and special interest communities can lead to remarkably rapid growth, especially when the programming is truly synergistic with this vibrant new medium.

Internet video offers a fresh media opportunity that virtually all of us expect to have an extraordinarily bright future. What we make of it is up to us.

Stay tuned.

RESOURCES

It's common sense, but frequently forgotten, that the Web itself is the most important resource for more information, especially on a technical subject such as this. Therefore, here are a few useful links. Broadcasters may want to start at "The Antenna," a site dedicated to TV and radio station sites that are using streaming video and audio: www.theAntenna.com. You may subscribe to very active Webcasting and Internet-Broadcaster mailing lists through: www.intervox.com/Webcast.htm.

Real Networks: www.real.com

Microsoft Windows Media Player: microsoft.com/windows/windowsmedia/

Apple QuickTime: www.apple.com/quicktime

Loudeye.com (formerly Encoding.com), by far the Web's largest encoding specialist: www.loudeye.com

InterVU, "the video delivery company": www.intervu.com

A comprehensive multicasting resource page: www.ipmulticast.com

Terran Interactive's Codec Central (provides an overview of different codecs and their applications): www.codeccentral.com

DUPLICATION:
THE REALITIES OF DIGITAL MEDIA

TIM WETMORE & TERENCE KEEGAN

It may seem an anachronism in this new century to talk about duplication and distribution of physical formats while television and film companies are busy making Internet distribution deals. Yet, in the here and now, the cold, hard truth is that those engagements are more about manipulation of stock prices than the realities of distributing high quality images.

Activity in streaming and "netcasting" continues to increase as the months go by, but until broadband delivery is common in almost every home and in almost every corporate and conference facility, it remains true in the year 2000 that physical media is the best route for high quality video distribution (aside from broadcasting and cable).

Of course, it's natural for the uninformed to think that since a production was done in digital video for digital (perhaps high definition) TV then it makes sense to release the program to the world, if not on the Internet, then on one of the newer digital media. In some cases this will be true, while in others it's the worst possible move. Either way, the decision on which medium to use for duplication and, thus, for distribution, should come in the early stages of planning the production itself, not as an afterthought.

Like every other part of producing video, duplicating and distributing have many hidden traps, with repercussions reaching back through the production chain. Also, invariably, it takes longer and costs more than originally thought. Proper planning will help the duplication process move quicker and smoother and will, in the long run, save money and result in a superior product.

It's amazing how several short months can make a difference in the choice of media for duplicating and distributing a video project. Not too long ago, smart money was on various tape formats, with some small applications for CD-ROM, while DVD was seen as viable for only high budget specialty work—and video streaming was laughably out of the question. Well, now it's a brave new world, baby!

DVD has arrived and in a big way. True, the most cost effective way to distribute video to the widest audience is still tape. Since this chapter is part of a DTV book, it should be noted, that there are special considerations regarding that form of distribution. If a program is digital, but not high definition, any of the standard formats will work. DVD, unlike most tape formats, does offer a 16:9 aspect ratio. If, however, the program is high def, then the picture is, shall we say, less clear. That's because tape is the best format for distributing high definition programming; in all probability it will be at least a year or so before a so-called HD-DVD standard is hatched out to support HDTV data transfer rates.

But if the higher ups are demanding digital programs that offer interactivity or, heaven forbid, surround sound, then DVD is your ONLY choice. And, with continued mass acceptance of the format after the 1999 Christmas buying season (when DVD-Video players sold for under $200) and a subsequent installed base well beyond five million units, program producers are more likely to find that people can play back DVD programs in board rooms and conference rooms and even at home. (In non-entertainment applications, some firms are finding it cost-effective to deliver to their non-wired clients a DVD player along with finished DVD projects!)

CHOOSING A FORMAT

With all this said, let's have a quick look at the formats.

CD-ROM, which was supposed to, by now, fall to DVD-ROM's domination, has been able to hang on as a viable distribution option thanks to a lack of widespread DVD-ROM development tools; end-user incompatibilities between DVD-ROM software and the multiple decoding solutions on the market; and a lingering price issue for DVD-ROM development and replication.

The installed base of DVD-ROM drives exceeds that of DVD-Video players, and since these drives are backwards-compatible with all CD formats (including CD-R and -RW), content owners continue to utilize CD-ROM as if nothing's changed. However, once again, the "pundits" are predicting a big push for DVD-ROM software in the coming months. And indeed, while development APIs and consumer hardware compatibility issues are ironed out, both Nintendo and Sony plan to release their next-generation, DVD-ROM-based videogame console systems this year—which will spur the PC gaming industry to exceed the console offerings with DVD-ROMs of its own. This, in turn, will work wonders in advancing DVD-ROM development operations and driving down costs.

Still in all, CD-ROM will remain a safe bet for the years to come—that is, if video quality is not an issue. If you are producing a linear program for general distribution, then your medium should be videotape. If you decide to do this, then you should take the highest quality digital videotape you can get from your post facility and hurry to your local video duplicator (most of them advertise in the phone book or can be recommended by your post facility).

If, however, you insist on the optical format, there are now three types of masters you can provide to your replicator: several CD-Rs (obviously not a blank one); DVD-R (which is now available in 4.7GB form); or DLT—Digital Linear Tape. DLT is by far the most preferable format and has become the defacto standard for optical video replication; some replicators are testing mastering from write-once DVD-R discs.

Disc replication can be the source of some controversy. There have been cases where replicated audio discs or CD-ROMs have not been up to the standard expected by the title holder (in this case, you). Fingers begin pointing at this stage. Some maintain the replication wasn't done right, others insist the mastering process was improperly handled while still others will say that the many phases of encoding/decoding through the digitization process from editing to final master to DLT to downloading the information to the LBR (laser beam recorder used in optical mastering) causes glitches.

After years of argument on this (bear in mind the number of problem discs compared to the billions that have been made is minuscule) someone decided, "Hey, what about the players?" An extensive, five-year survey was done to determine where problems come into the process of released discs and in over 90 percent of the cases, the problems were deemed to be in the players rather than the process. So the process for replicating a CD-ROM won't be your problem, while schedules and your perception of what the visual quality should be, are the likely problem areas.

Every once in a while, a DVD disc will still trigger a compatibility issue with a particular DVD player/drive. Again, this is usually due to the player manufacturer interpreting the DVD specification differently than the authoring hardware/software supplier. The rule here: QC early, and QC often—the longer you wait to check, the costlier the fix will be. Authoring houses, replicators and several dedicated quality-assurance firms are equipped to perform playback tests on a bank of DVD-Video players and -ROM drives.

DTV IN THE REAL WORLD

UNDERSTANDING DIGITAL

PRE-PRODUCTION

PRODUCTION

AUDIO

GRAPHIC & COMPOSITING

POST PRODUCTION

DELIVERY & DUPLICATION

ENGINEERING & TRANSMISSION

APPENDIX

GLOSSARY

THE REPLICATION PROCESS

Briefly, here is the process for making a CD after the DLT is delivered to the replicator. Any decent post production facility should be able to provide you with a DLT for duplication, in addition to any other formats you may wish.

The process described hereafter is the same for both CD-ROM and for single layer DVD discs, with a caveat. DVD can be single layer, one side, like CD-ROM, but after that everything is different. DVDs can also be single sided, dual layer; single layer, dual sided or dual layer, dual sided. The replication process for all of these versions of the DVD format has some very significant differences from CD-ROM, though fundamentally we are talking about forming pits in a plastic substrate and coating it with a reflective layer for subsequent readout.

But more on DVD later. For now, here is the basic process. A special glass is used (it's called float glass and is the same as that used in the great, glass office towers in big cities. This crossover, in fact, is one reason why replication costs have come down, since the building boom in recent years calling for the glass has allowed its price to come down to all customers). The glass disc is chemically and physically cleaned and then polished with a rare earth compound to remove anomalies, allowing for a perfectly smooth surface on which to spin coat the photoresist.

This process occurs in an inline mastering machine that holds up to five cleaned and polished glass substrates. Each glass disc is placed on the spin coater and rotated at a predetermined speed while the photoresist is dispensed. The thickness of the photoresist is very precise and is confirmed by the machine. The coated glass then moves on to master recording.

Here's where the LBR comes in. The laser beam recorder uses as its data source the formatted DLT and records the information onto the glass master using a laser with a certain focal length. The information is recorded onto the glass master by modulating the laser to create exposed areas in the surface of the light sensitive photoresist coating. The length of these exposed areas is determined by the various "books" specifying CD-ROM formats.

The glass master is rinsed with a developing solution and the polymerized areas of the light sensitive film that have been exposed to the laser are removed by the solution. This results in digitally encoded pits in the surface of the photoresist. The developed master is placed into a sputtering machine and a thin film of conductive metal is deposited onto the surface of the master and is then ready for electroplating.

Next comes what's called Galvanics which means the glass is dipped in a plating solution with a current running through it, and after a pre-determined time the current is turned off, the glass removed. This layer is then separated from the surface of the master and the encoded layer of pits in the photoresist have now been replicated in a series of mirror image bumps. This encoded layer is called the stamper.

After further, careful preparation, the stamper is put into the molding machine where polycarbonate resin is injected into the mold cavity. The melted plastic flows over the bumps, replicating them as pits, exactly like those in the original master. The replica is then transferred to a sputtering machine where a reflective metal coating is deposited onto the encoded surface.

That's a very brief, oversimplified description of how optical formats are replicated. As mentioned before, with DVD there are numerous complications which make it very different from CD-ROM replication. It would take most of this book to fully explain these differences; more importantly from the program producer's point of view, the critical difference comes in the DVD specification, i.e. compressed MPEG-2 video and Dolby Digital six channel surround sound.

The implications for this are vast, covering everything from the post production process to the replication procedure. These factors can, and should, influence your choice of release format. What this means is that if you are very concerned about video quality, then you will need an experienced, talented compressionist working on a state-of-the-art Variable Bit Rate (VBR) compression system and then it will have to go through a Dolby Digital encoding workstation (it should be noted that stereo and MPEG-2 audio are also part of the DVD spec, although the overwhelming majority of titles released in the United States so far have been Dolby Digital six channel with stereo capability).

One important factor is allowing enough time for compression since the VBR approach means your compressionist will make anywhere from four to 15 passes of the entire video program to get it just right, and will have to take time to make artistic decisions, probably with some discussion from the director, producer or other program representatives. You can imagine how long something like that might take.

A quick explanation of VBR: let's start with the "bit budget" concept. A single layer, single sided DVD has a total capacity of 4.7 gigabytes—that's your total budget. All the data has to fit into that size "bucket," including any and all audio channels. Since some scenes can be compressed more than others without showing the ill effects of MPEG compression (called artifacts), a compressionist will allocate a larger portion of the bit budget to some scenes and less to others. Scenes with great detail, lots of action and deep color density cannot stand a lot of compression and thus are allocated a greater number of bits than are static, talking head type scenes that can be compressed with few ill effects. The compressionist will, therefore, vary the amount of bits according to the scene, thus the term Variable Bit Rate. Part of the total information to be budgeted must include the data dedicated to navigation.

Another little wrinkle here. Does the duplication plan call for European distribution? If it does, remember that PAL has a higher resolution than NTSC and will therefore use up more bits. Since the bucket is only so big, that means more compression. Is that going to be acceptable? Better think about it. Also, if you know you are going into Europe or you have a complex program, ask your replicator

OTV IN THE REAL WORLD

UNDERSTANDING DIGITAL

PRE-PRODUCTION

PRODUCTION

AUDIO

GRAPHIC & COMPOSITING

POST PRODUCTION

DELIVERY & DUPLICATION

ENGINEERING & TRANSMISSION

APPENDIX

GLOSSARY

well in advance about Dual Layer DVD with its greater capacity. The authoring process is more involved and the schedule will tend to stretch out. (DVD-18 is also now available in limited quantities—offered only—as of February 2000—by Warner Advanced Media Operations (WAMO) in Olyphant, PA.)

Now comes the fun part—the authoring. This is much more involved than with CD-ROM, and for a number of reasons. These include the multiple channels of audio, the compression and the sheer amount of data stored on a DVD when compared to videotape or CD-ROM (seven times as great). This means the branching and menu structure are much more complex than anything you've seen in any format before.

Given this information, let's go back to what we looked at in the beginning of this chapter: the complexity of the format means you are going to have to pre-plan in the production phase for your replication stages because all of this will end up taking much more time than originally allotted. It won't work to hand off a digital Betacam master or even a D-1 to a dupe house and say, "Run me 500 copies (1,000 or a million, even)." Instead of taking a couple days, it will take six weeks! No joke. The large facilities, like WAMO, recommend you allow no less than six weeks for the process.

They also recommend a D-1 master, or DLT. Some replicators might soon suggest you use DVD-R, a write-once format that recently stepped up to a 4.7GB capacity over its former 3.95GB limit.

SHORT-RUNS

Insanely cheap prices for writers and blanks over the past two years have given rise to the proliferation of CD-Recordable (CD-R) technology everywhere from home offices to content development firms of all types. Thanks to improvements in duplication speed and disc printing, a "CD-R duplication" sub-industry has blossomed, making short-run jobs (from 50 to 1,000) on CD-R a viable alternative to more expensive "pressed" discs.

Replicators will now urge that runs of under 1,000 units for any CD format be completed on a CD-R duplication unit (basically a bunch of high-speed CD writers daisy-chained to a master -ROM drive, which takes a CD-R for its master). Glass mastering, the most time-consuming and costly of replication processes, is hence eliminated.

Along the same lines, DVD-R duplication is emerging—many of the CD-R duplication systems can accommodate DVD-R drive upgrades. Relatively stiff drive and disc prices (around $5,000 and $50, respectively) will continue to block widespread DVD-R duplication, along with lingering copyright protection issues still to be implemented in DVD-R's format specification.

DVD: AUTHORING IS EVERYTHING (ALMOST)

You can't overestimate the importance of the compression/authoring process. If you've chosen (or been forced into) the DVD format, it was probably because of the menu-driven navigation system native of the format and the relatively high visual quality of the medium (better than VHS). Either this interactive capability, or the fact that DVD is a bit bucket larger than any other and "marrying into the family" of DVD technologies may be an intelligent long-range strategy. The "family" means the various iterations of the format that are on the way. We have included a little glossary of the terminology often used when people refer to DVD that hint at the breadth of this family. Advance work is already being done on higher density storage that could bring the bit count up to as much as 50 GB per side, if manufacturing methods can be made more precise and the oft-hailed blue laser technology matures quickly enough.

In the meantime, DVD is a good choice for replication and distribution, if you really need the interactive menu system and you don't want to distribute to a huge base of users (though at the end of 1999 total worldwide DVD players had passed 5,000,000 units shipped and was on an upward swing—still nothing when compared with the 800,000,000-plus VHS players worldwide). The number on DVD-ROM players is much more elusive, but generally regarded to comfortably exceed DVD-Video's numbers, thanks to major computer manufacturers' integration of DVD-ROM drives as standard issue (or a cheap option at the worst).

If you want the best compromise between video quality and wide distribution, then VHS may be the ticket and the tab for the duplication will be much smaller, though the interactivity level of VHS is limited to how often you can rewind and fast forward. And this takes us back to deciding on your replication/duplication medium during the planning stages of the production. If it's not an interactive title at all, VHS will do you fine. If interactivity is important and video quality is not, then CD-ROM may work. If you want the best of both worlds and can live with a limited audience, then DVD is your jam.

DVD Storage Terminology

Name	Size	Number of sides	Number of layers per side
DVD-5	4.7 GB	1	1
DVD-9	8.5 GB	1	2
DVD-10	9.4 GB	2	1
DVD-18	17.0 GB	2	2
DVD-R	4.7 GB (write once)	1	1
DVD-RAM	2.6 GB (rewritable)	per side	1
DVD-RAM*	4.7 GB (rewritable)	per side	1

*4.7 GB DVD-RAM is expected to ship within 2000.

9

DTV IN THE REAL WORLD

UNDERSTANDING DIGITAL

PRE-PRODUCTION

PRODUCTION

AUDIO

GRAPHIC & COMPOSITING

POST PRODUCTION

DELIVERY & DUPLICATION

ENGINEERING & TRANSMISSION

APPENDIX

GLOSSARY

ENGINEERING & TRANSMISSION 9

Digital technologies have brought about a fundamental change in the "nuts and bolts" of broadcasting and teleproduction. What used to be simple signals that could be viewed on an analog wave-form monitor or oscilloscope, have evolved into more complex representations requiring more complex and sophisticated equipment. While our broadcast signals still use carrier waves, what they carry is now completely different. And just because a signal is a "digital" signal, it does not mean that the signal is perfect.

This section takes a look at digital engineering (the importance of test and measurement), transmission of signals within and outside of the facility, and offers primers on 8-VSB (U.S.'s ATSC), COFDM (Europe's DVB-T) and QAM (digital cable).

DTV TEST, MEASUREMENT AND MONITORING
WILLIAM C. MILLER

Test, measurement and monitoring are necessary evils. Collectively, they're one of those below-the-line expenses that'll never make you any money, but ignore them and they can cost you plenty. If you've been in the television business for any length of time, you know this. You also know how hard it is to find the capital funding to add to your arsenal of test equipment, or to find the manpower to regularly check out your systems.

Where DTV is concerned, I've got bad news and good news. The bad news is that DTV is an entirely new species of television, and it's going to require lots of new equipment and techniques. The good news is that all of this stuff is digital; that means there's an opportunity to automate it to a great degree. If done properly (and that includes test equipment manufacturers providing the proper tools), you could actually save money in the long run over the total cost of monitoring an analog plant.

WHY DO WE NEED SO MUCH NEW TEST EQUIPMENT?
Because you're adding a lot more layers to your system, and each layer has to be verified differently. Also, if you've decided to transmit anything other than 480-line interlaced video, you're dealing with another set of image formats operating at much higher frequencies, on a different interface.

WHAT ARE LAYERS?

A layer is a part of the signal that helps it hook to the next level. For instance, the NTSC video signal has a couple of layers; it comes out of the imagers as RGB, but at the camera output they get encoded into NTSC. You could look at the NTSC coding as a layer whose purpose is to encode the three color components into a single signal. At the monitor, a decoder undoes the NTSC coding and presents the RGB signals to the CRT for display.

In the digital world, there are many layers. The analog RGB layer is still there, of course, but there's also a digital component layer, a compression layer, a wrapper layer, a transport layer and an interface layer. Each of these has to be examined with different tools. There are also new bits of information about the signal, called metadata, which also have to be wrapped and transported. PSIP is an example. The good thing about digital systems is that everything eventually gets converted to bits, and they all get moved around on the same transport. However, from the troubleshooting point of view, the bad part about digital systems is that everything gets converted to bits and gets moved around on the same transport. If something goes wrong, you have to know how to dig it out of the transport and look at it.

ISN'T THIS DIGITAL STUFF SUPPOSED TO BE PERFECT?

Nothing yet devised by the hand of man is perfect. When it works properly, a digital transmission system can indeed exactly reproduce at its output the information fed into its input. The key here is *when it works properly*. As those who have worked with digital systems know all too well, when digital equipment fails it fails big time. If you want to be able to locate faults quickly, you have to design in that capability.

On the other hand, the serial digital interfaces, SMPTE 259 and 292, have one overwhelming advantage over their analog counterparts: automatic level adjustment and equalization. No more DA tweaks, no more adjusting proc amps to compensate for transmission losses. Leave your tweaker at the door. That's why nobody who's converted to digital ever wants to go back. Besides, once you master how the ATSC system works, you'll be able to analyze what you're transmitting to see how many bits you can afford to allocate to other services. This is where the new business opportunities will come from. After all, in the age of digital broadcasting, bits equal bucks.

THIS IS GETTING TOO COMPLICATED

Not really. NTSC is complicated, but we've all had lots of time to get used to its quirks and peculiarities. Remember the stories about blue bananas? Sure you do. Seen one lately? Of course not. The same thing will happen with DTV. To be comfortable with the system, however, you'll have to learn a new language. That's where books like this one can help.

SO WHAT IS ALL THIS STUFF, ANYWAY?

Well, let's start by separating the system into layers, as mentioned before. Then we'll examine each layer to determine how to measure it and troubleshoot it.

We'll begin with the analog layer. All of your audio and video starts as analog. Most modern cameras do the analog-to-digital conversion somewhere internally; what comes out the back of the CCU is a serial digital signal. Nonetheless, that serial digital signal contains a digital representation of the original analog, and you can't shade the camera without being able to see it. This was recognized years ago, and many manufacturers offer digital-input waveform monitors to let you see what your video looks like.

Many of those same waveform monitors can also diagnose problems in the baseband digital transport as well. By transport here I mean the serial digital signal; if it's standard definition you're probably dealing with SMPTE 259M; if it's high definition you're using SMPTE 292M. A blatant commercial plug: You need to get your hands on the SMPTE standards. The entire set of television standards is available on a single CD-ROM; details are on the SMPTE Web site, www.smpte.org.

In standard-definition video (SMPTE 259M) there's a tool available to check the integrity of the bitstream. SMPTE RP165 defines a method of embedding cyclical redundancy check codes (CRCs) in the serial digital signal. There are two codes; one for the active picture area and another for the full field. At the receiver, these are checked against CRCs computed from the signal itself; if the two disagree, an error has crept in. RP165 also defines a method of transmitting the fact that errors have been detected; the entire system is referred to as EDH, error detection and handling. Not all equipment out there supports EDH, but it can be a very useful tool for troubleshooting SDI problems, particularly finding paths that are too long.

In the high definition serial interface, a checksum is computed for each line and is carried in the EAV packet. This makes error detection much simpler; no separate encoder is required.

As discussed elsewhere in this book, to fit a 1.5 Gbps video signal into a 6 MHz channel, we have to use bit rate reduction, or compression as it's more commonly called. The ATSC system uses MPEG-2 compression, as defined in ISO 13818-2. Analyzing MPEG encoders to see if they're performing efficiently is a job for a laboratory; I expect most users will want to look at the decoded image with their eyes. However, it's extremely useful to be able to have a set of measurements that correspond with the subjective impairments you see. A considerable amount of work has gone into making tools for such measurements; they usually involve a set of test images and an analyzer. The analyzer measures the difference between the original image and the decoded image after compression, taking into account the fact that the eye sees some impairments more readily than others. You need one of these only if you're evaluating encoders for purchase or if you're considering upgrading the compression software that runs in the encoder. An individual station probably doesn't need one; a group might consider purchasing one.

Compression is also used elsewhere in the studio. All of the popular tape formats for high definition utilize compression, as do several for standard definition. Not all use MPEG compression; in fact, most use other types, such as M-JPEG or DV. We're now starting to see ways of connecting these machines together that keep the signal in compressed form. One of the more popular of these is SDTI (SMPTE 305M). At the moment I'm not aware of any SDTI analyzers, but I suspect they'll be developed. EDH also works on SDTI, and it's extremely important here. With regular SDI signals, EDH will report errors long before they're so numerous that they affect signal quality. SDTI signals, because they're compressed, are more fragile; each bit repre-

DTV IN THE REAL WORLD

UNDERSTANDING DIGITAL

PRE-PRODUCTION

PRODUCTION

AUDIO

GRAPHIC & COMPOSITING

POST PRODUCTION

DELIVERY & DUPLICATION

ENGINEERING & TRANSMISSION

APPENDIX

GLOSSARY

sents more of the original video. If you see problems, EDH will help you determine whether the codecs are broken or whether the path is at fault.

Now let's go back to the studio output. We've compressed the video to fit into an ATSC signal and added closed captioning; now it has to go into a transport stream. This transport stream will also have to carry the compressed audio, timing signals and metadata, including things like PMTs, PIDs and other directory information, plus PSIP. You'll need a way of looking at the structure of the transport stream multiplex and verifying that it's correct or receivers won't function properly. Transport stream analyzers are available; they're extremely useful. To my mind they're mandatory. Just as you now need a way to decode your VITS, you'll need a way to verify the transport stream.

Let's talk a bit about audio. Two issues have emerged that could become real showstoppers. The first develops from the migration to a multichannel world. Remember the grief we all had when TV went stereo? Multichannel is even more complicated. How do you know that the audio signal you're putting out is correct and complete? One common error is routing the Lf and Rf signals to the audio coder, assuming that they are Lt and Rt or Lo and Ro. The result? No dialogue! The music and effects are mixed to the Lf and Rf channels, so the opening credits sound fine. However, dialogue goes in the C channel, so as soon as the first actor starts speaking you're going to have a very obvious problem. (See table 1.)

CHANNEL DESIGNATIONS			TRACK ASSIGNMENTS		
Audio Channel	Abbreviation		Track	Assignment A	Assignment B
Left	L		1	L	L
Center	C		2	R	R
Right	R		3	C	C
Left surround	LS		4	LFE	LFE
Right surround	RS		5	LS	LS
Low-frequency effects	LFE		6	RS	RS
Mono surround	MS		7	Lt or Lo	F
Mono surround at −3 dB	MS(-3dB)		8	Rt Ro	F
Left total	Lt				
Right total	Rt		*table 1.*		
Stereo left	Lo				
Stereo right	Ro		*Multichannel Audio Channel*		
Monophonic	M		*Designations and Track Assignments*		
Freely usable	F		*(from SMPTE 320M-1999)*		
Unassigned/unused	U				

I know of only one way to resolve this issue. First, you need to have the ability to monitor multichannel sound in your master control room. Second, when you check slates and levels, roll past the opening credits and into the body of the show to where you can verify that you've got dialogue. Unfortunately, there's no way to automate this one.

The second killer issue is audio/video timing. It appears that no two types of receiver have equal audio/video delay, and the magnitude of the error can be far worse than the usual couple of frames of lip-sync error we have become used to handling. How we will deal with this is an open question, but we do need a simple, standard way of testing and measuring it. At the moment there is at least one piece of test gear that can analyze lip sync in an encoded stream. There are also test bitstreams that can be used to certify a decoder. One thing you cannot do is just assume that your ATSC encoder is correctly set; you have to verify it. Both encoder and receiver manufacturers are aware of the problem, and both the ATSC Implementation Subcommittee (IS) and the SMPTE Television Systems Technology Committee (S22) are working diligently to resolve it.

Now let's talk about getting this stuff on the air. The output of the transmission multiplexer will be carried on either the 270 Mbps asynchronous serial interface (ASI) as defined in the DVB standards, or on the SMPTE 310 synchronous serial interface (SSI). ASI is the same rate as the SMPTE 259M C level, but uses a different channel coding. SSI is a 40 Mbps interface using a simple channel code. It's designed for short connections between the transmission mux and the transmitter input. It has no forward error correction built in, so STLs will have to add their own. Whichever interface your transmitter uses, you'll have to be able to monitor it.

The modulator adds several layers of forward error correction and equalizer training signals before coding the transport stream into 8-VSB. You'll need to verify that this is being done properly. You'll also want to be able to look at the 8-VSB constellation to verify that it's correct. It should be possible to do both of these with a test demodulator; manufacturers should design these functions in. The test demodulator should provide you with a transport stream at one of its outputs, which you can feed into the transport stream analyzer to verify that it's correct (or determine where it's broken). Similarly, you'll need a reference MPEG decoder for the video, a reference AC-3 decoder for the audio, and a PSIP analyzer to make sure that's getting out OK. If you're also sending data, you'll need a way to look at that as well. At the beginning, at least, it's going to be quite a pile of equipment.

IF IT'S ALL DIGITAL, CAN'T IT BE SMART?

Yes. In fact, that's where having all that software can be a real help. Now the equipment can tell you when it's in trouble. That is, it can if the manufacturer has had the foresight to design in that capability. However, self-diagnosis is only half the battle. It's not much help if your super-duper whizzo box discovers it's in trouble, but only lights a small red LED on its front panel. In addition to error detection, you need error reporting. As a recent advertising campaign states, "Knowledge isn't power. Sharing it is." There are lots of ways to share diagnostic information; let's look at a few of them.

I've already mentioned EDH. Its error detection mechanism works quite well, but its error reporting leaves a lot to be desired. EDH works by setting flags in the signal; downstream equipment can read these. However, we really need errors to be reported out to a central monitoring system. SMPTE has standardized two ways to do this.

The simple method is SMPTE 273M, the simple fault-reporting interface. 273M specifies an isolated contact closure that is open if everything's OK, closed if there's a hard fault and closed once per field in the presence of EDH errors (one closure per errored field). Because the closure is isolated, you can connect a number of devices together in parallel to create a summary alarm for a subsystem. These in turn can be connected together, until at the end you have a system which works very much the same way that telco systems have for years; you follow the red lights to the source of the problem. A smarter way to do this would be to connect all devices to a central monitoring system; you could also use the signals to control automatic failover switches where you have redundant paths. 273M is designed to be cheap to implement. It's also designed to show a fault if it loses power. It is *not* suited to reporting status from complex devices such as servers and VTRs.

For complex devices there is SMPTE 269M, the status monitoring and diagnostic protocol (SMDP). SMDP is just a protocol, not a defined language; there's a lot of room for implementation flexibility. In this it resembles IEEE-488 (GPIB), which inspired it. At least one manufacturer implements SMDP (under its own trade name) across a wide range of its products; it began doing so when it got into the systems business and saw how such a reporting system could save it time and money in installing and servicing large systems. 269M is defined using a short, point-to-point serial interface, but nothing prevents it from being carried on a LAN; in fact, it was expected that LANs would be the most common implementation of such systems.

In practice SMPTE 269M has been overtaken by technology from the data networking world. Many of the newer monitoring devices on the market now sport embedded Web servers that allow them to be monitored by any computer with a browser. You simply bookmark the appropriate URLs on a PC on your technical intranet and you have a customized monitoring system with close to zero programming effort.

However, error reporting requires a push technology; you don't want to wait until a device is polled to know that it's in trouble. My colleague, George Berger, proposes using e-mail, the original push technology, for this. Most of the devices we need to monitor either have embedded controllers or are controlled by an external processor. Most of these run under operating systems that support mail and have a mail API. All we need is for the application software to send a mail message on change of status, particularly when that change of status calls the device's continued serviceability into question. Once notified, you can get the details by using your Web browser to interrogate whatever information the monitoring or reporting devices have published.

You should be able to define where you want the mail sent. I recommend a separate mail server for your diagnostic LAN. It would route messages to the appropriate people or departments, depending on what sent the message and what the contents were (status, warning or failure messages). You could link this system to your business LAN (using a router for isolation) to make communicating with departments outside Engineering simpler. Once your diagnostic messages are in e-mail form, you can use standard IT products for paging, voice notification, etc.

The importance of this concept is that it lets you leverage existing IT technology to extend the reach of your TV-specific diagnostic systems. It also makes it fairly simple for vendors to include this capability into their products. Logging troubles becomes a snap; e-mail includes dates and times. Just archive the message file. Later, you can sort it by the from: field to find out, for instance, how many messages you got from VTR A over the last month. It's one of those "why didn't I think of it" ideas, but it can only work if manufacturers are told to include it in their equipment.

A few years ago, I wrote a paper for a SMPTE conference titled "Monitoring and Diagnostics in Digital Television Systems."[1] In it, I described SMPTE 269M and SMPTE 273M, as well as the concept of the diagnostic LAN. I suggested that the real value of these diagnostic systems was not just that they would free up operators from having to constantly scrutinize the equipment, but that they could diagnose problems well before they became apparent on air. Consider, for example, the case of a server with error-correcting RAID drives. Clearly the RAID system must be aware of the occurrence of errors in order to correct them, but is this information reported out? If so, is it reported in a manner that makes it easy for a centralized monitoring system to receive, analyze and route it?

Knowing where a problem has occurred is helpful when sweeping up after a failure. It's also helpful after the fact in determining whether something should be replaced. However, in the environment in which we work, this information is of greatest value in averting problems before they affect air. In the analog world, we do the best we can with the information we have, but air failures do occur and they cost us money, both directly in the form of make-goods and indirectly in terms of our stations' reputation. In a digital world, the opportunity exists to make our diagnostic systems proactive rather than reactive, to fix or work around failures before they affect air. That's why I say there's good news; if our suppliers give us the tools, over the long run we can save more than we spend.

REFERENCES

[1] Miller, William C., "Monitoring and Diagnostics in Digital Television Systems," *SMPTE Journal*, September 1994, page 614.

The opinions presented here are solely those of the author, and do not necessarily represent the positions of his employer or of any professional society with which he is affiliated.

TRANSMISSION: DIGITAL WITHIN THE FACILITY

SHELDON LIEBMAN

The movement of digital video and audio information in and around a facility is the sum of three different parts. If these pieces do not speak with each other correctly, the result will be a signal that either won't move from point A to point B or won't be usable once it gets there.

The first piece of the puzzle is the physical connection between the various pieces of equipment. Not only must all the equipment be in place to create a physical link, but also all of the equipment must recognize and be able to use those links. For example, you can take a standard phone cord and plug the two ends directly into two different phones. This will create a physical connection, but does not allow a conversation to take place between them.

The second piece that must be dealt with is the communications interface between the equipment. This communications layer makes sure that the devices that are linked together can actually speak to each other using a common language. The simplest example of this may be connecting an ordinary VCR output into the antenna input of a television. If the VCR is set to output on channel 3 and the TV is tuned to channel 4, the physical connection exists but the communications interface is faulty.

Once the devices are properly connected to each other and communicating, the final issue to address is the data format of the information being sent between the devices. Every user of Microsoft Windows is familiar with the problem of trying to look at a file that is incompatible with the software loaded onto their machine. If you don't have a way to decode the information you've received, it's just a bunch of bits. Using the data requires that both the sending and receiving equipment can understand and process the digital information.

Before you can decide among the various types of networks that are available, it's important to look at the connection methods and file format issues to ensure that the decision you make can actually be implemented.

LINE SPEEDS

Just as there are speed issues within a computer and across a bus, there are limitations that are introduced based on the physical methods by which you connect devices together. For example, standard copper wire can't be used for gigabit per second connections. This is one of the reasons that Plain Old Telephone Service (POTS) is incompatible with high-speed networking. To move beyond a certain level, different types of wiring must be used. For the highest performance today, fiber optic cable is used.

When multiple locations are being connected, the right size "pipe" must be purchased or rented between them to ensure that the network can operate. Beyond POTS, which tops out at about 56 kilobits per second (kbps), there are alternatives like ISDN (128 Kbps) to be considered. For very high-speed networks, there is an alphabet soup of connection descriptions.

These descriptions usually start with T1 or DS1, which is rated at 1.544 megabits per second (Mbps). This number is the equivalent of 24 voice grade connections linked together. T3 or DS3 brings this up to approximately 45 Mbps. From this point, the designation changes to OC1, which is equivalent to DS3, and goes all the way up to OC192, which offers a speed of greater than eight gigabits per second (Gbps).

The higher speeds are accomplished using a physical layer called SONET, which stands for Synchronous Optical Network. SONET is an international standard that has been adopted in the United States, Europe and Japan. As described above, it has the ability both to satisfy much of today's bandwidth requirements and to grow in the future as the need for more bandwidth arises.

Whether a network uses SONET or standard copper wire, it can only operate effectively if the wiring and equipment requirements are understood and met. This includes not only the type of cable that is used but also how far it can travel between pieces of equipment and how it must be physically connected to the network nodes. If the wrong choice is made, it can be a very expensive error to correct.

FILE FORMATS

In the early days of video compression, almost every equipment supplier utilized Motion JPEG as the method for compressing video information and storing it on a computer disk. What they didn't tell us, however, was that the information was being stored differently by every company. This created a huge headache for companies that purchased equipment from multiple sources, only to find that the video captured by device "A" could only be viewed by device "A." If device "B" was used, the result was garbage.

Similar problems exist between videotape formats. A half-inch tape containing s-video (S-VHS) information cannot be played on a standard half-inch VCR (VHS). It is also true, for the most part, that the different DV format tapes from different manufacturers cannot be played on each other's equipment (note that certain Panasonic DVCPRO machines can play Sony DVCAM and consumer DV formats, Sony DVCAM machines can play consumer DV, and Sony consumer DV decks can play Sony DVCAM).

When digital video networks are being planned, it's crucial to consider the formats that will be used between the nodes on the network. Just moving the bit stream from one place to another isn't enough. If a 30-second stream of uncompressed digital video is placed in a file, that file will be approximately one gigabyte large. Moving the file from point A to point B, depending on the network used, can happen in less than 10 seconds or may take many hours. If the file can't be opened and viewed when it gets to the other end, why bother sending it at all? As we'll see, this can be a serious issue depending on the type of network that is being used.

ATM

Asynchronous Transfer Mode (ATM) is a very high bandwidth transmission, switching and multiplexing technology. Although ATM is usually described as a networking protocol for Wide Area Networks (WANs), it can be used quite successfully in a Local Area Network (LAN) environment. One of the best advantages offered by ATM is that it can move very large streams of data very quickly.

ATM utilizes "cells" to move data from one point to another. It is designed to handle a wide variety of data types including audio, video, graphics, data and voice, all through a single pipeline. Basically, the technology takes all of these different types of data and converts them into fixed length cells that are 53 bytes long. Within the cell, five bytes contain control information and the other 48 bytes contain data. The cells are moved through very large data pipes at a high rate of speed and are then reassembled into their original form at the receiving end of the connection.

Since the information is sent in small packages, ATM offers a highly reliable way of transmitting data from one point to another. If a cell does not get through, it can easily be resent. This process does not take a lot of time due to the high speeds at which ATM networks are typically configured. Today, these networks usually run at either 155 Mbps or 622 Mbps. This higher speed translates into over 60 megabytes per second (MBps), more than enough bandwidth to handle full resolution, uncompressed video streams. In the future, speeds of up to 10 Gbps are planned.

An ATM network can be configured with dedicated channels between two points, virtually guaranteeing that a large data pipe will always be available. Alternatively, it can allocate bandwidth on demand. In this type of environment, the network will constantly monitor the usage requirements of existing connections and will not allow new users to join the network if that will deteriorate the performance needed by existing connections.

Because ATM is used heavily in the WAN environment, using an ATM network (or at least providing a bridge to an ATM network) allows a facility to easily connect to other locations around the world. On the downside, the cost of ATM equipment is still very high. In many cases, only very large installations can justify the deployment of this type of network.

DTV IN THE REAL WORLD

UNDERSTANDING DIGITAL

PRE-PRODUCTION

PRODUCTION

AUDIO

GRAPHIC & COMPOSITING

POST PRODUCTION

DELIVERY & DUPLICATION

ENGINEERING & TRANSMISSION

APPENDIX

GLOSSARY

ETHERNET

Ethernet is probably the most widely used form of networking in the world. When it comes to moving standard data files, email and general-purpose documents, nothing can beat the ease of use and low cost of a standard Ethernet connection.

The original Ethernet specification moves data at a rate of 10 Mbps, which is definitely too slow for video applications. A few years ago, Fast Ethernet was introduced. With a tenfold increase in the pipeline, Fast Ethernet supports connections at up to 100 Mbps. In a compressed video environment, this type of network can be used effectively, although the number of users accessing data at the same time must be very small.

The newest member of the Ethernet family is Gigabit Ethernet, which can theoretically process data at 10 times the rate of Fast Ethernet or 100 times faster than standard Ethernet.

The reality of this standard is that it doesn't accomplish this goal when used in a video environment. All forms of Ethernet use very small data packets and have a high overhead associated with the handshaking and interrupt requirements at both ends. Because of this, transmitting large data files such as video and audio data end up getting bogged down in the handshaking.

The result is that the speed increase as you move up the ladder is less than 10 times the previous level. Fast Ethernet usually achieves only six to seven MBps and Gigabit Ethernet appears to top out at 30 to 40 MBps. While this is still fast enough to move around a single stream of uncompressed video, it doesn't provide the kind of performance that's available from other types of networks.

Ethernet can also exist in a switched format, where hubs make direct connections between the two devices communicating. The difference between a switched network and one that uses standard hubs is a concept that confuses many people. Basically, a switch has intelligence and communicates with every device connected to it. This results in a significant performance increase, although at a much higher price. A standard hub, on the other hand, just connects all of the devices to a single pipe and lets them determine on their own how to move data between them.

In effect, a switch makes every connection a point-to-point connection so that the maximum bandwidth possible between two devices is achieved. Standard Ethernet's bandwidth is shared between all the users on the network. Switched Ethernet allows the two communicating devices to share the entire bandwidth in a direct connection through a switched hub that all equipment is connected to. This is similar to how the telephone network functions—connecting two phones through a switched network. A benefit of Switched Ethernet is that all that is required is to replace the existing standard hub with a Switched Ethernet hub—current network interface cards (NICs) do not need to be replaced.

FIBRE CHANNEL

The original goal for Fibre Channel was to create a new standard for host-to-host connectivity with very high speed and over very long distances. During its development, however, additional functionality was added to address the need for connecting high-speed storage devices directly to the network. In this respect, Fibre Channel and Serial Storage Architecture (SSA) are very similar.

Fibre Channel is unique, however, in that it is the only connection standard that can be used in a point-to-point, loop or switched environment. This flexibility gives a facility the ability to start small and grow without having to change the basic networking infrastructure.

Fibre Channel's point-to-point configuration is the easiest way to start creating a Fibre Channel network. It is also the least flexible. Compared with traditional methods of connecting storage and computers, however, it offers advantages in both speed and distance. Fibre Channel supports up to 30 meters between devices using standard cabling and can be stretched to 10 kilometers using long wavelength optical connections. The speed of the connections varies from 30 MBps up to at least 70 to 80 MBps. The newest Fibre Channel hardware promises speeds of up to 200 MBps.

As a company grows and wants to connect multiple computers and storage devices, it can move to the Fibre Channel Arbitrated Loop (FC-AL) topology. Fibre Channel Arbitrated Loop requires the installation of a hub that is connected to all the nodes. As the network grows, more or larger hubs can be added so that all of the devices are connected together in a single system.

The advantage of FC-AL is that it allows a Fibre Channel network to be configured at a lower cost than if a full blown switch-based fabric is created. The disadvantage of FC-AL, however, is that there is a limit to just how large you'll want to make the network. Since all of the devices share the network bandwidth, performance degrades after four to six devices are connected.

Fibre Channel also supports a switched configuration that represents the original intention of the standard.

In the Fibre Channel standard, a switch knows where to find every asset in the network and can control them from a single location.

To gain maximum results for minimum costs, the latest generation of Fibre Channel switches now contain a "Fabric to Loop" feature, or FL. This means that you can take a hub and plug it into a switch. The entire group of devices on the hub then appears as a single device on the switch. While this does not provide the full benefits of a switched environment, it does increase the flexibility of growing a Fibre Channel network while reducing the cost.

IEEE 1394 (FIREWIRE)

Since 1987, the search has been on to find a replacement for SCSI (see below) and to bring peripheral connectivity to a new level. One of the contenders for this title is the IEEE 1394 standard (also known by the Apple trademark "FireWire"). This interface first appeared on commercial products in 1996 and continues to make inroads in video applications.

Although it was not exclusively designed for video, 1394 is seeing its largest application in this area. This is being driven by the inclusion of a 1394 connector on a number of digital camcorders and nonlinear editors. The decision to use 1394 was influenced by the number of advantages it offers.

First of all, the connectors used in 1394 are based on those used in video games. This makes them very inexpensive to produce and also ensures that they can put up with a lot of abuse. The cable used to connect devices is also thin and easy to manipulate.

The 1394 specification supports up to 63 devices on a single bus. Perhaps more importantly, it allows buses to be bridged together so the theoretical maximum is thousands of devices. It also uses no terminators and supports hot plug-in and dynamic configuration. When you add 64-bit addressing with automatic address selection, it's clear that 1394 has truly been designed to be a plug-and-play interface.

1394 also works well with video streams. Standard computer data is sent in small packets of information with lots of handshaking from both sides. 1394 supports large packets of information that don't need the constant handshaking of more volatile types of data. As a result, the interface can handle at least 10 MBps of continuous data (not just burst). Improvements to the design promise continuous throughput reaching over 100 MBps or more.

Since fully uncompressed video requires throughput of approximately 30 MBps, 1394 is not yet ready to play in this area. However, very high quality results can still be achieved with a compression rate of 4:1, which brings the throughput requirement down under eight MBps. The current generation of 1394 can easily handle this load.

Because 1394 is a digital serial bus, multiple devices can access the data on the bus without affecting the quality received by any of the other devices. This means that there is no loss of data or quality when multiple devices process the video information. For example, a digital video camera can send data to a digital monitor and to a computer at the same time—with no loss between devices, no termination problems and no need for a distribution amplifier.

The one big negative with 1394 is that it was not developed to function as a full-fledged network. The protocol does not include functions that are necessary to handle the demanding requirements of accessing and sharing information between more than one user. However, it can be very beneficial as an entry point or exit point for digital video information that is moved around within a facility. As the speed of the interface increases, the format of the video data can move from compressed to uncompressed and from standard resolution up to high definition formats.

HIPPI

The High Performance Parallel Interface (HIPPI) was originally developed as a way for supercomputers to communicate with each other at very high speeds. It was also one of the first standards designed to allow direct connection of storage devices. HIPPI operates at 800 Mbps, which provides enough bandwidth for multiple streams of uncompressed video to move around simultaneously. For this reason, at least one very high-end graphics and special effects supplier has been touting this network architecture to its customers.

The two biggest drawbacks to HIPPI are its cost and wiring requirements. Since the original form of HIPPI is a parallel technology, it requires a very large connector and thick, bulky wiring that contains 50 pairs of wires and which can be run up to 50 meters between network nodes.

A newer alternative is called Serial HIPPI. Serial HIPPI runs at 1.6 Gbps speed and supports distances between nodes of up to 10 kilometers if fiber connections are used. An even newer version of HIPPI is being planned called HIPPI 6400. This proposed standard is designed to support 6.4 Gbps (over 600 MBps) connections between devices.

HIPPI is also much more costly to install than many of the alternatives. Since HIPPI has never achieved the large installation volumes of other solutions, the switches, routers and interface cards are typically priced at least two to three times higher than other gigabit alternatives.

For installations that have already installed HIPPI networks, the benefits to this technology are obvious. To extend their reach and to expand their systems, however, it is probably a better idea to link the existing HIPPI network to another standard using a switch that handles both.

SCSI

The Small Computer System Interface (SCSI) is the standard by which direct connection of peripherals to personal computers is measured. Over the years, this standard has been expanded and tweaked in an attempt to stay current with advances in other types of computer technology.

The original SCSI specification is an 8-bit wide bus that supports up to eight devices including the host adapter. The maximum bandwidth available is five MBps and only two devices can exchange data at one time. The first improvement, Wide SCSI, increased the bus to 16-bits, effectively doubling the transfer rate to 10 MBps.

Next came Fast SCSI, which doubled the throughput for both 8-bit and 16-bit devices to a maximum of 20 MBps. Another doubling of the bus clock was introduced with UltraSCSI, bringing the maximum bandwidth to 40 MBps. In addition, UltraSCSI increased the number of devices that could be connected to a maximum of 15.

The evolution of SCSI is not over. Further developments have been announced (and are starting to appear) that raise the transfer rate to 80 MBps and even to 160 MBps. At these speeds, the movement of data across SCSI rivals the speed of other storage connection alternatives, but the limit on the number of devices is still a serious drawback.

SCSI is also defined primarily as a method for connecting storage and other peripheral devices, rather than connecting multiple computers. At least one company currently markets a networking solution based on SCSI technology, but there are limitations that make it unattractive to many users.

SDI/SDTI

The Serial Digital Interface (SDI) is the video world's answer to the transmission of digital video (with embedded audio). As defined in SMPTE specification 259M, SDI provides a method for transmitting uncompressed digital video, audio and other data between video devices that can be separated by as much as 300 meters.

In order for digital video to be transmitted inside a facility, all of the equipment that is used must be able to recognize and use the digital video format. In the video world, the central device to this process is a router, which corresponds to the hub or switch used in a standard computer style network.

The original CCIR-601 specification on which SDI is based was an 8-bit signal. This has since been upgraded to include a 10-bit version and includes both composite and component formats. Other more proprietary enhancements to SDI communications have been implemented as well, creating something of a problem.

Sony introduced SDDI (Serial Digital Data Interface). The enhancement specified a method by which data streams could be seamlessly transmitted along with video data. Panasonic countered with CSDI (Compressed Serial Digital Interface), which provides a method for sending compressed data across a serial digital connection. Because they incorporated proprietary components, equipment that was compatible with one of these formats could not be used with another.

In an effort to bridge the gap and provide a common solution for all video professionals, there is now another standard. The new format, called SDTI (Serial Digital Transport Interface), is an open standard so that all manufacturers can make equipment that is compatible with it. The goal is to allow all of the existing forms of SDI (including CSDI and SDDI) to be bridged across a single environment with support for video, audio, data and compression.

The advantage to using digital video is obvious—there is no generation loss as the streams are processed. When multiple layers of video are used or required, the ability to stay in a digital format allows more complex imagery to be used.

Today, the number of all-digital facilities is very small due to the high cost of the equipment and the incompatibility between the formats. This cost is driven higher by the need to support multiple pieces of equipment to deal with the multiple, incompatible versions of SDI. If an open standard can be agreed upon, it will be easier for all video professionals to shift to this format.

SSA

Serial Storage Architecture (SSA) was originally developed as a high-speed storage interface. During its development, the definition expanded to include high speed networking capabilities. Today, SSA is primarily sold as SSA-80, which supports a total communications bandwidth between devices of 80 MBps. The next generation of SSA, which is SSA-160, has been designed to double that bandwidth and should be commercialized during 1998.

SSA was designed to bring important pieces of mainframe technology to storage and networking connections, including no single point of failure, data protection and host connectivity. Since it was expected to be connected with storage subsystems in most instances, the cost of the interface was also very important. As a result, SSA is a single chip, CMOS integrated solution that is very inexpensive to implement.

The power of the SSA interface provides enough bandwidth to move around multiple video streams with or without compression. The SSA-80 interface runs at 200 MHz, with 20 MBps of read and write to any device from two directions. Every node has two ports, every port handles 20 MBps in and out simultaneously, so there is a total of 80 MBps for every device. SSA-160 calls for twice as much speed, up to 40 MBps in and out for a total of 160 MBps for every device.

With up to 128 devices on a loop, there is room for multiple machines and multiple storage devices to be connected at the same time. SSA also offers enough distance between devices to allow an entire facility to exist on a single loop. The con-

DTV IN THE REAL WORLD

UNDERSTANDING DIGITAL

PRE-PRODUCTION

PRODUCTION

AUDIO

GRAPHICS & COMPOSITING

POST PRODUCTION

DELIVERY & DUPLICATION

ENGINEERING & TRANSMISSION

APPENDIX

GLOSSARY

nections can use four-wire (two-pair) twisted pair cables and there can be up to 20 meters between each point-to-point link with pricing comparable to SCSI. If this distance is too small, fiber optic connections can be used to increase the distance to almost a kilometer per node without performance loss.

Because SSA was designed with mainframe technology in mind, it is highly reliable. An SSA loop has no single point of failure and supports auto-configuration and hot swapping of components. This is especially important if SSA is used to create video subsystems. Finally SSA is a simple and cost effective solution compared to some other alternatives.

USB

After a number of years of promises-and-false starts, the Universal Serial Bus (USB) is finally a reality. This is a plug and play interface that allows up to 127 peripherals to be connected to a single computer using only one port address and a single interrupt. The downside, at least in the initial version of this specification, is the speed. The USB supports a maximum bandwidth of only 12 Mbps (1+MBps), which makes it the slowest interface in this list.

Of course, USB wasn't designed to be a full-fledged network. Rather, it was designed to allow a large number of devices to plug into a PC with a single interface. These devices can include video cameras, but it is more likely they would include multiple VTRs. If USB ports start to show up on these and other video devices, machine control for an entire facility might be handled using a single computer.

CONCLUSION

There are a large number of ways that digital video can be captured, compressed, processed and transmitted within a facility today, and more are coming in the near future. To get started, it's important to be sure that the bandwidth required can be met by the network that's desired. As more equipment is added, most of these networks can be expanded. Whichever method is used, the results will be high quality video that doesn't get lost from one generation to the next.

INTRA-FACILITY AND INTER-FACILITY TRANSMISSION: COPPER VERSUS FIBER

GEORGE MAIER

The movement of digital video from point-to-point, or from point-to-multipoint, falls in one of two areas: transport within a facility or transport between facilities. The fundamental technologies are similar in either case, but the methods, protocols and hardware needs vary considerably depending on the task.

INTRA-FACILITY CABLE

The advent of SMPTE 259M (ITU-R 601) as a dominant digital serial digital standard at 270 Mbps, has forced facility owners to take a second look at their infrastructure—as it exists now and as it will exist five years from now. The coming of

HDTV has forced an even closer examination of facilities and will have a lasting affect on the infrastructure planning process.

Coaxial cables are still the practical solution for many digital applications, but their limitations are becoming apparent. Table 1 is a summary of five types of cables rated for digital video transmission rates. This data was supplied by Belden, however similar products may be supplied by Com/Scope and others. The pricing shown is suggested retail and may vary at the distributor level.

It can be seen that the best case is 151 meters at 1.5 Gbps with the largest available cable. Newer coaxial designs provide respectable reach at 1.5 Gbps and will work well in a large majority of facilities, but distance limitations at the HDTV end of the performance curve suggests that coaxial cables can no longer support all of the video needs in a facility.

For transmission distances beyond 100 meters (328 feet) only the larger RG-11/U type will meet the requirement. Some facility planners will avoid going to the absolute distance limit of a cable and will build in a 10 to 15 percent safety margin. (*Editors' note: Some cable manufacturers already put a 10 percent safety margin on their recommended distances—see* Better Cables, Better Distances *following this section.*) The safety margin is necessary to allow for cable aging, connector losses, physical compression and excessive bending. Once a digital signal drops out, it's gone and there's no way to recover it. The solution for long cable runs is the addition of reclocking distribution amplifiers with auto equalization at the far end of the cable. Such devices allow extending the range of cable beyond the specified limits of the cable itself. The equalization range of chips used in SDTV and HDTV distribution amplifiers is constantly being improved and we can expect to see these limits increase over time.

In rebuilding facilities to support digital video, many took comfort in the fact that they could use much of the existing copper cable plant in conjunction with SDI capture, switching, edit and playback operations. Many facilities have been upgraded to a 270/360 Mbps infrastructure, but stopped there. One of the major reasons was the promise of mezzanine compression, which has not become a practical reality, as mezzanine compression systems are expensive. Currently, the lowest cost MPEG-2 encoder and decoder combinations are priced between $20,000 and $30,000, which is actually more expensive than a small HDTV router and the compression system would add frame delays at each pass. In addition, most router manufacturers have engineered their HDTV routers to operate from the same control systems that their SDI routers respond to.

A hidden issue in older facilities with 8281 style cabling is that their original connectors were not optimized for 75 ohms and are producing significant reflections and VSWR anomalies at high bit rates, which seriously limit their digital range. Many broadcast and production folks are finding they must overbuild their plants once again to support video data rates above the 270/360 Mbps levels.

Cable Type	Basic Type	Max Dist 270 Mbps	Max Dist 360 Mbps	Max Dist 1.5 Gbps	Price/ 1000'	Cable Diameter	Weight /1000'
1505A	RG-59/U	305 M	265 M	83 M	$225	0.235"	29 lbs
1694A	RG-6/U	366 M	320 M	102 M	$292	0.275"	40 lbs
1855A	Mini-59	201 M	174 M	59 M	$190	0.159"	18 lbs
7731A	RG-11/U	560 M	484 M	151 M	$520	0.405"	100 lbs
8281	RG-59/U	274 M	236 M	73 M	$415	0.305"	68 lbs

table 1. Coaxial cable characteristics.

INTRA-FACILITY FIBER

Fiber optics have proven especially important in the area of field production, sports, news and entertainment events, because fiber systems can provide far greater reach and fiber cables are light and easy to work with. Side benefits include EMI and noise immunity, ground loop elimination and the most obvious, unlimited bandwidth.

The need for low cost fiber components to support DTV/HDTV within the facility has been answered by a growing number of manufacturers. Familiar names like Axon, CSI Math, Force, Leitch, NVISION, Telecast Fiber Systems and others have introduced digital products that are optimized for in-building or campus video transmission.

There are two general categories of optical fiber: multimode and single mode. While both fibers are 125 micrometers (or "microns") in diameter and identical in their outer appearance, upon examination one finds that the inner light-carrying "core" glass layer of the single mode is much smaller than the multimode fiber's core. This 9 micron single mode core, compared to 50 micron or 62.5 micron multimode core, is partially responsible for its virtually unlimited bandwidth. Single mode is the fiber type that is routinely installed outside the plant in telephone and cable TV companies and it is the fiber that is required for high data rates, such as uncompressed 1.5 Gbps HDTV, over long distances.

Multimode fiber is more commonly used for limited distance runs, say up to five or 10 kilometers, of analog video and audio, or just a couple of kilometers for SDTV at 270 Mbps. This is because the multimode fiber permits several modes of light to travel through the core at the same time. While the multimode fiber can send more optical power, it suffers greater dispersion of the high frequency modulated pulses, such as the optical representation of the bits of digital video and the resultant output pulses can become smeared together, resulting in an indistinguishable signal. This problem becomes more pronounced as data rates increase and as distances become greater.

Single mode fiber cable is approximately the same price as multimode cable, but transceiver electronics tend to be more expensive, since single mode systems are generally laser based, where multimode systems may be LED based. In addition, more care in handling and use is required, since single mode cables are more sensitive to attenuation losses due to improper bending and dirt on connector faces.

Fiber cable construction varies depending on the job at hand. Because fiber strands are so small, they are usually bundled with anywhere from four to over one hundred fibers in the same sheath. Within a facility, standard, flame retardant, PVC jacketed cables are normally used, while Teflon jacketed, plenum rated (high temperature) cables are optional. For outdoor use in campus or metro area applications, gel filled loose tube fiber is recommended. In mobile production applications, an extremely rugged "tactical" fiber is usually the choice. As the name implies, tactical fiber was developed for military applications, but lends itself well to the pounding that field production cables are subjected to.

For certain applications, SMPTE is supporting hybrid cables, which include both fiber and copper strands. Table 2 provides a few reference points for six and eight fiber bundles of single mode in various jacketing schemes. Single mode fiber was chosen over multi-mode due to the bandwidth limitations as explained earlier. This data was gathered from Mohawk Cable, but similar cables are available from Com/Scope and others.

DTV IN THE REAL WORLD

UNDERSTANDING DIGITAL

PRE-PRODUCTION

PRODUCTION

AUDIO

GRAPHIC & COMPOSITING

POST PRODUCTION

DELIVERY & DUPLICATION

ENGINEERING & TRANSMISSION

APPENDIX

GLOSSARY

Single Mode Fiber Type	Price/ 1000'	Cable Diameter	Weight/ 1000'
6 Fiber - PVC Jacketed	S310	0.190"	18 lbs
8 Fiber - PVC Jacketed	S400	0.212"	21 lbs
6 Fiber - Plenum Rated	S340	0.190"	18 lbs
8 Fiber - Plenum Rated	S430	0.212"	21 lbs
6 Fiber - Tactical	S638	0.255"	25 lbs
8 Fiber - Tactical	S750	0.276"	30 lbs
6 Fiber - Loose Tube	S390	0.375"	83 lbs
8 Fiber - Loose Tube	S450	0.375"	83 lbs
Hybrid 2 Fibers + 4x20 Ga + 2x24 Ga	S1350	0.362"	84 lbs

table 2. Comparison of fiber optic cables.

As the chart suggests, fiber is significantly less expensive, lighter and smaller than virtually any coaxial cables available for digital video, but that is only half of the story. To be useful, electrical to optical and optical to electrical conversion is required and is where the majority of expense lies. The issue for many is how the total expense compares with copper.

As discussed previously, optical hardware is now available from a number of manufacturers that can allow you to rack-mount optical interfaces for serial digital transport within a facility. The nature of rapid component developments for fiber optic systems is such that a myriad of low-cost products is now possible that were not previously.

Figure 1 is a composite of typical fiber and copper applications in an SDTV/HDTV digital facility. In a typical facility, some of the connections will be made by coaxial cable alone, while longer runs need line amplifiers with automatic equalization and reclocking, while others will be fiber optic. Figure 2 shows the relative range of 1694A coaxial cable versus fiber optic cables. We chose an RG-59/U style cable, like 1694A as the most popular of the newer designs from both a cost and size standpoint. Of course one could choose to implement an RG-11/U size cable, such as 7731A, but the 0.405 inch diameter would fill a conduit rather quickly.

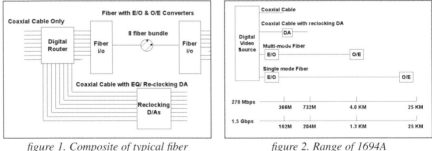

figure 1. Composite of typical fiber and copper applications.

figure 2. Range of 1694A coax vs. fiber optical cable.

Figure 3 is a basic view of fiber in the field. Systems like the one outlined in the diagram have been deployed in both 270 Mbps and 1.5 Gbps configurations. Field units like the Viper, offered by Telecast Fiber Systems, include such amenities as intercom and data circuits as well as the capability of being used for any bit rate in the SMPTE 259M and SMPTE 292M recommendations.

Although private fiber is still fairly rare, a growing number of television stations and post production facilities are finding dark (unused) fiber that they can utilize.

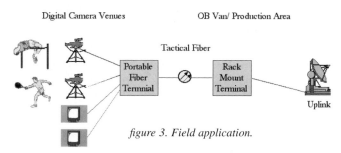

figure 3. Field application.

Figure 4 is representative of several different approaches to fiber optic ATSC STL systems now in operation. In one case, the network downlink is located at the transmitter; about 25 percent of all network affiliates are in a similar situation. If the link from the studio should totally fail, the output of the network decoder could be routed locally to the ATSC encoder, which feeds the DTV transmitter.

figure 4.
Fiber optic STL
applications.

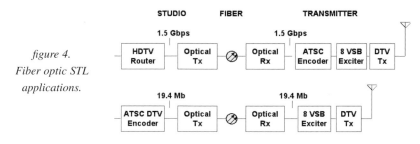

In the second case, the reverse is true and the ATSC data stream is generated at the studio, but still needs a path to the transmitter. Again fiber optic transmission systems can be of use, particularly in light of overcrowding in the broadcast auxiliary microwave bands and the constant threat of encroachment by non-broadcast interests.

COPPER OR FIBER?

There is a constant debate over this issue and the answer is not as clear as it once was. In a situation where a digital facility manager must cover distances that are well within the range of coaxial cables, as defined earlier, the issue is simple. Straight copper coax cable is an easy winner. Once the need for equalizers and reclocking has been established, the choice becomes much more difficult. To provide some guidance, we

figure 5. Cable vs. fiber
comparison at 1.5 Gbps.

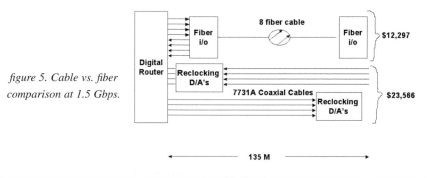

looked at a hypothetical, but realistic different situation and drew a comparison.

In a situation where four bi-directional 270 Mbps contribution circuits are to be run 200 meters (656 feet), all that is required is a good quality cable, like 1694A. At some point, these same eight circuits must carry 1.5 Gbps so a shelf of reclocking distribution amplifiers is needed at each end. The total cost breaks down as follows:

8 x 200M (656') cables	=	$ 1,532
BNC Connectors	=	$ 71
Distribution/Reclocking	=	$21,963
Total		$23,566

If the same project were done using fiber optics, the cost would be as follows:

200M of 8 fiber cable	=	$ 262
SC Connectors	=	$ 205
Fiber optic Tx's & Rx's	=	$11,830
Total		$12,297

These numbers were arrived at using Belden 1694A cable, Amphenol 75 ohm BNC connectors and Tektronix M9602HD reclocking distribution amplifiers in a MAX-900 shelf for the coaxial cable analysis. The fiber optic analysis used Mohawk 8 fiber PVC cable, AMP duplex SC connectors and the Telecast Python multiple fiber I/O. Interestingly, there is a major difference in price for even this modest scenario. The final decision is left to the user, but the cost of fiber can no longer be an objection in studio infrastructure.

INTER-FACILITY

The only feasible way to move digital video between facilities is to use either microwave radio or fiber optic systems, and both offer very specific advantages and disadvantages.

Microwave: For many years, microwave has been the best choice for studio to transmitter links and for news gathering, but has fallen out of favor for long haul intercity networks due to the availability of fiber and satellites. As the nation and the world move to digital, microwave will continue to provide a large percentage of the all-important final links to the transmitter and may find new uses as extensions of digital fiber networks.

Familiar names like Microwave Radio Communications, Nucomm and RF Technology, have been joined by Alcatel, Itelco and Moseley, with new digital products. A number of products appear to be emerging to support any one of several situations that a broadcaster might be in.

Baseband Modulators And Demodulators: If you have an existing FM microwave system and would like to use it to carry an ATSC video stream, these devices will allow it by generating a 4FSK signal that is friendly to a directly modulated FM baseband radio. The advantages are simplicity and not having to buy a new radio. The disadvantages are some loss of fade margin and having to dedicate a radio for this purpose.

Digital IF Modulators And Demodulators: In some cases, existing 70 MHz analog FMT and FMR shelves may be replaced by new digital modulators and demodulators. The linearity of the existing radio will play a major role in determining whether it can still be used, needs upgrading or must be replaced by a completely new digital radio. Most companies have been selling "digital ready" radios for some time now and those will require only minor adjustments.

Digital Radios: Digital radios are essentially new, IF or directly modulated digital transmission systems specifically designed for the job at hand. The key factor, as mentioned above, is linearity in the microwave and IF amplifier stages, plus error correction and automatic countermeasures against multipath.

The digital modems that are being offered for video applications can be configured to run in QPSK or QAM modes, depending on the spectral efficiency requirement, as dictated by the data speed and channel width. At 7 GHz for example, QPSK modulation would be a good choice for 45 Mbps transmission. With a spectral efficiency of 1.66 bits/Hz, QPSK provides a robust transmission medium within the allotted 25 MHz channels. At 2 GHz, where the channels are 17 MHz wide and may soon be 12 MHz, a higher form of modulation, like 16-QAM, will be required to pass the same 45 Mbps signal.

Thanks to years of development for the utility and cellular markets, sophisticated digital radios are readily available with spectral efficiency high enough to allow transmission of 19.4 Mbps in a 5 or 7 MHz wide RF channel and transmission of 45 Mbps in a 10 or 12 MHz RF channel. Although new to the broadcast world, similar technology has been used in common carrier microwave systems for nearly two decades.

Dual Video: With reference to figure 6, several of the companies mentioned earlier are offering a 45 Mbps microwave radio, that will simultaneously transport the ATSC data stream at 19.4 Mbps and an NTSC signal that has been digitized and compressed using MPEG-2 encoding equipment. The major advantage in using this type of approach is that both ATSC data and the NTSC video may be transported in a single RF channel; a must in areas where additional microwave frequencies are not available in 7 or 13 GHz and the STL path is too long for an 18 or 23 GHz radio.

Figure 7 shows an alternate approach to spectrum congestion by Alcatel, which includes adding a new digital radio for ATSC next to the old analog radio in the same band and possibly in the same channel, by using a dual polarized antenna system and added filtering.

Another new variation, shown in figure 8 is called the Twin Stream by Microwave Radio Communications, which combines both digital and analog ele-

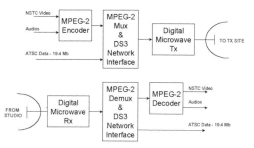

figure 6. Dual video 45 mbps digital radio.

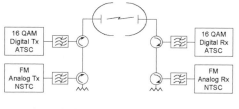

figure 7. dual radios in the same brand.

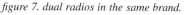

ments in the same radio. It allows a non-compressed NTSC carrier to be combined with a 16-QAM modulated ATSC carrier in the same channel and on the same polarization. The advantage is in not having to use MPEG-2 compression NTSC video.

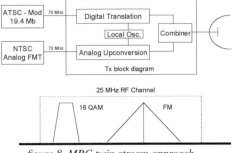

figure 8. MRC twin stream approach.

Fiber Optics: With few exceptions, the broadcaster rarely owns inter-facility fiber. In metro areas, a large percentage of new video circuits are being supplied by local exchange carriers, metro area carriers and increasingly cable television companies. Because the local phone company is a regulated carrier, new types of services are slow to materialize. Their unregulated counterparts are quicker to look at new digital opportunities and may decide to push ahead with services if the economics are sound. A substantial number of telco-and CATV-based SDI networks are now providing compressed and non-compressed point-to-point and switched SDI service in most major metro areas.

Companies like ADC, Artel Video Systems, Video Products Group and others have been very active with regulated and non-regulated carriers in providing uncompressed 270 Mbps equipment for broadcast and post production local loop networks. Compression equipment to support 270 Mbps SDI has been supplied by ADC, Alcatel, Barco/RE, Nortel, Synctrix and others. At this point, none of the carriers are discussing 19.4 Mbps ATSC or 1.5 Gbps HDTV transmission at native rates, despite the fact that fiber equipment is readily available for either.

Should you find that leased services are the only option, it is vitally important to negotiate a deal based on video service, not on a data rate. Even though most compressed digital circuits are carried via DS-3 facilities, do not approach a carrier and ask for a DS-3, or you'll pay the DS-3 rate, which is considerably higher than a video tariff that uses DS-3 as its transmission medium. Discuss the nature of the requirement in video terms first. For uncompressed 270 Mbps SDI circuits, tariffs similar to the old analog TV-1 services are now available in major metro areas.

BETTER CABLES, BETTER DISTANCE FOR HDTV

STEVE LAMPEN

Uncompressed, high definition video signals run at a data rate of 1.485 Gbps and a bandwidth of 750 MHz. It is no surprise, therefore, that cables designed to operate at 4.2 MHz for analog video have a much harder time at 750 MHz. These high frequencies require greater precision and lower loss than analog. Where effective cable distances were thousands of feet for analog, the distance limitations are greatly reduced for HD.

When SMPTE first addressed this problem, they looked at the bit error rate at the output of various cables. Their purpose was to identify the "digital cliff", the point where the signal on a cable goes from "zero" bit errors to unacceptable bit errors. This can occur in as little as 50 feet.

The SMPTE 292M committee cut cables until they established the location of this cliff, *cut that distance in half*, and measured the level on the cable. From there they came up with the standard: where the signal level has fallen 20 dB, that is as far as your cable can go for HD video. It should be apparent, therefore, that these cables can go up to twice as far as their 'recommended' distance, especially if your receiving device is good at resolving bit errors. Of course, you could look at bit errors yourself, and that would determine whether a particular cable, or series of cables, would work or not.

There is one other way to test HD cable and that is by measuring return loss. Return loss shows a number of cable faults with a single measurement, such as flaws in the design, flaws in the manufacturing, or even errors or mishandling during installation of a cable. Ultimately, return loss shows the variations in impedance in a cable, which lead to signal reflection, which is the "return" in return loss.

A return loss graph can show things as varied as the wrong impedance plugs attached to the cable, or wrong jacks or plugs in a patch panel. It can also reveal abuse during installation, such as stepping on a cable or bending a cable too tightly, or exceeding the pull strength of the cable. Return loss can even reveal manufacturing errors.

Broadcasters are familiar with VSWR—Voltage Standing Wave Ratio, which is a cousin to return loss. For instance, SMPTE recommends a return loss of 15 dB up to the third harmonic of 750 MHz (2.25 GHz), this is equivalent to a VSWR of 1.43:1. If you know VSWR, you will recognize this as a very large amount of return. Others have suggested that 15 dB return loss is insufficient to show many circuit flaws.

It is suggested that a two-band approach be taken, since return loss becomes progressively more difficult as frequencies increase. In the band of 5 to 850 MHz, a minimum of 23 dB would be acceptable (equivalent to a VSWR of 1.15:1) and from 850 to 2.25 GHz a minimum 21 dB (equivalent to a VSWR of 1.2:1). Some manufacturers are sweeping cables and showing 21 dB return loss out to 3 GHz, which is even better.

So what cables should you use and what cables should you avoid? Certainly, the standard video RG-59 cables, with solid insulations and single braid shields lack a number of requirements. First their center conductors are often tin-plated to help prevent oxidation and corrosion. While admirable at analog video frequencies, these features can cause severe loss at HD frequencies. Above 50 MHz, the majority of the signal runs along the surface of the conductor, called "skin effect". What you need is a bare copper conductor, since any tinned wire will have that tin right where the high-frequency signal wants to flow. And tin is a poor conductor compared to copper.

Around the conductor is the insulation, called the "dielectric." The performance of the dielectric is indicated by the "velocity of propagation," as listed in manufacturer's catalogs. Older cables use solid polyethylene, with a velocity of propagation of 66 percent. This can easily be surpassed by newer gas-injected foam polyethylene, with velocities in the +80 percent range. The high velocity provides lower high-frequency attenuation.

However, foam is inherently softer than a solid dielectric, so foam dielectrics will allow the center conductors to "migrate" when the cable is bent, or otherwise deformed. This can lead to greater impedance variations, with a resultant increase in return loss. Therefore, it is essential that these foam cables have high-density hard-cell foam. The best of these cables exhibit about double the variation of solid cables (±3Ω foamed versus ±1-1/2Ω solid), but with much better high frequency response.

This is truly cutting-edge technology for cables, and can be easily determined by stripping the jacked and removing the braid and foil from short samples of cables that you are considering. Just squeeze the dielectric of each sample. The high-density hard cell one should be immediately apparent.

Over the dielectric is the shield. Where a single braid was sufficient coverage for analog video, it is not for HD. Older double braid cables have improved shielding, but the ideal is a combination of foil and braid. Foil is superior at high frequencies, since it offers 100 percent coverage at "skin effect" frequencies. Braid is superior at lower frequencies, so a combination is ideal. Braid coverage should be as high as possible. Maximum braid coverage is around 95 percent for a single braid.

The jacket has little effect on the performance of a cable, but a choice of color, and consistency and appearance, will be of concern. There are no standards for color codes (other than red/green/blue indicating RGB-analog video), so you can have any color indicate whatever you want.

DIGITAL TELEVISION BROADCASTING

RON MERRELL

Major equipment manufacturers laboring to deliver educational seminars and short courses on the industry's transition to DTV openly admit that answers which worked just a year ago have been revised many times by now, with even more revisions coming.

While it's tempting to jump into the RF plant and start thinking about what brand of new transmitter will surface as your best choice, it's a good idea to back off and start at a much more elementary point in the chain of RF plant: the tower.

THE TOWER

It's not nearly as exciting, because once you have one, you have it for so many years everyone forgets just how long it's been there. In fact, some stations have towers that are icons of their city's skyline, such as KCMO in Kansas City, MO. Lights strung up each leg to the top of the tower let you know you're in Kansas City.

The reason we suggest starting with the tower is that many of them have been around so long that they've outlived their chief engineers many times over.

With towers that old, who's still around to point out the old gal is already overloaded with antennas for other services? Overloading can mean two things: weight and windloading. Except in very rare cases where a tower was first supporting a minimal antenna and has long since been converted to a very high gain version, basic tower/transmission line/antenna weight is seldom an overlooked problem. All station engineers fear the day when freezing rain collects on the tower, antenna(s), transmission line(s) and perhaps on the guys. For a short period of time, there can be an incredible weight overload, especially if the tower lives in a climate where freezing rains are rare. In that case, it probably wasn't a consideration in the original design. What station engineers should be concerned about in the transition to

DTV has more to do with what additional services added to the tower will mean, and a little less to do with mother nature playing nasty tricks. What does catch the eye of tower manufacturers and consultants is how much is on the tower. They'll expect to see the transmission line, the antenna and obstruction lights, but antennas for other services will get their attention. The problem is windloading.

Wind pushes against the tower and anything on the tower that the wind hits. In general, towers are rated for the wind speed they can handle. Look at the specs and you'll see it expressed other ways, but that's what it means. So, after various chiefs and administrations over the years have leased space on their towers for additional income or new services of their own, it's possible that many towers are seriously endangered by the extra windloading, or the extra force that will be exerted against the structure as a whole.

Should any of these over-windloaded towers also be subjected to freezing rain, the problem is exaggerated because the ice adds extra surface area that, in turn, helps multiply the windloading on the whole structure and everything tied to it.

The fact is, there are stations on the air today that are so far removed from their original specs that no one on staff knows for sure how much leeway their tower has for making it through the next storm season, let alone how it would fare when a second antenna and transmission line is run up its legs.

The first step in the transition process is to bring in experts who understand how to assess the health of your tower and its ability to carry any added load. Their assessment could drastically alter your plans.

If the inspection reveals an overloaded tower, don't throw in the towel. There are options, as you'll see in the next section of this chapter.

TOWER SURVEY

In some cases, tower consultants such as ITI and companies like Dielectric, Landmark, LeBLANC and Micro Communications can suggest ways to strengthen their tower, or how many service antennas and their feed lines need to come down. Landmark is known for its tall towers and towers that require lots of ingenuity to construct. Still, the company is well-known for its tower strengthening strategies. According to the company, most towers can be saved.

What could be overlooked is checking into the proposed changes with an eye toward how a new antenna will react with the old one(s). The first stop in the transition to DTV belongs here, because if the antenna won't stay in the air, you're worse off than finding yourself at the end of the transmitter waiting line.

Over the past four years, attention has been focused on whether or not the transmitter manufacturers can produce transmitters fast enough to meet the demand expected across the industry. A recent manufacturers' survey in *Television Broadcast* indicated that this shouldn't be a major problem for stations.

However, in some markets, and among the networks, engineers decided that while they contemplated brand buys and partnerships, they should have their towers inspected and assessed for current and future performance. For example, tower and antenna studies have long been concluded on the Mt. Sutro complex in San Francisco and on those atop the World Trade Center in New York.

Sutro has been in operation for decades now, and its design may hold the answer for many broadcasters today. The candelabra-type design, with many stations sharing a common structure, is one way to insure no one needs to bear the sole brunt of new tower expenses. DTV Utah and other cooperative, shared sites are becoming a trend in the industry. While they come loaded with legal baggage, they are gaining popularity, because once the legalities are worked out, the expenses are shared. What's more, in this arrangement, no one station lays sole claim to the very best site. Whatever approach you choose, the problem becomes all the more focused when you realize that there isn't exactly a glut of tower installers lined up for the big push. Some have suggested that this is just a perceived problem that could be overcome by attracting installers from the cellular industry.

While that's an interesting proposal, most chiefs and directors of engineering get white-knuckled at such talk.

Once again, the reason for making the tower the first priority is because you might be okay with additional loading. Then again, maybe not. So if any changes are needed, or if a second tower is appropriate, if you aren't looking into it now, you will be waiting in a line that's a lot longer than the one originally predicted for DTV transmitters. Depending on how deep a station can afford to go into financing, having a thorough understanding of your tower's condition and capabilities could affect how you enter the DTV transition.

For example, if money isn't available for a full, near-term commitment because of your tower's capabilities, you might consider putting up a shorter, interim tower and running lower power for the time being. There are several scenarios along this line that could be played out sensibly, but only when the tower's actual condition is known.

CHECKS AND BALANCES

While technical questions abound concerning adjacent channel separation and interference, cable head-end reception, area coverage versus fall-off, efficiencies, pattern changes, STL linking and the headaches of sorting out who's affecting what on multi-antenna structures, finding some relief isn't as daunting as it might at first seem.

Among these considerations, cable system problems should get a leg up, based on the findings of experimental DTV stations such as WHD (Washington, DC). They've already run head-on into that experience, but it's something to keep on your agenda of subjects to be considered. Also, there's a whole other area to investigate, as it concerns the connection of the station to its remote transmitter site. You'll have to check out the potential for fiber optics, additional microwave STL capabilities, as well as ENG and STL links.

In fact, even the Canon CanoBeam lightwave link could become a player, as it is another linking alternative.

EVERYBODY GRAB A PARTNER

Partnering is a term that surfaced in the industry just a few years ago, and now it's almost a byword for the transition to DTV. The term is self-defining, because partners are brought together for their common goals. Long before it became a popular expression, engineers had grown comfortable with a partnership normally (but not always) put together by the transmitter manufacturer of choice. This would include the antenna manufacturer or supplier (who also dealt, if necessary, with a transmission line and RF components company) and the tower company. Even if a new tower wasn't needed, their reps should always have been involved if for nothing more than to assure that the tower's integrity wasn't compromised. But partnering in the late 1990s has come to mean the old team (just mentioned), which was joined first by a cast of integrators/installers, has now also been joined with production and post production players who will supply the new equipment compatibly so that everything works for the benefit of all.

For perhaps the first time in the history of television broadcasting, a multitude of chief engineers and directors of engineering are asking for and getting help to make certain that all video chain possibilities are explored and that all plant knowledge is shared for the common end of developing a very sophisticated video and RF chain. Manufacturers holding DTV seminars with these titled station people are quick to admit that many very elementary questions are being asked, questions that in the future will probably be answered in a variety of ways by some form of partnering.

And don't think that because the transmitter manufacturer you prefer won't be making forays into other product areas that they can't play a major role for your station. Their ability to cross lines to meet your needs is waiting for your test questions.

One of the major misconceptions is that only the megabuck RF manufacturers are capable of putting together a team deep enough to satisfy your RF plant and studio needs. This just isn't true.

Harris can offer (and will offer even more) studio-type products of their own along with RF plant equipment. Comark has struck agreements with a number of well-known studio box manufacturers. And in some cases, it's likely that both Harris and Comark will be involved in equipment designs on units that are not now in existence.

But when you check out the alliances and partnerships being forged by the other manufacturers, you'll discover they, too, have the ability to bring a team together for a turnkey system. It would be a huge mistake, for example, to assume that companies such as Acrodyne, Automated Broadcast Systems (ABS), Continental Electronics, EMCEE, Itelco, Larcan and others can't or aren't interested in working out turnkey contracts.

As this handbook went to press, EMCEE has acquired ABS and its high power UHF transmitter lineup.

These companies, working with systems integrators who have vast broadcast experience, can help you set up a partnership and also make arrangements on the financial end to make certain that no stations will be left behind for lack of financing.

As everyone knows, there have been many bottom line transition estimates. It isn't cheap. But most forms of partnerships can offer capital financing on some or all of the equipment required for the transition to DTV. If you find this turn of events a bit unusual, consider that if partnerships were left to the black box studio manufacturers, the opportunity for incompatibility would be maximized. And there already is some history here of successful turnkey operations that were forged by RF manufacturers.

ENTER THE TRANSMITTER

You won't get very far into transmitter discussions before you run head-on into the 8-VSB exciter, and this is a very technical subject. So for a detailed technical description of 8-VSB, see What Exactly Is 8-VSB Anyway later in this chapter.

DTV IN THE REAL WORLD

UNDERSTANDING DIGITAL

PRE-PRODUCTION

PRODUCTION

AUDIO

GRAPHICS & COMPOSITING

POST PRODUCTION

DELIVERY & DUPLICATION

ENGINEERING & TRANSMISSION

APPENDIX

GLOSSARY

Depending on how well financed they are, stations are considering everything from putting their names on the list for one of the first transmitters all the way to asking about retrofitting. Retrofitting in most cases is like grabbing for straws. After all, if the main transmitter is retrofitted, the alternate main transmitter would be put back on the air for NTSC, where the majority of the viewers will be. There are so many old horse main transmitters still chugging along where, in many cases, the alternate is either a newer but lower power rig, or it's good only for emergencies.

However, don't dismiss retrofitting altogether. At some point, stations will want to consider it for the transmitter forced into the alternate role because of a DTV transmitter purchase. It'll be a consideration at the point where the station is mandated to be DTV all the way. Financing, discussed earlier under partnering, plays its first role here, because if it can't be arranged by the group or the individual station to cover the big transition numbers, RF can be an area of relief. A number of transmitter manufacturers offer lower power transmitters, and they can put you in a partnership for antennas with high gain and the appropriate transmission lines, along with installers. The savings against a full power RF installation could be substantial, perhaps allowing some money in the budget to be moved into the studio chain. Along these same lines, solid state becomes a cost/operational question. If you're thinking in this direction, the operating costs for solid state (at least currently) versus IOTs cross over at 20 kW. At that point, the choice falls to the IOTs, and you may recall that EEV introduced its IOT digital tube recently, so even these devices are changing. Watch for more developments along those lines at future NABs. It'll surprise everyone if Silicon Carbide can change the crossover point, but that's how NAB news is made. While Silicon Carbide awaits its turn, the LDMOS is now the solid-state device of choice. Since our last edition, Acrodyne has built its first IOT transmitter and brought in Rhode & Schwarz to shore up its solid state medium and low power lineup. The Rhode 8-VSB modulator will sit at the heart of the new Acrodyne IOT transmitter. New to the American television market, Continental Electronics is offering a cutting-edge transmitter designed by Telefunken, a company that traces its television roots to the very beginning of television. The choices are compounded by Litton's entry of the Constant Efficiency Amplifier, a device that combines a klystron and MDSC technology.

LINKS

Again, a warning: don't get sidetracked with production equipment until you can at least pass along a DTV program through the RF chain...all the way through it.

The STL is the most important link, as both an ATSC program stream and an NTSC program must both go to the transmitter site (assuming both ATSC and NTSC transmitters are co-located). The problem is that, typically, there is only one link with insufficient bandwidth to carry both signals. One way around this is to use an STL based on a single DS-3 (45 Mbps) or equivalent channel and multiplexing the ATSC and NTSC streams together for STL transport. At the transmitter site, the DS-3 signal is demultiplexed into separate ATSC and NTSC program streams and fed to the appropriate exciter/transmitter.

History has shown us that, left to the production box manufacturers, incompatibility could stop this revolution as surely as a major stock market crash. Transmitter manufacturers, sometimes acting as catalysts, sometimes as entrepreneurs, turned this into a bull market technology through partnering and sheer will.

Acting in this role, whatever their individual goals, all RF manufacturers have helped form the nucleus of partnerships that won't tolerate incompatibilities. And, as you'll begin to see at upcoming NAB conventions, where some RF equipment manufacturers are hesitant to join the team, others will introduce equipment you'd have expected from other areas of the equipment exhibition halls.

But, lest you get lost again in the whirlwind of announcements that will be forthcoming, take another look at that tower. If DTV won't work here, it makes little difference what else you have in mind.

REPACKING: SO MUCH FUN, LET'S DO IT AGAIN

The primary reason that broadcasters are being "loaned" a second channel is so television transmission can be converted from analog to digital. The theory is that at some time in the future (tentatively 2006), analog broadcasting will be shut off and the spectrum used by analog broadcasting will be "recaptured" for auction by the federal government.

Currently, the television broadcast spectrum is covered with mostly analog stations. In a few years, we'll have both analog and digital stations throughout the spectrum. In addition, we have taboo channels and have had to avoid co-channel and adjacent-channel interference issues.

When the analog channels are returned, the television broadcast spectrum will be marked with holes where those stations used to be. This is not very efficient. So the plan is to take all the digital channels and "repack" them into a smaller slice of the spectrum. While "virtual" channel numbers will remain the same (just as a digital channel number is based on an analog channel number—see DTV Transmission Realities), the actual frequency will most likely change.

Does that mean that broadcasters will have to buy a new transmitter again? Possibly. Or at least some components of their transmission system.

Repacking will mean spectrum efficiency for the federal government, but it will mean a second DTV transmission transition for broadcasters.

DTV INTERFERENCE:
NEW CHANNELS, NEW PROBLEMS

Mark J. Pescatore

When WFAA, the ABC affiliate in the Dallas/Ft. Worth area, turned on its DTV transmitter in February 1998, their signal interfered with heart monitors in nearby hospitals. This was not a life-threatening development, but it served as a wake-up call for the broadcast industry.

Many broadcast industry insiders weren't surprised by the interference, since so many secondary and unlicensed pieces of equipment use parts of the broadcast spectrum for transmission. In fact, these experts promise many more of the same types of interference problems in the coming years. The problems aren't restricted to telemetry devices—your own wireless microphones could also fall victim to the new DTV channels (better check those frequencies). Plus, a select few markets with new DTV channels 3 or 4 *might* experience interference with cable set-top boxes and other devices (like video games and VCRs) that use an RF output modulated on channels 3 or 4. (The FCC believes such interference is unlikely, especially if the equipment has channel-switchable capabilities.)

There are more than 4,000 hospitals across the country, and each one has the potential to be hindered by new DTV transmissions. Many of your own wireless microphones could fall victim to progress as well. How many health care facilities will be affected in *your* area when DTV comes to town?

Since there were no DTV sets on the market when WFAA ran into interference problems, staying off the air was a relatively painless way for the station to help solve the problem. By the time your local stations are ready to make the jump to DTV, though, there will probably be an audience out there. Then, the thought of turning off a signal for a week might seem less like charity and more like financial suicide—especially if those stations have already sold air time.

And testing a DTV signal doesn't guarantee that all interference will be detected. All the interference with WFAA wasn't reported (or discovered) when the station first signed-on with their digital signal. In fact, WFAA had to turn off their signal *three* different times to solve separate interference problems with three health care facilities.

Solving this problem isn't about assessing blame. After all, broadcasters have done nothing wrong. They've been allocated a portion of the spectrum for digital television transmission, and they are legally broadcasting their signal. In this case, the television station is the primary service. That means if the hospitals want to continue to use their monitors, they are going to have to change their frequencies or change their equipment, neither of which is a "quick fix" option.

In a joint statement on March 25, 1998 the FCC and the Food and Drug Administration (FDA) outlined courses of action to help prevent this interference in the future. For its part, the FCC will be working to ensure that TV broadcasters communicate with area health care facilities about the potential problem, and will ask manufacturers to help their customers determine if they may be affected by new DTV channels assignments. The FCC will also provide information about spectrum sharing and an area-specific DTV channel listing on their Web site, www.fcc.gov.

Meanwhile, the FDA has sent a public health advisory to all U.S. hospitals and nursing homes, and will work with manufacturers to have equipment labeled to alert users about potential interference. Together, both agencies will explore long-term spectrum needs for medical devices in an effort to avoid future interference problems, and, according to the statement, will "work with equipment manufacturers and the health care community to consider various long term technology improvements that might ameliorate the interference problem."

Despite this effort by the FCC and FDA, broadcasters need to take the initiative to work with the hospitals and caregivers in their area *before* their DTV signal hits the airwaves. This means taking the extra time to send a member of the engineering staff to the local hospitals to explain the potential interference in detail. Not only does this promote a caring image in the community, it helps stations avoid negative publicity (imagine all the accusatory headlines like "TV Station Is Killing Patients" you won't have to endure). A little preventative engineering assessment today helps keep the doctor(s) away.

DTV TRANSMISSION REALITIES

MICHAEL SILBERGLEID

Quality. Is that why we're doing DTV? Or is it other non-traditional television services like data broadcasting and digital coupons? Is it multicasting or HDTV? Or is it all of these things? Or none, since television broadcasters, to stay in television broadcasting, must do this by law?

As an industry, broadcasters will be able to do a great deal of things with the 19.39 Mbps that can go into the 6 MHz of bandwidth the FCC has allocated for digital television. We will have crystal clear CD-like sound and, if we so choose, high definition film-like television. But there is one thing that can potentially cause havoc with all of this—compression.

We've been living with compression since the beginning of television with interlace. And now we have the ability to trade interlace for progressive, but to transmit that signal to the home, we'll still have to use MPEG-2 compression.

Through the years, there has been research that shows interlace compresses better than progressive. Not to be outdone, there has also been research that shows that progressive compresses better than interlace. So now what? Do we produce the best picture we possibly can and hope that transmission doesn't muck it all up? Basically, yes. And it will take some trial and error as the encoders get better. If you've ever seen a DBS signal, you've probably seen macroblocks—a compression artifact.

In 1997 and 1998, ATSC encoders used in experimental and volunteer DTV/HDTV stations did *not* encode signals perfectly. Critical viewers (experts—not consumers) could see compression artifacts as macroblocks within the picture. This was especially evident in fast-action programming like basketball.

The big question is: What can the encoder handle, and specifically what will it choke on?

Which leads the purchaser of an ATSC encoder (or encoders if multicasting will occur) to wonder if it will come with a "no choke" guarantee, or if viewers will even see the same picture that we as professionals will see.

DISPLAY TECHNOLOGY

The Consumer Electronics Association (CEA) has stated that the digital television sets made by their members will display all of the formats in the ATSC's Table 3 on whatever display type the television actually has (this means that HDTV signals will be down-converted to SDTV if a SDTV display is what is in the television).

If the TV set is a 4:3 display, how will 16:9 images be displayed? Decoders are capable of sending to the display: letterbox, center protected area, and pan and scan. In theory the choice is up to the consumer, in reality, the choice is made by the broadcaster.

Today's displays are interlace and 30 frames per second. What if the original signal is something different? Well, whatever is sent will have to be converted to whatever the display is. So although new digital television sets may be capable of displaying 24, 30 or 60 frames in progressive or interlace, today's televisions with a digital television set-top box will still only display 30 frames per second interlace. What this means is that 3:2 pulldown would move from the telecine to the ATSC decoder. And, if you believe that 720 progressive looks better than 1080 interlace, but the public believes that 1080 interlace is a better picture than 720 progressive, because 1080 is a larger number than 720, then we'll see a great deal of interlace digital television displays in a great deal of houses.

CHANNEL NUMBERS

The way we talk about channel numbers in the DTV world has also changed—we now have virtual channels. The ATSC, in document A/65, specifies how the new numbering system works. There are two types of channel numbers: the major channel number and the minor channel number (or sub-channel number). A "virtual channel number" must be associated with a major and a minor channel number, with the minor channel number on the right-hand part of the "virtual channel number," such as 4-2. To state that another way, the major channel number, along with the minor channel number, act as the user's reference number for the virtual channel.

Major channel number: Numbered between 1 and 99. In the U.S., numbers 2 to 69 are for ATSC television purposes (using the same channel number as the station's NTSC analog license, or the ATSC channel number if the broadcaster does not have an ATSC license) and numbers 70 to 99 are for other services (such as data) and repositioning other services within the ATSC multiplex (for example, a local broadcaster transmitting community college lectures in its bit stream may want to use a major channel number different than its own major channel number for the virtual channel carrying the lectures.

Minor channel number: Numbered between 0 and 999 (one thousand channels). In the U.S., the zero minor channel number is the NTSC analog channel (ATSC channel 5 would be ATSC channel 5-0). Numbers 1 to 99 are used for ATSC television and ATSC audio-only services while numbers 1 to 999 can be used for data services. (Note that receivers can go up to minor channel number 1,024.)

MONITORING WHAT PEOPLE SEE

There are a large number of television stations that have inexpensive color and black and white television sets in their studio and master control rooms so that staff can monitor more closely what a viewer is seeing at home. In the digital television world, with the varying degree of decoders that will be available to consumers within digital television sets and set-top boxes, what is the station to do, monitor every possible display? No.

What a station should do is look at off-air signals with three levels of decoders—the best, the mid-range, and the least expensive. And looking at the station's signal from your cable company or companies (and whose decoder will they have if they convert to analog?) will be just as important.

If the cable company feed is less than adequate, will the broadcast station have to "loan" them a better decoder so the signal looks as good as it can be? Stations might want to budget that in as well. And if stations multicast, how will that decoder know what to pass on to your single cable channel (with the future of multicasting Must Carry unknown)?

Most people will not notice what a professional can see, so the real question is: What can stations get away with, and does the station truly want to get away with it?

(For a discussion on the relationship between 4:3 and 16:9 screen sizes, see the Measuring Screen Size section in DTV in the Real World.)

• • • • •

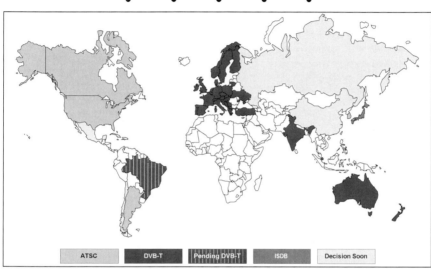

Worldwide DTV commitments as of February 2000. Image: Grass Valley Group.

WHAT EXACTLY IS 8-VSB ANYWAY?

DAVID SPARANO

The U.S. invented it, the ATTC tested it, the FCC accepted it, everyone is talking about it, and soon we'll all get it in our homes—but what is 8-VSB anyway? Simply put, 8-VSB is the RF modulation format utilized by the recently approved ATSC digital television standard to transmit digital bits over the airways to the home consumer. Since any terrestrial TV system must overcome numerous channel impairments such as ghosts, noise bursts, signal fades, and interference in order to reach the home viewer, the selection of the right RF modulation format is critical. Being one of the most crucial aspects of the DTV system, the 8-VSB format has received a great deal of attention and scrutiny recently.

In the alphabet soup world of digital communications, there are two big names to remember when thinking about the complete DTV system: 8-VSB and MPEG-2. 8-VSB is the RF modulation format and MPEG-2 is the video compression/packetization format. To convert high definition studio video into a form suitable for over-the-air broadcast, according to DTV standards, two stages of processing are needed:

MPEG-2 encoding and 8-VSB modulation. Accordingly, two major pieces of equipment are required: an MPEG-2 encoder and an 8-VSB exciter.

The MPEG-2 encoder takes baseband digital video and performs bit rate compression using the techniques of discrete cosine transform, run length coding and bi-directional motion prediction—all of which are discussed elsewhere in this book. The MPEG-2 encoder then multiplexes this compressed video information together with pre-coded Dolby Digital (AC-3) audio and any ancillary data that will be transmitted. The result is a stream of highly compressed MPEG-2 data packets with a data rate of only 19.39 Mbps. This is by no means a trivial task since the high resolution digital video (or multiple standard resolution video) input to the MPEG-2 encoder could easily have a data rate of one Gbps or more. This 19.39 Mbps data stream is known as the *DTV Transport Layer.* It is output from the MPEG-2 encoder and input to the 8-VSB exciter.

Although MPEG-2 compression techniques can achieve stunning bit-rate reduction results, still more tricks must be employed to squeeze the 19.39 Mbps DTV Transport Layer signal into a slender six MHz RF channel and transmit it (hopefully without errors) to the eager consumer waiting at home in front of the

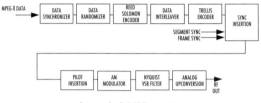

figure 1. 8-VSB exciter.

TV set. This is the job of the 8-VSB exciter.

Figure 1 is a block diagram of a typical 8-VSB exciter. In this section, we will walk through the major processes that occur in the 8-VSB exciter—identifying the major components of the 8-VSB signal and explaining how this signal is generated.

DATA SYNCHRONIZATION

The first thing that the 8-VSB exciter does upon receiving the MPEG-2 data packets is to synchronize its own internal circuits to the incoming signal. Before any signal processing can occur, the 8-VSB exciter must correctly identify the start and end points of each MPEG-2 data packet. This is accomplished using the MPEG-2 sync byte. MPEG-2 packets are 188 bytes in length with the first byte in each packet always being the sync byte. The MPEG-2 sync byte is then discarded; it will ultimately be replaced by the ATSC segment sync in a later stage of processing.

DATA RANDOMIZER

With the exception of the segment and field syncs (to be discussed later), the 8-VSB bit stream must have a completely random, noise-like nature. This is because our transmitted signal frequency response must have a flat noise-like spectrum in order to use the allotted channel space with maximum efficiency. If our data contained repetitious patterns, the recurring rhythm of these patterns would cause the RF energy content of our signal to "lump" together at certain discrete points of our frequency spectrum—thereby leaving holes in other parts. This implies that certain parts of our six MHz channel would be over-used while other parts would be under-used. Plus, the large concentrations of RF energy at certain modulating frequencies would be more likely to create discernible beat patterns in an NTSC television set when DTV-to-NTSC interference is experienced.

In the data randomizer, each byte value is changed according to known pattern of pseudo-random number generation. This process is reversed in the receiver in order to recover the proper data values.

REED-SOLOMON ENCODING

Reed-Solomon encoding is a Forward Error Correction (FEC) scheme applied to the incoming data stream. Forward Error Correction is a general term used to describe a variety of techniques that can be used to correct bit errors that occur during transmission. Atmospheric noise, multipath propagation, signal fades, and transmitter non-linearities may all create received bit errors. Forward Error Correction can detect and correct these errors, up to a reasonable limit.

The Reed-Solomon encoder takes all 187 bytes of an incoming MPEG-2 data packet (the packet sync byte has been removed) and mathematically manipulates them as a block to create a sort of "digital thumbnail sketch" of the block contents. This "sketch" occupies 20 additional bytes which are then tacked onto the tail end of the original 187 byte packet. These 20 bytes are known as Reed-Solomon parity bytes.

The receiver will compare the received 187 byte block to the 20 parity bytes in order to determine the validity of the recovered data. If errors are detected, the receiver can use the parity "thumbnail sketch" to locate the exact location of the errors, modify the disrupted bytes, and reconstruct the original information. Up to 10 byte errors per packet can be corrected this way. If too many byte errors are present in a given packet, the parity "thumbnail sketch" no longer resembles the received data block, the validity of the data can no longer be confirmed, and the entire MPEG-2 packet must be discarded.

DATA INTERLEAVER

The data interleaver disturbs the sequential order of the data stream and disperses the data throughout time (over a range of about 4.5 msec through the use of memory buffers) in order to minimize the transmitted signal's sensitivity to burst-type interference.

This is the equivalent of spreading all of your eggs (bytes) over many different baskets (time). If a noise burst punches a hole in the signal during propagation and "one basket" (i.e., several milliseconds) is lost, many different segments lose one egg instead of one data segment losing all of its eggs. This is known as *time diversity*.

Data interleaving is done according to a known pattern; the process is reversed in the receiver in order to recover the proper data order.

TRELLIS ENCODER

Trellis coding is yet another form of Forward Error Correction. Unlike Reed-Solomon coding, which treats the entire MPEG-2 packet simultaneously as a block, trellis coding is an evolving code that tracks the progressing stream of bits as it develops through time. Accordingly, Reed-Solomon coding is known as a form of *block* code, while trellis coding is a *convolutional* code.

For trellis coding, each 8-bit byte is split up into a stream of four, 2-bit words. In the trellis coder, each 2-bit word that arrives is compared to the past history of previous 2-bit words. A 3-bit binary code is mathematically generated to describe the transition from the previous 2-bit word to the current one. These 3-bit codes are substituted for the original 2-bit words and transmitted over-the-air as the eight level symbols of 8-VSB (3 bits = 23 = 8 combinations or levels). For every two bits that go into the trellis coder, three bits come out. For this reason, the trellis coder in the 8-VSB system is said to be a 2/3 rate coder.

The trellis decoder in the receiver uses the received 3-bit transition codes to reconstruct the evolution of the data stream from one 2-bit word to the next. In this way, the trellis coder follows a "trail" as the signal moves from one word to the next through time. The power of trellis coding lies in its ability to track a signal's history through time and discard potentially faulty information (errors) based on a signal's past and future behavior.

This is somewhat like following one person's footsteps through the snow on a busy sidewalk. When the trail becomes confused with other tracks (i.e., errors are received), the trellis decoder has the ability to follow several possible "trails" for a few footprints and make a decision as to which prints are the correct ones. (Note: change this analogy to "footprints in the sand on a crowded beach" if you are reading this in a warm climate.)

SYNC AND PILOT INSERTION

The next step in the signal processing chain is the insertion of the various "helper" signals that aid the 8-VSB receiver in accurately locating and demodulating the transmitted RF signal. These are the ATSC pilot, segment sync, and frame sync. The pilot and sync signals are inserted after the data randomization, Reed-Solomon coding, data interleaving and trellis coding stages so as not to destroy the fixed time and amplitude relationships that these signals must possess in order to be effective.

Recovering a clock signal in order to decode a received waveform has always been a tricky proposition in digital RF communications. If we derive the receiver clock from the recovered data, we have a sort of "chicken and egg" dilemma. The data must be sampled by the receiver clock in order to be accurately recovered. The receiver clock itself must be generated from accurately recovered data. The resulting clocking system quickly "crashes" when the noise or interference level rises to a point that significant data errors are received.

When NTSC was invented, the need was recognized to have a powerful sync pulse that rose above the rest of the RF modulation envelope. In this way, the receiver synchronization circuits could still "home-in" on the sync pulses and maintain the correct picture framing—even if the contents of the picture were a bit snowy. (Everyone saw the need for this except the French; sync there is the weakest part of the signal—*vive la différence*). NTSC also benefited from a large residual visual carrier (caused by the DC component of the modulating video) that helped TV receiver tuners zero in on the transmitted carrier center frequency.

8-VSB employs a similar strategy of sync pulses and residual carriers that allows the receiver to "lock" onto the incoming signal and begin decoding, even in the presence of heavy ghosting and high noise levels.

The first "helper" signal is the ATSC pilot. Just before modulation, a small DC shift is applied to the 8-VSB baseband signal (which was previously centered about zero volts with no DC component). This causes a small residual carrier to appear at the zero frequency point of the resulting modulated spectrum. This is the ATSC pilot. This gives the RF PLL circuits in the 8-VSB receiver something to lock onto that is independent of the data being transmitted.

Although similar in nature, the ATSC pilot is much smaller than the NTSC visual carrier, consuming only 0.3 dB or 7 percent of the transmitted power.

The other "helper" signals are the ATSC segment and frame syncs. An ATSC data segment is comprised of the 187 bytes of the original MPEG-2 data packet plus the 20 parity bytes added by the Reed-Solomon encoder. After trellis coding, our 207 byte segment has been stretched out

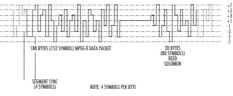

figure 2: ATSC baseband data segment.

into a stream of 828 8-level symbols. The ATSC segment sync is a repetitive four symbol (one byte) pulse that is added to the front of the data segment and replaces the missing first byte (packet sync byte) of the original MPEG-2 data packet. Correlation circuits in the 8-VSB receiver home in on the repetitive nature of the segment sync, which is easily contrasted against the background of completely random data. The recovered sync signal is used to generate the receiver clock and recover the data. Because of their repetitive nature and extended duration, the segment syncs are easy for the receiver to spot. The result is that accurate clock recovery can be had at noise and interference levels well above those where accurate data recovery is impossible (up to 0 dB SNR—data recovery requires at least 15 dB SNR). This allows for quick data recovery during channel changes and other transient conditions. Figure 2 shows the make-up of the ATSC data segment and the position of the ATSC segment sync.

An ATSC data segment is roughly analogous to an NTSC line; ATSC segment sync is somewhat like NTSC horizontal sync. Their duration and frequencies of repetition are, of course, completely different. Each ATSC segment sync lasts 0.37 msec.; NTSC sync lasts 4.7 msec. An ATSC data segment lasts 77.3 msec.; an NTSC line 63.6 msec. A careful inspection of the numbers involved reveals that the ATSC segment sync is somewhat more "slender" when compared to its NTSC counterpart. This is done to maximize the active data payload and minimize the time committed to sync "overhead."

Three hundred and thirteen consecutive data segments are combined to make a data frame. Figure 3 shows the make-up of an ATSC data frame. The ATSC frame sync is an entire data segment that is repeated once per frame (24.2 msec.) and is roughly analogous to the NTSC vertical interval. (FYI: The NTSC vertical interval occurs once every 16.7 msec.). The ATSC frame sync has a known data symbol pattern and is used to "train" the adaptive ghost-canceling equalizer in the receiver. This is done by compar-

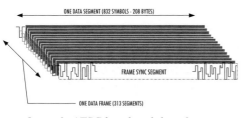

figure 3: ATSC baseband data frame.

ing the received signal with errors against the known reference of the frame sync. The resulting error vectors are used to adjust the taps of the receiver ghost-canceling equalizer. Like the segment sync, the repetitive nature of the frame sync, and correlation techniques used in the 8-VSB receiver, allow frame sync recovery at very high noise and interference levels (up to 0 dB SNR).

The robustness of the segment and frame sync signals permits accurate clock recovery and ghost-canceling operation in the 8-VSB receiver—even when the active data is completely corrupted by the presence of strong multipath distortion. This allows the adaptive ghost-canceling equalizer "to keep its head" and "hunt around in the mud" in order to recover a useable signal—even during the presence of strong signal echoes.

AM MODULATION

Our eight-level baseband signal, with syncs and DC pilot shift added, is then amplitude modulated on an intermediate frequency (IF) carrier. With traditional amplitude modulation, we generate a double sideband RF spectrum about our carrier frequency, with each RF sideband being the mirror image of the other. This represents redundant information and one sideband can be discarded without any net information loss. This strategy was employed to some degree in creating the vestigial lower sideband in traditional NTSC analog television. In 8-VSB, this concept is taken to greater extremes with the lower RF sideband being almost completely removed. (Note: 8-VSB = **8** level—**V**estigial **S**ide **B**and.)

(There are several different ways to implement the AM modulation, VSB filtering, and pilot insertion stages of the 8-VSB exciter, some of which are completely digital and involve direct digital synthesis of the required waveforms. All methods aim to achieve the same results at the exciter output. This particular arrangement was chosen in the interest of providing a clear, easily understandable, signal flow diagram.)

NYQUIST FILTER

As a result of the data overhead added to the signal in the form of forward error correction coding and sync insertion, our data rate has gone from 19.39 Mbps at the exciter input to 32.28 Mbps at the output of the trellis coder. Since 3 bits are transmitted in each symbol of the 8-level 8-VSB constellation, the resulting symbol rate is 32Mb / 3 = 10.76 Million symbols/sec. By virtue of the Nyquist Theorem, we know that 10.76 Million symbols/sec can be transmitted in a VSB signal with a minimum frequency bandwidth of 1/2 X 10.76 MHz = 5.38 MHz. Since we are allotted a channel bandwidth of 6 MHz, we can relax the steepness of our VSB filter skirts slightly and still fall within the 6 MHz channel. This permissible excess bandwidth (represented by a, the Greek letter alpha) is 11.5 percent for the ATSC 8-VSB system. That is, 5.38 MHz (minimum band-

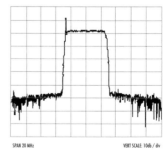

SPAN 20 MHz   VERT SCALE: 10db / div

figure 4: 8-VSB RF frequency spectrum. Note presence of ATSC pilot at lower edge of channel. Lower sideband (below pilot frequency) is almost completely removed.

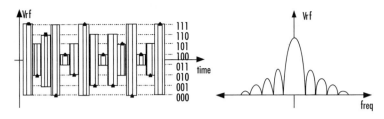

figure 5: Impossible 8-VSB RF envelope.
This eight-level AM signal, although easy to visualize, would produce a frequency spectrum far too wide for our 6 MHz channel bandwidth.

width per Nyquist) + 620 kHz (11.5 percent excess bandwidth) = 6.00 MHz (channel bandwidth used). The higher the alpha factor used, the easier the hardware implementation is, both in terms of filter requirements and clock precision for sampling.

The resulting frequency response after Nyquist VSB filter is shown in figure 4.

This virtual elimination of the lower sideband, along with the narrowband filtering of the upper sideband, creates very significant changes in the RF waveform that is ultimately transmitted. For the NTSC-hardened veteran, there is a great temptation to imagine the 8-VSB RF waveform as being a sort of "8-step luminance stairstep" signal transmitting the eight levels of 8-VSB. Unfortunately, there is a fundamental flaw with this notion. As figure 5 illustrates, such a crisp stairstep signal with "squared off" abrupt transitions would generate a frequency spectrum that is far too wide for our single 6 MHz channel. A "square symbol pulse" -type signal generates a rich spectrum of frequency sidelobes that would interfere with adjacent channels.

We know that this type of RF waveform is incorrect since our Nyquist VSB filter has already pared our RF spectrum down to a slender 6 MHz channel.

As any video or transmitter engineer knows, when a square pulse is frequency bandlimited, it will lose its square edges and "ring" (oscillate) in time before and after the initial pulse. For our digital 8-level signal, this would spell disaster as the pre- and post-ringing from one symbol pulse would interfere with the preceding and following pulses, thereby distorting their levels and disrupting their information content.

Fortunately, there is still a way to transmit our 8-VSB symbol pulses if we observe that the 8-level information is only recognized during the precise instant of sampling in the receiver. At all other times, the symbol pulse amplitude is unimportant and can be modified in any way we please—so long as the amplitude at the precise instant of sampling still assumes one of the required eight amplitude levels.

If the narrowband frequency filtering is done correctly according

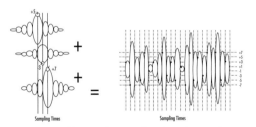

figure 6a: Addition of narrowband, orthogonal symbol pulses. At any given sampling time (vertical line), only one symbol pulse contributes to total signal amplitude, all other pulses experience a zero crossing. The resulting RF envelope corresponds to the eight digital levels only during the precise instant of sampling.

figure 6b: The 8-VSB RF waveform as seen at the 8-VSB exciter output. The black regions represent the current oscilloscope trace; the gray regions show the stored value of all past traces.

to the Nyquist Theorem, the resulting train of symbol pulses will be *orthogonal*. This means that at each precise instant of sampling, only one symbol pulse will contribute to the final RF envelope waveform; all preceding and following symbol pulses will be experiencing a zero crossing in their amplitude. This is shown in figure 6a. In this way, when the RF waveform is sampled by the receiver clock, the recovered voltage will represent only the current symbol's amplitude (one of the eight possible levels).

At all times in-between the instants of sampling, the total RF envelope waveform reflects the addition of the "ringing" of hundreds of previous and future symbols (since all symbols have non-zero amplitudes between sampling times). Note that, in the interest of simplicity, figure 6a shows our narrowband symbol pulses as ringing for only 10 sampling periods; in reality they ring for a much longer time. These non-zero values (between sampling times) from hundreds of symbols can add up to very large signal voltages. The result is a very "peaky" signal that most closely resembles white noise. This is shown in figure 6b. The peak to average ratio of this signal can be as high as 12 dB, although RF peak clipping in the transmitter can limit this value to 6 to 7 dB with minimal consequences.

8-VSB SIGNAL CONSTELLATION

In 8-VSB, the digital information is transmitted exclusively in the amplitude of the RF envelope and not in the phase. This is unlike other digital modulation formats such as QAM, where each point in the signal constellation is a certain vector combination of carrier amplitude and phase. This is not possible in 8-VSB since the carrier phase is no longer an independent variable under our control, but is rather "consumed" in suppressing the vestigial lower sideband.

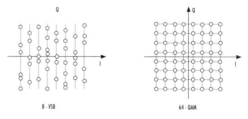

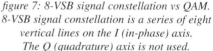

figure 7: 8-VSB signal constellation vs QAM. 8-VSB signal constellation is a series of eight vertical lines on the I (in-phase) axis. The Q (quadrature) axis is not used.

The resulting 8-VSB signal constellation, as compared to 64-QAM, is shown in figure 7. Our eight levels are recovered by sampling an in-phase (I channel) synchronous detector. Nothing would be gained by sampling a quadrature channel detector since no useful information is contained in this channel. Our signal constellation diagram is therefore a series eight vertical lines that correspond to our eight transmitted amplitude levels. By eliminating any dependence on the Q-channel, the 8-VSB receiver need only process the I channel, thereby cutting in half the number of DSP circuits required in certain stages. The result is greater simplicity, and ultimately cost savings, in the receiver design.

THE REST OF THE 8-VSB CHAIN

After the Nyquist VSB filter, the 8-VSB IF signal is then double up-converted in the exciter, by traditional oscillator-mixer-filter circuits, to the assigned channel frequency in the UHF or VHF band. The on-channel RF output of the 8-VSB exciter is then supplied to the DTV transmitter. The transmitter is essentially a traditional RF power amplifier, be it solid state or tube-type. A high-power RF output system filters the transmitter output signal and suppresses any spurious out-of-band signals caused by transmitter non-linearities. The last link in the transmitting chain is the antenna that broadcasts the full-power, on-channel 8-VSB DTV signal.

In the home receiver, the over-the-air signal is demodulated by essentially applying in reverse the same principals that we have already discussed. The incoming RF signal is received, downconverted, filtered, then detected. Then the segment and frame syncs are recovered. Segment syncs aid in receiver clock recovery and frame syncs are used to train the adaptive ghost-canceling equalizer. Once the proper data stream has been recovered, it is trellis decoded, deinterleaved, Reed-Solomon decoded, and derandomized. The end result is the recovery of the original MPEG-2 data packets. MPEG-2 decoding circuits reconstruct the video image for display on the TV screen and Dolby Digital (AC-3) circuits decode the sound information and drive the receiver loudspeakers. The home viewer "receives his DTV" and the signal chain is complete.

CONCLUSION

The goal of this section has been to provide some insight into the inner workings of the 8-VSB transmission system. Like many things in life, 8-VSB can appear formidable at first, but is really quite simple "once you get to know it." Hopefully the knowledge conveyed in this section will dispel some of the fear factor that many NTSC engineers experience when faced with the unknown world of digital TV broadcasting.

So what then is 8-VSB? Simply put, 8-VSB is the future of American television. And the future doesn't have to be such a scary thing.

REFERENCES

[1] Davis, Robert and Twitchell, Edwin, "The Harris VSB Exciter for Digital ATV" NAB 1996 Engineering Conference. April 15-18, 1996.
[2] Citta, Richard and Sgrignoli, Gary, "ATSC Transmission System: 8-VSB Tutorial" ITVS 1997 Montreux Symposium. June 12-17, 1997.
[3] Totty, Ron, Davis, Robert and Weirather, Robert, "The Fundamentals of Digital ATV Transmission" *ATV Seminar in Print*. Harris Corporation Broadcast Division, 1995.

ACKNOWLEDGEMENTS

Special thanks go to Joe Seccia, Bob Plonka and Ed Twitchell of Harris Corporation Broadcast Division for their contributions of time, material and assistance in writing this section.

THE HOW AND WHY OF COFDM

J. H. Stott

Coded Orthogonal Frequency Division Multiplexing (COFDM) is a form of modulation which is particularly well-suited to the needs of the terrestrial channel. COFDM can cope with high levels of multipath propagation with wide delay spreads. This leads to the concept of single-frequency networks in which many transmitters send the same signal on the same frequency, generating 'artificial multipath'. COFDM also copes well with co-channel narrowband interference, as may be caused by the carriers of existing analog services.

COFDM has therefore been chosen for two recent new standards for broadcasting, for sound (Digital Audio Broadcasting, DAB) and television (Digital Video Broadcasting-Terrestrial, DVB-T), optimized for their respective applications and with options to fit particular needs.

The special performance of COFDM in respect of multipath and interference is only achieved by careful choice of parameters and attention to detail in the way in which the forward error-correction coding is applied.

INTRODUCTION

Digital techniques have been used for many years by broadcasters in the production, distribution and storage of their program material. They have also been used in 'supporting roles' in broadcasting itself, with the introduction of Teletext and digital sound (NICAM) for television, and Radio Data (RDS) to accompany FM sound broadcasts. These have all used relatively conventional forms of digital modulation.

Sound and television terrestrial broadcasting is now entering a new age in which the main audio and video signals will themselves be broadcast in digital form. Systems have been standardized [ETSI 1 and 2], for use in Europe and elsewhere in the world for Digital Audio Broadcasting (DAB) and Digital Video Broadcasting-Terrestrial (DVB-T).

These systems have been designed in recognition of the circumstances in which they will be used. DAB (unlike its AM and FM predecessors) was especially designed to cope with the rigors of reception in moving cars—especially multipath, in this case time-varying. For DVB-T, less emphasis was placed on true mobility, but reception via the often-used set-top antennas still implied the need to cope with multipath reception—and higher data capacity than DAB was also required. A new form of modulation—COFDM—was chosen for both cases, albeit with detail differences and appropriate changes of parameters to suit the different requirements. Both include a degree of flexibility.

COFDM involves modulating the data onto a large number of carriers ("FDM"). The key features which make it work, in a way so well suited to terrestrial channels, include *orthogonality* (the "O" of COFDM), addition of a *guard interval*, and the use of *error coding* (the "C"), *interleaving* and *channel-state information* (CSI).

This section is a brief attempt to explain these features and their significance.

WHY USE MULTIPLE CARRIERS?

The use of multiple carriers follows from the presence of significant levels of multipath.

Suppose we modulate a carrier with digital information. During each symbol, we transmit the carrier with a particular phase and amplitude which is chosen from the constellation in use. Each symbol conveys a number of bits of information, equal to the logarithm (to the base 2) of the number of different states in the constellation.

Now imagine that this signal is received via two paths, with a relative delay between them, and that the receiver attempts to demodulate what was sent in say symbol n by examining the corresponding symbol's-worth of received information.

When the relative delay is *more* than one symbol period, figure 1 (left), the signal received via the second path acts purely as interference, since it only carries information belonging to a previous symbol or symbols. Such *inter-symbol interference* (ISI) implies that only very small levels of the delayed signal could be tolerated (the exact level depending on the constellation in use and the acceptable loss of noise margin).

When the relative delay is *less* than one symbol period, figure 1 (right), part of the signal received via the second path acts purely as interference, since it only carries information belonging to the previous symbol. The rest of it carries the information from the wanted symbol—but may add constructively or destructively to the main-path information.

This tells us that if we are to cope with any appreciable level of delayed signals, the symbol rate must be reduced sufficiently that the total delay spread (between first- and last-received paths) is only a modest fraction of the symbol period. The information that can be carried by a single carrier is thus limited in the presence of multipath. If one carrier cannot then carry the information rate we require, this leads naturally to the idea of dividing the high-rate data into many low-rate parallel streams, each conveyed by its own carrier—of which there are a large number. This is a form of FDM—the first step towards COFDM.

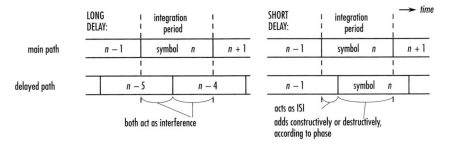

figure 1. How a delayed path causes inter-symbol interference (ISI), with two examples of delay.

Even when the delay spread is less than one symbol period, a degree of ISI from the previous symbol remains. This could be eliminated if the period for which each symbol is transmitted were made longer than the period over which the receiver integrates the signal—a first indication that adding a *guard interval* may be a good thing. (We shall return to this idea shortly).

ORTHOGONALITY AND THE USE OF THE DFT/FFT

Orthogonality: The use of a very large number of carriers is a prospect which is practically daunting (surely, we would need many modulators/demodulators, and filters to accompany them?) and would appear to require an increase of bandwidth to accommodate them. Both these worries can fortunately be dispelled if we do one simple thing: we specify that the carriers are evenly spaced by precisely $f_u = 1/T_u$, where T_u is the period (the 'useful' or 'active' symbol period) over which the receiver integrates the demodulated signal. When we do this, the carriers form what mathematicians call an *orthogonal set*:

The kth carrier (at baseband) can be written as $\psi_k(t) = e^{jk\omega_u t}$, where $\omega_u = 2\pi/T_u$, and the orthogonality condition that the carriers satisfy is:

$$\int_\tau^{\tau+T_u} \psi_k(t)\psi_l^*(t)dt = 0, \quad k \neq l$$

$$= T_u, k = l$$

More intuitively, what this represents is the common procedure of demodulating a carrier by multiplying by a carrier[1] of the *same* frequency, ('beating it down to zero frequency') and integrating the result. Any other carriers will give rise to 'beat tones' which are at integer multiples of ω_u. All of these unwanted 'beat tones' therefore have an integer number of cycles during the integration period T_u and thus integrate to zero.

Thus without any 'explicit' filtering[2], we can separately demodulate all the carriers without any mutual cross-talk, just by our particular choice for the carrier spacing. Furthermore, we have not wasted any spectrum either—the carriers are closely packed so that they occupy the same spectrum in total as if all the data modulated a single carrier, with an ideal very sharp-cut filter.

Preserving Orthogonality: In practice, our carriers are modulated by complex numbers which change from symbol to symbol. If the integration period spans two symbols (as for the delayed paths in figure 1), not only will there be same-carrier ISI, but in addition there will be *inter-carrier interference* (ICI) as well. This happens because the beat tones from other carriers may no longer integrate to zero if they change in phase and/or amplitude during the period. We avoid this by adding a guard interval, which ensures that all information integrated comes from the same symbol *and* appears constant during it.

Figure 2 shows this addition of a guard interval. The symbol period is extended so it exceeds the receiver integration period T_u. Since all the

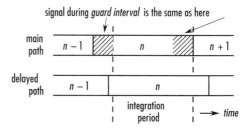

figure 2. The addition of a guard interval.

carriers are cyclic within T_u, so too is the whole modulated signal, so that the segment added at the beginning of the symbol to form the guard interval is identical to the segment of the same length at the end of the symbol. As long as the delay of any path with respect to the main (shortest) one is less than the guard interval, all the signal components within the integration period come from the same symbol and the orthogonality criterion is satisfied. ICI and ISI will only occur when the relative delay exceeds the guard interval.

The guard interval length is chosen to match the level of multipath expected. It should not form too large a fraction of T_u, otherwise too much data capacity (and spectral efficiency) will be sacrificed. DAB uses approximately[3] $T_u/4$; DVB-T has more options, of which $T_u/4$ is the largest. To tolerate very long delays (as in the 'artificial multipath' of a single-frequency network, SFN) T_u must therefore be made large, implying a large number of carriers—from hundreds to thousands.

The paths of figure 2 may still add constructively or destructively. In fact it is possible to show that the signal demodulated from a particular carrier equals that transmitted, but simply multiplied by the effective frequency response of the (multipath) channel at the carrier frequency[4].

Many other things can cause a loss of orthogonality and hence also cause ICI. They include errors in the local-oscillator or sampling frequencies of the receiver, and phase-noise in the local oscillator [Stott 3 and 4]. However, the effects of all these can, with care, be held within acceptable limits in practice.

Use of FFT: We've avoided thousands of filters, thanks to orthogonality,—what about implementing all the demodulating carriers, multipliers and integrators?

In practice, we work with the received signal in sampled form (sampled above the Nyquist limit, of course). The process of integration then becomes one of summation, and the whole demodulation process takes on a form which is identical to the Discrete Fourier Transform (DFT). Fortunately there exist efficient, so-called Fast Fourier Transform (FFT) implementations of this, and integrated circuits are already available, so that we are able to build COFDM equipment reasonably easily. Common versions of the FFT operate on a group of 2^M time samples (corresponding to the samples taken in the integration period) and deliver the same number of frequency coefficients. These correspond to the data demodulated from the many carriers. In practice, because we sample above the Nyquist limit, not all of the coefficients obtained correspond to active carriers that we have used[5].

The inverse FFT is similarly used in the transmitter to generate the OFDM signal from the input data.

CHOICE OF BASIC MODULATION

In each symbol, each carrier is modulated (multiplied) by a complex number taken from a constellation set. The more states there are in the constellation, the more bits can be conveyed by each carrier during one symbol—but the closer the constellation points become, assuming constant transmitted power. Thus there is a well-known trade-off of ruggedness versus capacity.

At the receiver, the corresponding demodulated value (the frequency coefficient from the receiver FFT) has been multiplied by an arbitrary complex number (the response of the channel at the carrier frequency). The constellation is thus rotated and changed in size. How can we then determine which constellation point was sent?

One simple way is to use *differential demodulation*, such as the DQPSK used in DAB. Information is carried by the change of phase from one symbol to the next. As long as the channel changes slowly

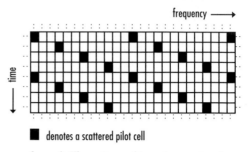

denotes a scattered pilot cell

figure 3. The pattern of inserting scattered pilot cells used in DVB-T.

enough, its response does not matter. Using such a differential (rather than coherent) demodulation causes some loss in thermal noise performance—but DAB is nevertheless a very rugged system.

When higher capacity is needed (as in DVB-T) there are advantages in *coherent demodulation*. In this, the response of the channel for each carrier is somehow determined, and the received constellation is appropriately *equalized* before determining which constellation point was transmitted, and hence what bits were transmitted. To do this in DVB-T, some pilot information is transmitted (so-called *scattered pilots*[6]), so that in some symbols, on some carriers, known information is transmitted (figure 3) from which a sub-sampled[7] version of the frequency response is measured. This is then interpolated, using a 1-D or 2-D filter, to fill-in the unknown gaps and used to equalize all the constellations carrying data.

USE OF ERROR CODING

Why Do We Need Error Coding? In fact, we would expect to use forward error-correction coding in almost any practical digital communication system, in order to be able to deliver an acceptable bit-error ratio (BER) at a reasonably low signal-to-noise ratio (SNR). At a high SNR it might not be necessary—and this is also true for uncoded OFDM, but only when the channel is relatively flat. *Uncoded* OFDM does not perform very well in a selective channel. Its performance could be evaluated for any selective channel and any modulation scheme, by: noting the SNR for each carrier, deducing the corresponding BER for each carrier's data and finally obtaining the BER for the whole data signal by averaging the BERs of all the carriers used.

Very simple examples will show the point. Clearly, if there is a 0 dB echo of delay such that every mth carrier is completely extinguished, then the 'symbol' error ratio, SER, (where 'symbol' denotes the group of bits carried by one carrier within one OFDM symbol) will be of the order of 1 in m, *even at infinite SNR*. An echo delay of say $T_u/4$, the maximum for which loss of orthogonality is avoided when the guard-interval fraction is 1/4, (as in DAB and some modes of DVB-T) would thus cause the SER to be 1/4. Similarly, if there is one carrier, amongst N carriers in all, which is badly affected by interference, then the SER will be of the order of 1 in N, even with infinite SNR.

This tells us two things: *uncoded* OFDM is not satisfactory for use in such extremely selective channels, and, for any reasonable number of carriers, CW interference affecting one carrier is less of a problem than a 0 dB echo.

However, just adding hard-decision-based coding to this uncoded system is not enough, either—it would take a remarkably powerful hard-decision code to cope with an SER of 1 in 4! The solution is the use of convolutional coding with soft-decision decoding, *properly integrated* with the OFDM system.

Soft Decisions And Channel-State Information: First let us revise, for simplicity, 2-level modulation of a single carrier: one bit is transmitted per symbol, with say a '0' being sent by a modulating signal of -1V and a '1' by +1V. At a receiver, assuming that the gain is correct, we should expect to demodulate a signal always in the vicinity of either -1V or +1V, depending on whether a '0' or a '1' was transmitted, the departure from the exact values ±1V being caused by the inevitable noise added in transmission.

A *hard-decision* receiver would operate according to the rule that negative signals should be decoded as '0' and positive ones as '1,' 0V being the *decision boundary*. If the instantaneous amplitude of the noise were never to exceed ±1V then this simple receiver would make no mistakes. But noise may occasionally have a large amplitude, although with lower probability than for smaller values. Thus if say +0.5V is received, it most probably means that a '1' was transmitted, but there is a smaller yet still finite probability that actually '0' was sent. Common sense suggests that when a large-amplitude signal is received we can be more confident in the hard decision than if the amplitude is small.

This view of a degree of confidence is exploited in soft-decision Viterbi decoders. These maintain a history of many possible transmitted sequences, building up a view of their relative likelihoods and finally selecting the value '0' or '1' for each bit according to which has the *maximum likelihood*. For convenience, a Viterbi decoder *adds log*-likelihoods (rather than multiplying probabilities) to accumulate the likelihood of each possible sequence. It can be shown that in the case of BPSK or QPSK the appropriate log-likelihood measure or metric of the certainty of each decision is indeed simply proportional to the distance from the decision boundary. The slope of this linear relationship itself also depends directly on the signal-to-noise ratio. Thus the Viterbi decoder is fed with a *soft decision* comprising both the hard decision (the sign of the signal) together with a measure of the amplitude of the received signal.

With other rectangular-constellation modulation systems, such as 16-QAM or 64-QAM (see QAM In Cable Transmission in this chapter), each axis carries more than one bit, usually with Gray coding. At the receiver, a soft decision can be made separately for each received bit. The metric functions are now more complicated than for QPSK, being different for each bit, but the principle of the decoder exploiting knowledge of the expected reliability of each bit remains.

Metrics for COFDM are slightly more complicated. We start from the understanding that the soft-decision information is a measure of the confidence to be placed in the accompanying hard decision.

When data are modulated onto a single carrier in a time-invariant system then *a priori* all data symbols suffer from the same noise power on average; the soft-decision information simply needs to take note of the random symbol-by-symbol variations that this noise causes.

When data are modulated onto the multiple COFDM carriers, the metrics become slightly more complicated as the various carriers will have different signal-to-noise ratios. For example, a carrier which falls into a notch in the frequency response will comprise mostly noise; one in a peak will suffer much less. Thus in addition to the symbol-by-symbol variations there is another factor to take account of in the soft decisions: data conveyed by carriers having a high SNR are *a priori* more reliable than those conveyed by carriers having low SNR. This extra *a priori* information is usually known as *channel-state information* (CSI).

The CSI concept can be extended to embrace *interference* which affects carriers selectively.

Including channel-state information in the generation of soft decisions is the key to the unique performance of COFDM in the presence of frequency-selective fading and interference.

We return to the simple example in which there is a 0 dB echo of such a delay (and phase) as to cause a complete null on one carrier in 4. Figure 4 illustrates the effect of this selective channel: 1 carrier in 4 is nulled out, while 1 carrier in 4 is actually boosted, and the remaining 2 are unaffected. Note that received *power* is shown, to which the SNRs of the carriers will be proportional if the receiver noise is itself flat, as is usual. The 'mean power' marked is the mean of all carriers. It is equal to the total received power (via both paths) shared equally between all carriers.

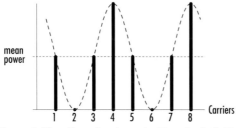

Received Power

mean power

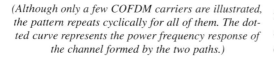

Carriers

figure 4. The effect of a channel with a single 0 dB echo of long delay, such that exactly 1 carrier in 4 is nulled out.

(Although only a few COFDM carriers are illustrated, the pattern repeats cyclically for all of them. The dotted curve represents the power frequency response of the channel formed by the two paths.)

In COFDM, the Viterbi metrics for each bit should be weighted according to the SNR of the carrier by which it traveled. Clearly, the bits from the nulled carriers are effectively flagged as having 'no confidence.' This is essentially the same thing as an *erasure*—the Viterbi decoder in effect just records that it has no information about these bits.

There is another well-known case of regularly-occurring erasures, namely *punctured codes*. Typically, convolutional codes intrinsically have code rates expressed as simple fractions like 1/2 or 1/3. When a code having higher rate (less redundancy) is needed then one of these lower-rate 'mother' codes is *punctured*, that is to say certain of the coded bits are just not transmitted, according to a regular pattern known to the receiver. At the receiver 'dummy bits' are re-inserted to replace the omitted ones, but are marked as erasures—bits having zero confidence—so that the Viterbi decoder treats them accordingly. Punctured codes obviously are less powerful than the mother code, but there is an acceptable steady trade-off between performance and code rate as the degree of puncturing is increased.

Suppose we take a rate-1/2 code and puncture it by removing 1 bit in 4. The rate-1/2 code produces 2 coded bits for every 1 uncoded bit, and thus 4 coded bits for every

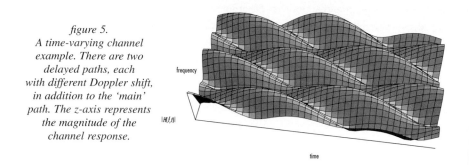

figure 5.
A time-varying channel
example. There are two
delayed paths, each
with different Doppler shift,
in addition to the 'main'
path. The z-axis represents
the magnitude of the
channel response.

frequency

|H(f,t)|

time

2 uncoded bits. If we puncture 1 in 4 of these coded bits then we clearly finish by transmitting 3 coded bits for every 2 uncoded bits. In other words we have generated a rate-2/3 code. Indeed, this is exactly how the rate-2/3 option of DVB-T is made.

Now return to our simple COFDM example in which 1 carrier in 4 is nulled out by the channel—but the corresponding bits are effectively flagged as erasures thanks to the application of channel-state information. 2 out of 3 of the remaining carriers are received at the same SNR as that of the overall channel, while 1 is actually boosted, having an improved SNR. Suppose that rate-1/2 coding is used for the COFDM signal. It follows that the SNR performance of COFDM with this *selective* channel should be very slightly better (because 1 carrier in 4 is boosted) than that for a single-carrier (SC) system using the corresponding punctured rate-2/3 code in a *flat* channel. In other words, the effect of this very selective channel on COFDM can be directly estimated from knowledge of the behavior of puncturing the same code when used in a SC system through a flat channel.

This explains how the penalty in required CNR for a COFDM system subject to 0 dB echoes may be quite small, provided a relatively powerful convolutional code is used together with the application of channel-state information.

Interleaving: So far we have considered a very special example so as to make it easy to explain by invoking the close analogy with the use of code puncturing. But what of other delay values?

If the relative delay of the echo is rather shorter than we just considered, then the notches in the channel's frequency response will be broader, affecting many adjacent carriers. This means that the coded data we transmit should not simply be assigned to the OFDM carriers in order, since at the receiver this would cause the Viterbi soft-decision decoder to be fed with clusters of unreliable bits. This is known to cause serious loss of performance, which we avoid by *interleaving* the coded data before assigning them to OFDM carriers at the modulator. A corresponding de-interleaver is used at the receiver before decoding. In this way the cluster of errors occurring when adjacent carriers fail simultaneously (as when there is a broad notch in the frequency response of the channel) is broken up, enabling the Viterbi decoder to perform better.

As just described, the process could be called *frequency interleaving*; as is used in DVB-T. It is all that is needed if the channel only varies slowly with time. In mobile operation (a key application for DAB) we may expect the various paths to be subjected to different and significant Doppler shifts, making the frequency response vary with time, figure 5. Furthermore, a vehicle may drive into shaded areas like underpasses so that all signals are severely attenuated for a period (not shown in figure 5). For this reason, in DAB the coded data are in addition re-distributed over time, providing *time interleaving*.

More coding: DAB conveys audio data, which, despite being compressed in source coding, is relatively robust to the effects of transmission errors[8]. The BER remaining after correction by the Viterbi decoder is adequate. On the other hand, the compressed video data of DVB-T is more susceptible to errors so that the residual BER at the output of the Viterbi decoder is too high.

Thus DVB-T includes a second stage of error coding, called the 'outer' coding, since in an overall block diagram it sandwiches the ('inner') convolutional coding. Data to be transmitted are first coded with a Reed-Solomon code, interleaved with an additional 'outer' interleaver, then passed to the 'inner' convolutional coder. At the receiver, the Viterbi decoder is followed by an 'outer' interleaver and the 'outer' R-S decoder. The R-S decoder uses hard decisions, but is able to reduce the BER substantially despite very modest extra redundancy having been added at the transmitter.

SINGLE-FREQUENCY NETWORKS

Our simple example of a 0 dB echo often crops up when considering SFNs. If two synchronized COFDM transmitters operate on a common frequency there will somewhere be locations where the two signals will be received at equal strength (and with a relative delay, depending on the geometry of the situation, which we assume to be within the system limits). An obvious question is: does reception suffer or benefit from this situation?

Clearly, compared with receiving either transmitter alone, the total-received-signal-to-noise power ratio (CNR) is doubled, i.e. increased by 3 dB, expressed in familiar decibel notation. However, the presence of the two transmissions makes reception *selective* rather than *flat* (as we might hope to have with a single transmission, without 'natural' echoes). This increases the CNR required to achieve the same BER, in a way which depends on the error-correcting code in use.

We have already seen a qualitative argument how this increase in CNR requirement may be closely related to the performance of punctured codes. Simulation shows that the increase in CNR requirement between flat and 0 dB-echo channels is just below 3 dB for a rate-1/2 code, while it is greater for higher-rate codes which have already been punctured. Practical experience supports the order of 3 dB for a rate-1/2 code, while for rate-2/3 the increase is of the order of 6 dB.

It follows that with rate-1/2 coding, receiving two signals of equal strength, in place of either one alone, increases the received CNR by 3 dB while also increasing the CNR required for satisfactory reception (in the now highly-selective channel) by about the same amount. The performance is thus unchanged by adding the second path.

Since for most practical purposes the case of the 0 dB echo appears to be more or less the worst one, this is very encouraging for planning and developing SFNs.

SUMMARY OF KEY DAB AND DVB-T FEATURES

Both DAB and DVB-T have flexibility built-in to cope with a range of circumstances and uses.

DAB has four modes with 192, 384, 768 or 1536 carriers and corresponding guard intervals from 31 to 246 µs. All occupy 1.536 MHz, use DQPSK and use both time- and frequency-interleaving.

DVB-T has two modes with either 1705 or 6817 carriers in 7.61 MHz bandwidth, with a wide range of guard intervals from 7 to 224 µs. Coherent demodulation is used, with QPSK/16-QAM/64-QAM constellations. Together with options for inner-code rate this provides extensive trade-off between ruggedness and capacity (from 5 to 31.7 Mbps). No time interleaving is used. The convolutional inner code is supplemented by a Reed-Solomon outer code. (The figures quoted above relate to the use of nominally 8 MHz channels. The DVB-T specification can be adapted to 6 or 7 MHz channels by simply scaling the clock rate; the capacity and bandwidth scale in proportion.)

CONCLUSIONS

COFDM, as used in DAB and DVB-T is very well matched to the terrestrial channel, being able to cope with severe multipath and the presence of co-channel narrowband interference. It also makes single-frequency networks possible.

COFDM is also adaptable to various uses by appropriate choice of parameters, both DAB and DVB-T having a range of options to facilitate this.

COFDM only works because all the key elements are correctly integrated: many orthogonal carriers, added guard intervals, interleaving, soft-decision Viterbi decoding and the use of channel-state information.

FOOTNOTES

1: Actually a complex conjugate, corresponding to the standard I-Q quadrature demodulation process.

2: In fact the 'integrate-and-dump' process can itself be shown to be equivalent to a filter with a $\mathrm{sinc}(\omega/\omega_u)$ characteristic, with nulls on all the carriers except the wanted one.

3: Actually it is precisely $63T_u/256 \approx 0.246T_u$.

4: For the mathematically inclined, the addition of the guard interval has in effect turned the normal process of convolution of the signal with the impulse response of the channel into a *circular convolution*, which corresponds to multiplication of DFT frequency coefficients.

5: Note that this does not lead to any loss of capacity or inefficient use of bandwidth. It merely corresponds to 'headroom' for the analogue filtering in the system.

6: Some carriers always carry further *continual-pilot* information which is used for synchronization.

7: Sub-sampled in both frequency and time.

8: Some more-susceptible data have special treatment.

REFERENCES

[1]: ETS 300 401 (1994): Radio broadcast systems; Digital Audio Broadcasting (DAB) to mobile, portable and fixed receivers. www.etsi.fr.

[2]: ETS 300 744 (1997): Digital broadcasting systems for television, sound and data services; framing structure, channel coding and modulation for digital terrestrial television. www.etsi.fr.

[3]: Stott, J.H., 1995. The effects of frequency errors in OFDM. *BBC Research and Development Report No. RD 1995/15.* www.bbc.co.uk/rd/pubs/reports/1995_15.html.

[4]: Stott, J.H., 1998. The effects of phase noise in COFDM. *EBU Technical Review*, No 276 (Summer 1998), pp. 12 to 25. www.bbc.co.uk/rd/pubs/papers/pdffiles/jsebu276.pdf.

The following further reading is recommended:

European Broadcasting Union (EBU), 1988. Advanced digital techniques for UHF satellite sound broadcasting. Collected papers on concepts for sound broadcasting into the 21st century.

Maddocks, M.C.D., 1993. An introduction to digital modulation and OFDM techniques. *BBC Research Department Report No. RD 1993/10.*

Stott, J.H., 1996. The DVB-Terrestrial (DVB-T) specification and its implementation in a practical modem. *Proceedings of 1996 International Broadcasting Convention, IEE Conference Publication No. 428*, pp. 255 to 260.

Oliphant, A., Marsden, R.P., Poole, R.H.M., and Tanton, N.E., 1996. The design of a network for digital terrestrial TV trials. *Proceedings of 1996 International Broadcasting Convention, IEE Conference Publication No. 428*, pp 242 to 247.

Møller, L.G., 1997. COFDM and the choice of parameters for DVB-T. *Proceedings of 20th International Television Symposium, Montreux.* www.bbc.co.uk/validate/paper_17.htm.

Stott, J.H., 1997. Explaining some of the magic of COFDM. *Proceedings of 20th International Television Symposium, Montreux.* www.bbc.co.uk/rd/pubs/papers/paper_15/paper_15.html.

Oliphant, A., 1997. VALIDATE—verifying the European specification for digital terrestrial TV and preparing for the launch of services. *Proceedings of 20th International Television Symposium, Montreux.* www.bbc.co.uk/rd/pubs/papers/paper_16/paper_16.html.

Morello, A., Blanchietti, G., Benzi, C., Sacco, B., and Tabone, M., 1997. Performance assessment of a DVB-T television system. *Proceedings of 20th International Television Symposium, Montreux.*

Mitchell, J. , and Sadot, P. The development of a digital terrestrial front end. *Proceedings of 1997 International Broadcasting Convention, IEE Conference Publication No. 447*, pp. 519-524 www.bbc.co.uk/rd/pubs/papers/paper_12/paper_12.html.

Nokes, C.R., Pullen, I.R., and Salter, J.E., 1997. Evaluation of a DVB-T compliant digital terrestrial television system. *Proceedings of 1997 International Broadcasting Convention, IEE Conference Publication No. 447*, pp. 331-336. www.bbc.co.uk/rd/pubs/papers/paper_08/paper_08.html.

Oliphant, A., 1998. VALIDATE—a virtual laboratory to accelerate the launch of digital terrestrial television. ECMAST Conference, May 1998. Berlin, Germany.

www.bbc.co.uk/rd/pubs/papers/ecmast22/ecmast22.html.

Nokes, C.R., 1998. Results of tests with domestic receiver IC's for DVB-T. *Proceedings of 1998 International Broadcasting Convention*, pp. 294-299.

ACKNOWLEDGEMENTS

The author wishes to thank the many colleagues, within the BBC and collaborating organizations throughout Europe, who have helped him to develop his understanding of COFDM. This section is based on a paper the author gave in July 1997 to an IEE Summer School in the U.K.

QAM IN CABLE TRANSMISSION

JOHN WATKINSON

Digital transmission consists of converting data into a waveform suitable for the path along which it is to be sent. The generic term for the path down which the information is sent is the channel, in this case a cable.

In real cables, the digital signal may originate with discrete states which change at discrete times, but the cable will treat it as an analog waveform and so it will not be received in the same form. Various loss mechanisms will reduce the amplitude of the signal. These attenuations will not be the same at all frequencies. Noise will be picked up in the cable as a result of stray electric fields or magnetic induction. As a result the voltage received at the end of the cable will have an infinitely varying state along with a degree of uncertainty due to the noise. Different frequencies can propagate at different speeds in the channel; this is the phenomenon of group delay. An alternative way of considering group delay is that there will be frequency-dependent phase shifts in the signal and these will result in uncertainty in the timing of pulses.

In a digital transmission, it is not the cable which is digital; instead the term describes the way in which the received signals are interpreted. When the receiver makes discrete decisions from the input waveform, it attempts to reject the uncertainties in voltage and time. The technique of channel coding is one where the transmitted waveforms are restricted to a set which allow the receiver to make discrete decisions despite the degradations caused by the analog nature of the cable.

Cables have the characteristic that as frequency rises, the current flows only in the outside layer of the conductor effectively causing the resistance to rise. This is the skin effect and is due to the energy starting to leave the conductors. As frequency rises still further, the energy travels less in the conductors and more in the insulation between them, and their composition becomes important and they have to be called dielectrics.

The conductor spacing and the nature of the dielectric determine the characteristic impedance of the cable. A change of impedance causes reflections in the energy flow and some of it heads back towards the source. Constant impedance cables with fixed conductor spacing are necessary, and these must be suitably terminated to prevent reflections.

At high frequencies, the time taken for the signal to pass down the cable is significantly more than the bit period. There are thus many bits in the cable which have been sent but which have yet to arrive. The voltage at the input of the cable can be quite different to that at the output because the cable has become a transmission line.

In a transmission line, the spectrum of the input signal is effectively split into different frequencies. Low frequencies travel as long wavelength energy packets and high frequencies travel as short wavelengths. The shorter the wavelength, the more times the energy has to pass in and out of the dielectric as it propagates. Unfortunately dielectrics are not ideal and not all of the energy stored per cycle is released. Some of it is lost as heat. High frequencies thus suffer more dielectric loss than low frequencies.

This frequency-dependent behavior is the most important factor in deciding how best to send data down a cable. As a flat frequency response is elusive, the best results will be obtained using a coding scheme that creates a narrow band of frequencies. Then the response can be made reasonably constant with the help of equalization. The decoder might adapt the equalization to optimize the error rate.

In digital circuitry, the signals are generally accompanied by a separate clock signal. It is generally not feasible to provide a separate clock in transmission applications. Cable transmission requires a self-clocking waveform. Clearly if data bits are simply clocked serially from a shift register, in so-called direct transmission, this characteristic will not be obtained. If all the data bits are the same, for example all zeros, there is no clock when they are serialized. This illustrates that raw data, when serialized, have an unconstrained spectrum. Runs of identical bits can produce frequencies much lower than the bit rate would suggest. One of the essential steps in a cable coding system is to narrow the spectrum of the data and ensure that a sufficient clock content is available.

The important step of information recovery at the receiver is known as data separation. The data separator is rather like an analog-to-digital converter because the two processes of sampling and quantizing are both present. In the time domain, the sampling clock is derived from the clock content of the channel waveform. The sampler makes discrete decisions along the time axis in order to reject jitter due to group delay variation.

In the voltage domain, the process of slicing converts the analog waveform from the channel back into a binary representation. The slicer is thus a form of quantizer which has a resolution of only a few bits. The slicing process makes a discrete decision about the voltage of the incoming signal in order to reject noise. Clearly the less noise there is in the channel, the more discrete levels can be distinguished by the quantizer and so the more bits it can output per sample. This is the principle of multi-level signaling.

Multi-level codes need less bandwidth because the more bits are carried in each symbol, the fewer symbols per second are needed for a given bit rate. The bandwidth efficiency of such codes is measured in bits/second/Hz. Cables have the advantage of low noise compared to radio broadcasting, and so they can use more levels. This compensates for the reduced bandwidth available in cables due to frequency dependent loss. As a result cable codes tend to use more signaling levels than radio transmission codes, which in turn use more levels than transmissions from satellites, which have plenty of bandwidth but poor noise characteristics because of the limited power available.

QUADRATURE AMPLITUDE MODULATION (QAM)

Quadrature Amplitude Modulation (QAM) is an ideal code for cable transmission. Figure 1 shows the example of 64-QAM. Incoming 6-bit data words are split into two three-bit words and each is used to amplitude modulate a pair of sinusoidal carriers which are generated in quadrature. The modulators are four-quadrant devices such that eight amplitudes are available, four which are in phase with the carrier and

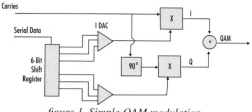

figure 1. Simple QAM modulation.

four which are antiphase. The two AM carriers are linearly added and the result is a signal which has 64 combinations of amplitude and phase. There is a great deal of similarity between QAM and the color subcarrier used in analog television in which the two color difference signals are encoded on in-phase and quadrature carriers. To visualize how QAM works, simply replace the analog R-Y and B-Y signals of NTSC with a pair of eight level signals. The result will be 64 possible vectors.

Like analog chroma, the QAM signal can be viewed on a vectorscope. Each bit pattern produces a different vector, resulting in a different point on the vectorscope screen. The set of 64 points is called a constellation. At the encoder, the constellation should be ideal, with regular spaces between the points. At the receiver, cable noise and group delay effects will disturb the ideal constellation and each point will become a "vector ball." The size of these balls gives an indication of the likely error rate of the cable. Clearly if they overlap, the decoder will be unable to distinguish discrete levels and phases and bit errors become inevitable.

The error correction coding of the system is designed to overcome reasonable bit error rates so that the transmitted data are essentially error free. This is important for digital television because MPEG compressed video data are sensitive to bit errors.

In a typical application, the data are randomized by addition to a pseudo-random sequence before being fed to the modulator. The use of randomizing and error correction is not part of QAM which is only a modulation technique. Practical systems need these additional processes.

The sampling clock is recovered at the decoder using a phase-locked loop (PLL) to regenerate it from the clock content of the QAM waveform. In phase-locked loops, the voltage-controlled oscillator is driven by a phase error measured between

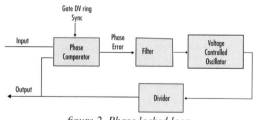

figure 2. Phase locked loop.

the output and some reference, as shown in figure 2, such that the output eventually has the same frequency as the reference. If a divider is placed between the VCO and the phase comparator, the VCO frequency can be made to be a multiple of the reference. This also has the effect of making the loop more heavily damped. Clearly data cannot be separated if the PLL is not locked, but it cannot be locked until it has seen transitions for a reasonable period. There will inevitably be a short delay on first applying the signal before the receiver locks to it.

ENGINEERING & TRANSMISSION

The QAM decoder can easily lock to the symbol rate so that it can set the PLO to the right frequency, but it also needs to be able to sample in the right phase. This can be done by sending a periodic synchronizing signal in a reference phase, much like analog chroma sends a burst at the beginning of every line.

Quadrature modulation appears to achieve the impossible by combining two signals into the space of one. Figure 3 shows how it works. At a) is shown the in-phase signal, which is a sine-wave. At two points per cycle the sine wave passes through zero, which it will do irrespective of the amplitude of the wave. At b) is shown the quadrature signal which is a cosine wave. This also passes through zero twice per cycle, but the points at which this happens are exactly half way between the points for the sine wave.

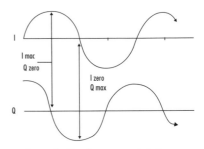

figure 3. Quadrature modulation.

When the cosine wave is at zero, the sine wave is at a peak. Thus if the waveform is sampled at that point, only the amplitude of the sine wave will be measured. One quarter of a cycle later, the sinewave will be at zero and the cosine wave will be at a peak. If the waveform is sampled at this point, only the amplitude of the cosine wave will be measured. The signals are independent and are said to be orthogonal.

If the receiver is synchronized so that the quadrature modulated signal is sampled at exactly 90-degree increments starting at zero degrees, the samples will represent alternate components which are effectively interleaved. In a sense quadrature modulation is an analog version of data multiplexing where two data streams can be sent down the same bitstream.

In a QAM receiver, the waveform is sampled twice per cycle in phase with the two original carriers so that each sample will represent the amplitude of one of the carriers alone. A sampler of this kind is effectively a phase sensitive rectifier and effectively it simultaneously demodulates and demultiplexes the QAM signal into a pair of 8-level signals.

The cable will have a certain amplitude loss which is a function of its length. The decoder will need an automatic gain control (AGC) system which produces a signal having a stable amplitude as an input for the slicing process. The synchronizing signal can also be used as an amplitude reference. The decoder gain is adjusted until the synchronizing signal has the correct amplitude. This will place the discrete levels of the signal in the center of quantizing intervals of the slicer.

In a digital decoder, the ADCs can be multi-bit devices so that a high resolution version of each sample is available. In the digital domain the AGC can be performed by multiplying the sample values by constants. The slicing process can be performed by comparing the values from the ADC with reference values. The digital decoder has the advantage that it can easily be integrated into an LSI chip at low cost.

APPENDIX A
DIGITAL TELEVISION
PRODUCTION AND TRANSMISSION

DTV IN THE REAL WORLD

UNDERSTANDING DIGITAL

PRE-PRODUCTION

PRODUCTION

AUDIO

GRAPHIC & COMPOSITING

POST PRODUCTION

DELIVERY & DUPLICATION

ENGINEERING & TRANSMISSION

APPENDIX

GLOSSARY

PRODUCTION AND
TRANSMISSION STANDARDS

The following three charts outline popular current analog and digital television production standards as well as the ATSC Table 3 transmission standards. ATSC Table 3 formats are not required and broadcasters can legally transmit any format they choose.

Following the charts is an essay on the difference between the production standard and the transmission standard centering around 704 pixels versus 720 pixels, and an essay on MPEG-2 splicing, editing and keying.

POPULAR ANALOG TELEVISION PRODUCTION AND TRANSMISSION STANDARDS (i=interlace)			
total lines	active lines	aspect ratio information	frame rate and scan
525 (NTSC)	483.5	4:3 (non-square pixel)	29.97i
625 (PAL/SECAM)	575.5	4:3 (non-square pixel)	25i
625 (PAL Plus)	575.5	16:9 (non-square pixel)	25i

DIGITAL TELEVISION PRODUCTION STANDARDS (i=interlace, p=progressive)					
vertical size value (active)	vertical size value (total)	horizontal size value (active)	horizontal size value (total)	aspect ratio information	frame rate and scan
1,080	1,250	1,920	2,376	16:9 (square pixel)	50p, 25i
1,035	1,125	1,920	2,200	16:9 (non-square pixel)	30i
1,080	1,125	1,920	2,640	16:9 (square pixel)	25p, 25i
1,080	1,125	1,920	2,200	16:9 (square pixel)	60p, 59.94p, 30p, 29.97p, 30i, 29.97i
1,080	1,125	1,920	2,750	16:9 (square pixel)	24p, 23.98p
720	750	1,280	1,650	16:9 (square pixel)	60p, 59.94p
483	525	720	858	16:9 (non-square pixel)	59.94p
486	525	720	858	16:9 (non-square pixel)	29.97i
486	525	960	1,144	16:9 (non-square pixel)	29.97i
576	625	720	864	4:3 (non-square pixel)	25i
486	525	948	1,135	4:3 (non-square pixel)	29.97i
576	625	948	1,135	4:3 (non-square pixel)	25i
486	525	768	910	4:3 (non-square pixel)	29.97i

ATSC TABLE 3 FORMATS FOR DTV TRANSMISSION (i=interlace, p=progressive)			
vertical size value (active)	horizontal size value (active)	aspect ratio information	frame rate and scan
(HD) 1,080	1,920	16:9 (square pixel)	24p, 30p, 30i
(HD) 720	1,280	16:9 (square pixel)	24p, 30p, 60p
(SD) 480	704	4:3 (non-square pixel)	24p, 30p, 30i, 60p
(SD) 480	704	16:9 (non-square pixel)	24p, 30p, 30i, 60p
(SD) 480	640	4:3 (square pixel)	24p, 30p, 30i, 60p

Note: These formats are known as the 18 "ATSC Table 3" formats (see Glossary). Each frame rate has a 1000/1001 frequency change to accommodate NTSC color (24=23.98, 30=29.97, 60=59.94), for a total of 36 formats. The fractional frame rate will remain part of the DTV landscape until NTSC is no longer needed.

Other organizations have their own version of Table 3; for example, the OCI-N OpenCable interim specification (www.opencable.com/pubdocs/OCI-N-INT01-991022.pdf) has 640x480 at 60p and 59.94p as an HDTV format and the draft of EIA-818, known as the DTV Cable Compatibility Specification, has 480 vertical lines matched with 720, 704, 640, 544, 528 and 352 active horizontal pixels.

SWEET 16 AND NEVER BEEN MISSED

MARK SCHUBIN

First, nothing is wrong with the number 704. It's divisible by two six times. That means it's divisible by 16, 16 x 2, and 16 x 4—nice features for MPEG compression. It's 11/10 of VGA's 640 horizontal pixels. And it's the star of ATSC A/53 Annex A Table 3; 16 of the 36 formats in that table have 704 active pixels per scanning line. There's just one problem with 704: It's not 720.

What's 720? Besides being 16 more than 704, it's the number of active pixels per scanning line in Recommendation 601, the first global video standard and the first for component digital video. That was followed by ANSI/SMPTE 125M, the D1 DVTR format, Quantel's Henry, Panasonic's D5, Sony's Digital Betacam,

Ampex's DCT, Tektronix's Profile—there's an awfully long list of teleproduction products with 720 active pixels.

Nevertheless, when Table 3 was being hashed out in 1995, it ended up with 704, not 720. Why? The key factor was probably the idea that some cable-TV and satellite programmers seemed to prefer half-resolution images to save bandwidth. Half of 720 is not divisible by MPEG's 16-pixel-wide macroblocks; half of 704 (352) is.

The number 352 doesn't exist, however, in Table 3. In places where it does exist, like the European ETSI standard ETR 154, the full resolution listed is 720, not 704.

In fact, just about every standard for component digital video worldwide features 720 and not 704. That includes European, Japanese, American and global standards. ATSC's own A/63 standard, intended for countries currently transmitting 625-line television, calls for 720, not 704.

It could be argued that it doesn't make any difference. The eight pixels shaved off each edge of the picture will never be seen. Any changes in aspect ratio that result will be insignificant. If DTV encoders accept standard inputs, who cares what they do to the edges?

The same year the ATSC standardized 704 pixels (1995), SMPTE approved a recommended practice on blanking, RP 187. It specifies a "clean" aperture of 708 x 480—not quite ATSC's 704 x 480 but closer than Rec. 601's 720 x 483.5. Why? Video processing "operations (including most filters) produce edge-related artifacts."

Consider an image where the first pixel is white. Coming out of blanking, the video signal will have to hit full level in just 74 ns. That could produce overshoots and ringing after filtering. SMPTE, therefore, defined a "clean aperture" that an "ideal display" would show and "a region where artifacts are acceptable" outside the clean aperture.

In other words, the clean aperture doesn't stay clean unless the unclean area surrounds it. To put it in SMPTE's words, "It should be noted that it is not the intent of this practice that information outside the clean aperture be discarded."

If only 704 pixels are transmitted, and any processing occurs after transmission (such as upconversion, fading to black, re-encoding for transmission on cable TV, consumer recording, etc.), then the artifacts enter the visible portion of the signal. An equivalent SMPTE clean aperture for 704 pixels would be just 692.

More recently, the issue of MPEG transcoding has been raised. If a video signal is compressed by a factor of, say, 10:1, then the encoder must throw away 90 percent of the information. It will make certain decisions about which 90 percent to discard. Succeeding stages of compression may or may not end up discarding the same. If they throw away previously undiscarded information, the effect is that of using a higher compression ratio, usually leading to worse pictures, the dreaded "concatenated compression."

Transcoding carries information about compression decisions from one stage to the next so that each encoder can discard the same information. As a result, the losses of concatenation are either reduced or eliminated.

Achieving transcoding requires matching MPEG macroblocks, with their associated motion-vectors. Unfortunately, the macroblocks of 720 don't align with those of 704. Transcoding, therefore, cannot be used where it may be needed most: in the heavy compression of DTV.

There are two solutions to these problems. One is to change 720 to 704—in every one of the world's standards, in all of the production equipment that exists, in the vast libraries of programming, in the SCTE digital cable-TV standard, and, presumably, even in the ATSC's A/63 standard.

The other is to allow 720-pixel lines in A/53. The FCC already does. Rejecting Table 3, they did not demand 704 pixels, but they kept Section 5, which says, "The allowable parameters shall be bounded by the upper limits specified for the Main Profile [of MPEG-2] at High Level."

Based on publicity about the chipsets being used, that's what DTV receiver manufacturers are doing, too—they're not decoding 36 different formats; they're simply decoding MPEG-2 MP@HL. It would seem, then, that 720-pixel video is not a problem for DTV.

ATSC-compliant encoders, however, must lop the edges off of 720- pixel imagery because 720 keeps being rejected by the ATSC Executive Committee, comprised in part by manufacturers who sell 720-pixel production equipment. Go figure.

MPEG-2 ART: SPLICING, EDITING AND KEYING

MICHAEL SILBERGLEID

Television, as we know it, has changed. Then again, television has always changed. From black and white to color, mono to stereo to multichannel, composite to component, analog to digital, baseband to compressed.

Perhaps the biggest changes are still to come—NTSC to ATSC and PAL to DVB. These changes mean a new way of working with video and audio in MPEG-2 compression, which is the specification for both transmission standards. This has led to a desire by broadcasters and broadcast equipment manufacturers on both sides of the Atlantic (as well as both sides of the Pacific) to remain either in baseband as long as possible before compression, or once compressed to stay compressed.

The reasons for this are simple: When you compress a signal, you are throwing away part of that signal—something you might need later, and compression encoding and decoding cycles can have an unwanted effect on the quality of the image and sound.

So ever since manufacturers, broadcasters and regulatory bodies decided that MPEG-2 would be a good idea for one part of the broadcast chain (transmission), the industry has been trying to adopt MPEG-2 to all of the other parts of the chain—production, post and storage so that once in MPEG-2, you could stay that way throughout the chain.

Unfortunately, we tend to want to do things to our video (like dissolves, wipes and keys) which make life in the MPEG-2 world rather difficult. The consensus has been that you couldn't switch, splice, edit, key or do effects in the MPEG-2 realm accurately. That isn't, and has never been altogether true.

WHAT MPEG-2 IS AND ISN'T

MPEG-2 is just a set of compression tools. It is not a tape format or a transmission format (although there are MPEG-2 tape recorders). For production and post, we use the MPEG-2 4:2:2 toolkit. For transmission, we use the MPEG-2 4:2:0 toolkit. While this is an ultra-simplistic way of looking at MPEG-2, it is accurate.

Keep in mind that there are three types of MPEG-2 frames and that you can use different combinations of these frames during compression.

I frame: Intraframe. This frame contains all the information needed to construct a complete frame of video. It is exactly like a M-JPEG or DV frame in that it contains all the information needed to construct a single video frame. Video that is encoded using only I frames can be switched and edited (cuts only) without having to decompress the signal. Provides the least encoding efficiencies since the complete frame is encoded.

P frame: Predictive. The frame is encoded using motion-compensation prediction from a past reference picture. Contains the difference between the actual image and the predicted image. Provides better encoding efficiencies than I frames.

B frame: Bi-directional predictive. The frame is encoded using motion-compensation prediction from both a past and future reference picture. Contains the difference between the actual image and the predicted image—it is not an average of the previous and future frames. Provides the best encoding efficiencies, however, a third memory buffer is required in addition to the buffers for past and future reference (I and P) frames. Fast search modes ignore B frames.

MPEG-2 streams can be encoded using I frames only, I and P frames, I and B frames, or I, P and B frames. I frames are always needed and are the first frame in a Group of Pictures (GoP), which then ends just before the next I frame. GoPs can have a length of one (all I frames) or more. The larger the GoP, the more efficient the compression encoding, but the harder it is to manipulate and survive errors in transmission (since an I frame is needed as a reference).

So, MPEG-2 causes problems because:

- If you try to manipulate anything other than an I frame, it's like trying to edit or switch on a frame that doesn't exist...because it doesn't.
- You can't manipulate something, like an MPEG-2 frame, that really isn't video.

Unfortunately, television has progressed from its early days when camera lens turret moves would be seen on the air and the viewing public accepted them. (If you've never seen a lens turret move, imagine seeing a wide shot, your picture going blurry then black for a second and then seeing a close-up). Today, we want everything to be seamless and perfect. Unfortunately, MPEG-2 makes that rather difficult. Here's why:

SPLICING

You want to switch between two MPEG-2 streams. To do this perfectly, the streams need to be synchronized. To do it when you push the "take" button, they also must have an I-frame pass by the switch at the right moment. With I frame only this is simple, but imagine having a GoP where I frames come every half a second or more.

There are some ways around this. The NDS System 3000 MPEG Splicer/ Transcoder can switch between three MPEG-2 streams. The catch is that you can only splice in non-seamless and near-seamless modes. During a non-seamless splice, the viewer would see either a blank or frozen frame generated by the viewer's decoder for anywhere from three to 26 frames depending on the splice point and when the next I frame appears.

For near-seamless splicing, there must be control over one of the sources according to Mike Knowles, manager of business development-digital terrestrial for NDS. Therefore that source must be local and on disk. With near-seamless splicing, the delay happens at the station. When the "take" button is pressed, the splice doesn't occur until after the last frame in the GoP, so the next I frame comes from local material. The latency for near-seamless splicing is dependent on the size of the GoP from the outside source and where in the GoP the "take" button is pressed.

The Philips DVS 4800 StreamCutter currently provides seamless splicing, but in a slightly different way. The StreamCutter supports local insertion (remember the need to have control of at least one local source) and switching between a single high definition source and multiple standard definition programs for ATSC. For DVB, the StreamCutter handles up to five program streams.

While StreamCutter does not rely on the existence of splicing points (a marker for clean splices within the MPEG-2 bitstream), it can utilize them when they are present (and available) for its Seamless Splicing Point Mode, where the main and local streams must contain compatible and aligned splicing points.

The Seamless Uniform Color Pictures (UCP) mode is somewhat visually similar to NDS's non-seamless splice except that a uniform color (or black) is sent by the StreamCutter and seen by the viewer instead of a decoder-generated frozen picture or black. The UCP period is fixed and is less than half a second. But there is a slight delay as the system waits for the end of the GoP before sending the color.

One of the best features of the StreamCutter is that it can simultaneously switch four bitstreams each containing a single video component, or a single bitstream containing up to four video components. With StreamCutter, if you're already multiplexed for four channels, you can replace any one of those channels without having to demux.

StreamCutter supports DVB-compliant streams up to at least 80 Mbps as well as 19.39 Mbps ATSC streams. All interfaces are DVB-ASI.

Hewlett-Packard used a buffering technique within their MPEG-2 MediaStream family of products for MPEG switching. HP's "CleanCut" technology provides seamless cuts-only capability between bitstreams coming off the server as video. This may seem fairly simple, but is actually very complex due to timing issues. What happens is that the server 'pre-charges' the 'cut-to' decoder with the complete GoP so that a splice can be made on any frame within the video domain. Sort of like an MPEG-2 frame store and synchronizer.

C-Cube Microsystems has a lot to gain by folks wanting to decode then re-encode—since they make the chips that do the encoding and decoding. Their DVxpress-MX chip may be the world's first all-digital, mixed format compression chip for MPEG-2 (4:2:2 and 4:2:0) and DV25 (as well as another model that adds DV50) (4:2:2, 4:2:0 and 4:1:1), but in order to do the conversion, the single chip converts the compressed video to digital baseband—with a transcoding latency of seven to eight frames. Dr. Feng-Ming Wang, C-Cube's general manager for the PC/Codec division believes that "the MPEG domain is always limited" and that baseband provides the "least possible problems." Dr. Wang says that the biggest problem is maintaining a compliant MPEG bitstream after the signal is modified without being decoded. "Baseband," he says, "is easy."

Baseband may be easy, but most experts agree that it is not the most efficient way of dealing with the need to manipulate video encoded as MPEG-2.

Other solutions, like those under development from Lucent Technologies and Sony involve not just locating the I frame for splicing, but in forcing the creation of an I frame through transcoding so that a splice can take place at any time.

EDITING

How do you edit on a frame that doesn't exist? For the FAST silver. (formerly FAST601) MPEG-2 nonlinear editor the answer is easy...all frames exist. silver. encodes everything with I frames so each frame can stand on its own. If you want to do a cut, you can do it in the MPEG-2 realm and not loose quality by decompressing and recompressing. Of course if you want to do anything else (dissolve, key, wipe, etc.) silver. will still decode to baseband, manipulate the video, and re-encode the result to MPEG-2.

Sony's Betacam SX format works very differently. BetaSX uses I and B frames for efficient compression during recording. But for editing, Sony decodes back to baseband video. Since the frames that the B frame is using for bi-directional prediction are already recorded on the BetaSX tape, a memory buffer lets the B frame see ahead before conversion to baseband.

Sony's hybrid DNW-A100 Beta SX DVTR does MPEG cuts only editing without going to baseband since the file is being read off the disk and being manipulated by a playout list.

KEYING (AND EFFECTS)

On-screen logos are everywhere. Stations and networks branding themselves in the eyes of the viewer. But what if the signal coming into your plant is already compressed for transmission, like the recent Harris ATSC pre-compressed feed of the Space Shuttle Discovery launch with John Glenn? You might think that you would have to decode all of the picture. While that may have been the popular theory, technology is advancing to the point where you can do your keying without having to decode entirely to baseband.

Today, if you want to do a key on compressed video, you no longer have to decode the entire frame. Pro-Bel offers a logo inserter that enables logos and IDs that are stored as bitmapped files to be directly inserted into an MPEG-2 bitsream. By using a new transport stream manipulation technology developed by the Institut fÿr Rundfunktechnik (IRT), the research and development body of the public broadcasting authorities of Germany, Austria and Switzerland, the bitstream is only decoded in the area required for graphic insertion on a macroblock level, so that the remainder of the picture passes virtually unaltered. Both transparent and opaque graphics can be faded in and out using pre-set rates at user-defined screen locations.

While not just for keying, Snell & Wilcox is using MOLE technology, as developed by the ATLANTIC project (BBC [U.K.], Centro Studi e Laboratori telecomunicazione [Italy], Ecole Nationale Superieure des Telecommunications [France], Ecole Polytechnique Fédérale de Lausanne [Switzerland], Electrocraft [U.K.], Fraunhofer-Institut für Integrierte Schaltungen [Germany], Instituto de Engenharia de Sistemas e Computadores [Portugal], Snell & Wilcox [U.K.]) to keep concatenation errors to a minimum. MOLE decoders forward the previous encoding decisions at the macroblock level invisibly through the serial digital signal path, so that subsequent encoders can 'clone' the original encoding process, except where the picture has changed (wipes, dissolves and keys).

Thomson has what they call the "Helper Channel." Similar to MOLE technology, the helper channel has decoder-generated metadata placed in the vertical interval of a digital signal derived from a Helper Channel-equipped MPEG-2 decoder and used by a Helper Channel-equipped encoder to re-encode the signal after manipulation. While slightly less efficient (and less expensive) then MOLE technology, the Helper Channel is another way to get around the problem of having to decode the entire frame—and it's available now, while MOLE technology is awaiting SMPTE standardization.

Philips, however, is the technological leader in MPEG-2 keying and picture manipulation with their MPEG Object (Logo) Insertion system. At a demonstration at IBC 1998, hidden in a section of their booth, Philips' Vincent Boutroux of the Digital Signal Processing group in France showed what he could do with a business card.

First he would scan in the logo off a business card, then he would place that logo in the picture. The difference between other systems and the Philips system is that Vincent did not decode the background video to baseband. The system works by using transcoding technology and DCT coefficients.

Images can be any size and shape but are currently displayed transparent or up to about 80 percent opacity and their video levels follow the background video.

While there is some image flashing as the system learns the MPEG-2 sequence of the background video, the system does indeed work.

In fact, logos can be made to fly in and out if so desired, or a ticker can be placed on the screen. All without conversion to baseband.

ONE OTHER SMALL PROBLEM

Due to the latency between the encoder at the broadcast facility and the decoder at the viewing point, techniques that we take for granted in analog will have to find other solutions. Two of the most prominent are time and cueing.

If you give out a time tone at the top of each hour, you can compensate for your station's encoder latency, but there is no way to compensate for the viewer's decoder latency (and each brand will have a different latency). To the viewer, your top of-the hour chime will be close, but not exact.

For news organizations that use off-air cueing for live remote reports, the latency at the reporter's TV set will be too great for the signal to be useful. For this task, private radio frequencies (which will have to be coordinated since everyone will want one) with IFBs are one solution while reporters learn not to watch themselves on-air.

APPENDIX B
STORAGE AND ARCHIVING/
ASSET MANAGEMENT

DTV IN THE REAL WORLD

UNDERSTANDING DIGITAL

PRE-PRODUCTION

PRODUCTION

AUDIO

GRAPHIC & COMPOSITING

POST PRODUCTION

DELIVERY & DUPLICATION

ENGINEERING & TRANSMISSION

APPENDIX

GLOSSARY

STORAGE AND ARCHIVING
IN THE AGE OF DIGITAL

KEN KERSCHBAUMER

One of the biggest issues facing broadcast and teleproduction professionals is how to archive digital media. In the past, archiving was done one way and one way only—by creating shelf upon shelf of tape storage space to hold videotapes containing source material and completed programs.

But the digital age provides a number of options for archiving. They include:

- Archiving digital tapes in a way similar to today's archive process—placing tapes on a shelf, barcoded and indexed.
- Transferring data onto data storage tape, like the Ampex DST system, which allows for quick access to hours of material.
- Using disk arrays, once the cost point becomes low enough and storage capacity increases enough to make it cost effective.
- Combining any of the above, or modifications which include the use of robotic tape libraries and analog tape machines.

The traditional method of archiving will remain relatively the same—buy some shelves and stack some tapes. The advantage of the traditional method is cost, as you would be limited to the cost of the original media, the shelving, some database software, barcoding equipment, and an archivist. The disadvantage? You won't be taking advantage of other digital and computer technologies to improve the speed and accuracy with which users can retrieve video and audio content.

The second method, the use of data storage tapes require the digital video and audio material on the original tapes to be transferred to data tape drives. Once on the data storage tape, information can be gathered off the tapes quickly, and if a cache drive or similar products from companies like StorageTek are used, a "nearline" environment is created. Nearline takes the information you call up from tapes and then stores it in a disk cache, which allows for easy access to the desired information.

Because the information on data storage tapes is kept in compressed data mode, it will require far less bandwidth and fewer tapes than the traditional tape storage method. For example, data storage systems like the one available from Ampex can currently store approximately 30 hours of material per tape.

In addition, because the tape libraries have sustained transfer rates of 15 megabytes per second, compressed video files can be moved from tape to the cache disk via SCSI data ports at multiples of realtime, reducing wear on the machines, and freeing staff for other productive activities. Fibre channel networks can be used for even faster transfer time.

Another advantage of data storage tape is that because it has similarities to videotape storage the transition is easier. For example, on high-performance helical scan data drives, longitudinal tracks are used to identify the address of a file on tape. This is similar to the way longitudinal time code is used to locate video elements.

Data storage tape is not without its disadvantages. For instance, simple audio or video insert edits are no longer available, because there is no audio or video to insert edit into. The files are only a compressed digital data representation of the original analog or digital audio or video. When a file is overwritten, or replaced, it is referred to as an "append." Once a file is appended, all information already on the tape following the append is lost unless the tape drive is sophisticated enough to support partitioning. Partitioning permits administrators to divide a tape into many small segments where only the information contained within the partition will be affected by appending.

As a result, partitioning is a key feature for broadcasters who plan to store constantly changing video such as commercial spots. Standard partition sizes can be formatted to accommodate the size of the average commercial. This allows replacement of only a single spot within a given partition, and does not affect the rest of the items stored on the tape.

The other drawback to data storage tape is that it is still tape. Unless a disk system is used, you'll still have linear access tapes on a shelf. Granted, much fewer tapes, but tapes nonetheless.

VIDEO SERVERS

The introduction of video server and disk array technology into the video marketplace signaled a major turning point in the concept of how video content would be handled within a broadcast station or post production facility. In addition, because the servers use similar technology to that found in computer hard drives, the video market was introduced to the concept of rapid hardware introductions that offer vast improvements over previous generation's capabilities.

Today video server technology is still too new to provide a cost-effective, 100 percent archiving solution. Disk capacity is still too small to allow for cost-effective archive systems to be created and maintained. But video servers, for all their current limitations, do hold the key to a future filled with easy access to hour upon hour of video and audio.

Until the cost of server storage reaches a point where it's affordable to have 100 percent online storage, hybrid solutions will be needed. One example of a hybrid solution consists of RAID-based online storage used in conjunction with a nearline robotic tape library and an offline computer-controlled analog or digital videotape player array. With the use of a storage management software system that is based on a pre-programmed priority or history of usage, it's possible to contain the costs and access times involved in retrieving content.

FAST ACCESS

The biggest advantage video servers offer is online or nearline access to desired video content (also called Video On Demand—VOD and Near Video On Demand-NVOD, respectively). Over the years, video indexing has always been the top challenge to maintaining a simple-to-use archive. Archivists would watch a videotape and then type in the key words that would allow a future user to easily gain access to the desired footage.

The difficulty, however, is that the archive process is reliant on the judgment of the archivist, and therefore is subject to differences of interpretation as to which videos would be listed under which keywords.

But in order to fully take advantage of the speed and flexibility offered by video server archiving, a more complex system for properly indexing the video content is required.

One manufacturer of a video indexing system, IslipMedia, has an indexing process that consists of five steps. The first step is the digitizing of the audio and video material, either analog or digital, into a standards-based MPEG format. Then the material is sent to a fast processor that generates a time aligned full-content topical index using speech and language understanding.

Next the video is segmented into meaningful "video paragraphs" using language, image, and audio cues. Image analysis on the video portion of the data then creates the filmstrips and icons to include key scenes. Finally, a comprehensive full-content index of the video collection is built.

DTV IN THE REAL WORLD

UNDERSTANDING DIGITAL

PRE-PRODUCTION

PRODUCTION

AUDIO

GRAPHIC & COMPOSITING

POST PRODUCTION

DELIVERY & DUPLICATION

ENGINEERING & TRANSMISSION

APPENDIX

GLOSSARY

BUILDING AN INDEX

If the video information you're looking for is stored on a video server, calling up clips on a given subject will be as simple as calling up word documents on a word processor, or doing a term search on an Internet search engine with a browser. But unlike a word document, where a keyword text search is the most accurate, an accurate video search system should include text, edits, and images. The creation of complex video indexing systems is where much energy, time and money is being expended by a number of manufacturers. But the future of archive retrieval will be keyword, image, and even based on voices—quite an advantage over current retrieval systems.

The approaches taken by the different video indexing systems may vary slightly, but all will use three broad categories of technologies to create and search a digital video library or broadcast and unedited video and audio materials.

The first way to index material is through text processing. This technique will look at the textual representation of the words that were spoken, as well as other text annotations. These may be derived from the generated transcript, accompanying notes or from the closed captioning that might be available on broadcast material.

Text analysis of scripts can work on an existing transcript and segment the text into video paragraphs. In addition, an analysis of keyword prominence allows users to identify important sections in the transcript, and to more easily search for relevant video information. For instance, suppose you're looking for video that appears while the script mentions "the evolution of species." Simply type in the phrase and the system will pull up all clips that mention the whole phrase or the words "evolution" or "species."

Next is image analysis. This method looks at the images in the video portion of the MPEG-encoded stream. The analysis is used two ways: first, for the identification of scene breaks and to select static frame icons that are representative of a scene; second, to identify a specific image, such as that of a celebrity whose image and name are stored in a reference database and then compared to the archived material for a match.

For scene break identification, image statistics are computed for primitive image features such as color histograms, and these are used for indexing, matching, and segmenting images.

For example, color histograms will measure differences from scene to scene to automatically tell the server where to begin and end a given video paragraph. Those scenes with little change and disparity will be listed as one paragraph, while those with greater changes from frame to frame will be listed as individual scenes.

Optical flow analysis is another important method of visual segmentation and description based on interpreting camera motion. Pans, zooms and cuts can be interpreted by examining the geometric properties of the optical flow vec-

---

tors. According to a report in the August 1997 *SMPTE Journal*, using the Lucas-Kanade gradient descent method for optical flow, individual regions can be tracked from one frame to the next. By measuring the velocity that individual regions show over time, a motion representation of the scene is created. Drastic changes in this flow indicate random motion, and therefore, new scenes. These changes will also occur during gradual transitions between images, such as fades or special effects.

The final way to search through an archive will be by speech analysis. One method used to automatically transcribe the content of the video material for American English content is the Sphinx-II system, a large-vocabulary, speaker-independent continuous speech recognizer created at Carnegie Mellon is used. The process addresses three knowledge sources: acoustic modeling, pronunciation modeling and language modeling.

The Sphinx-II system uses semi-continuous Hidden Markov Models, a statistical representation of speech events (e.g. word), to characterize context-dependent phones (triphones), including between-word context. The recognizer processes a utterance in three steps. It makes a forward time synchronous pass using full between-word models, Viterbi scoring and a trigram language model. This produces a word lattice where words may have only one begin time but several end times. The recognizer then makes a backward pass that uses the end times from the words in the first pass and produces a second lattice that contains multiple begin times for words. An A algorithm is used to generate the best hypothesis from these two lattices.

CONCLUSION

The future of archiving promises to be one filled with greater accuracy, flexibility and ease of use compared to yesterday's systems. Shuttling through tape after tape could very well become a thing of the past, as users instead shuttle through thumbnail images of the first scene of a given clip on the video servers and RAID arrays, using tools similar to today's World Wide Web search engines. Archiving will become even more important, as consistency and thoroughness will be needed for optimum efficiency.

In addition, constant improvements in computer processing and bandwidth will change the capabilities of video servers and indexing systems. What tomorrow's archiving systems will eventually offer is anyone's guess, but constant improvements in server technology make future capabilities seem limitless.

REFERENCES

[1] Wactler, H.D., Hauptmann, A.G., Smith, M.A., Pendyala, K.V., and Garlington, D., "Automated Video Indexing of Very Large Video Libraries", *SMPTE Journal*, August, 1997.

[2] Pendyala, K.V., Wachtler, H.D., and Juliano, M.J., "Automated Indexing

and Retrieval From Large Digital Video Libraries", Islip Media Network, 1997 NAB Broadcast Engineering Conference Proceedings.

[3] Hennessy, John, "The Role of Data Storage in Broadcasting's Future", Director of Business Development, Ampex Corporation, *Television Broadcast*, November, 1997.

DIGITAL ASSET MANAGEMENT
CRAIG BIRKMAIER

"*The business of digital television broadcasting is the management of the data multiplex that feeds the 19 megabit per second channel, so as to maximize the revenue that can be produced at any given moment in time.*"

Welcome to the brave new world of digital television.

The statement above was the cornerstone of a paper presented by the author at the 31st SMPTE Advanced Motion Imaging Conference in February 1997. "A Visual Compositing Syntax for Ancillary Data Broadcasting," the paper explored the new medium of digital television and emerging requirements to re-engineer the way digital video and other forms of digital media content are conceived, produced, distributed and consumed.

The underlying premise of the business model suggested in the statement above infers that we can measure the tangible value of *bits*, in much the same way that program content and commercial inventories represent television industry assets today. The fundamental difference in this business model is that the broadcaster is no longer trying to maximize revenue by delivering the largest number of eyeballs; with digital broadcasting it will be possible to deliver bits to many different groups of eyeballs simultaneously, or multiple streams of information to a single viewer. Equally important, the broadcaster may find that it is better to deliver simultaneous "competing" services through the digital channel, rather than risk the possibility that viewers will tune into another multiplex to find the desired information.

The implications of managing a program multiplex will ripple back through every aspect of the content creation process. Major content producers will be expected to deliver not only the program content, but ancillary data about the program that enhances the viewing experience, and thus the value, of the asset.

The concept of digital asset management extends into every aspect of digital television, from concept to final delivery of content. This section will provide a quick overview of asset management and the role that it may play in the future of digital television.

MANAGING THE CONTENT CREATION PROCESS

Virtually every aspect of the processes we now use to create and distribute video content can be considered an asset management challenge. An asset is the actual piece of content to be tracked and catalogued. Thus, a digital asset may be a computer file that is or contains the content to be managed. When we think about the entertainment industry, we tend to think about assets as a movie, video program or commercial (in other words, a completed project) that has been digitized. In reality, any piece of a project—a frame, a cel, a scene, etc.—can become a digital media asset.

It is easy to compare the digital asset to the physical assets we work with every day.

In some cases, however, it may be difficult to actually digitize the asset, as with the costumes and props that fill up warehouses around movie studio lots. Even in this case, however, the physical asset can be managed by maintaining information about it in a database—text descriptions, photographs or the original computer generated drawings used to create the physical asset.

In most cases, there is a wealth of information about the digital assets we work with that is less tangible. We call this *metadata*—the data that describes the data. Metadata describes attributes of an asset that may be needed for further processing, or that may be of interest to someone who is consuming the final product.

For example, an attribute could be related to the digitized audio or video file:
- creation date
- creator
- file type
- name of file
- size of file
- project name
- episode
- scene
- scene description
- content rating (language, nudity, violence, etc.)
- actor(s)

Or, it could be related to the technical characteristics of the data:
- acquisition format
- audio track characteristics
- frame rate
- spatial resolution/aspect ratio
- colorimetry and gamma characteristics
- processing history
- composition information (e.g. related matte/alpha channels)

Or, it could relate to the presentation of the content:
- pan and scan coordinates
- motion vectors for path based animation of an overlay object
- versioning information (suggested editing to meet time or rating requirements)
- scene-based cropping or masking of content to comply with rating requirements
- storyline information and key scenes that can be used to generate promos

While all of this information is available at some point in the production process, it has been difficult, if not impossible, to keep track of it. Most of this data is discarded along the way, or stored in proprietary file formats that are meaningless, except to the computer that created the file.

The notion of appending metadata to the digitized asset has been enabled, in part, by the migration of virtually every aspect of the content creation process to computer-based tools. The next step is to build the links between these tools that allow the metadata to be appended to media files in a way that is virtually transparent to the artists and technicians who produce the content.

In addition to the need for computer-based tools, there are two important prerequisites that enable such an approach to the re-engineering of the content creation process:

1. The ability to network all of the systems that create and process the data together so that it can be shared; and

2. An asset management system that provides the framework for entering information about, and managing the digital assets.

An asset management system is a group of software applications and subsystems that work together to form a complete system for the customer. This could contain multiple client/server applications, database systems, as well as many different types of hardware: PC, Mac, SGI, media servers, and networked video processing devices.

It is not the intent of this section to fully describe the functionality of an asset management system. Suffice it to say that this is an area of intense product development activity among vendors of computer software, hardware and networking products, and film/video production systems.

METADATA:
THE DIGITAL VERTICAL BLANKING INTERVAL

The analog television systems we are replacing dedicated a significant portion of the available bandwidth to synchronization signals contained within the vertical and horizontal blanking intervals, when a CRT display is resetting the scanning beam to start a new line or new video field. There is no vertical interval (or horizontal blanking) in a digital video transmission; these are issues to be dealt with in the local decoding and display hardware.

The display system is now decoupled from the transmission system, and the format that will be used locally to display the content; the video decoder/display processor must accommodate all forms of content to the local display environment; it is highly likely that the display processor will generate visual objects locally and compose them with streaming audio and video content.

Even as the MPEG-2 video coding standards, upon which virtually all digital television systems are based, begin to be deployed, work is nearing completion within the MPEG-4 committee on a standard to allow elements of programs to be composed in the television appliance (including a video or still image background and multiple visual objects or sprites). This work is converging with the rapid growth of open Internet standards to redefine the expected role of digital television appliances.

We can now begin to think of a digital television receiver as a computer with an Internet address. It will be able to receive content customized for viewer preferences or to which a viewer subscribes. In-home digital media servers will be able to filter information from a broadcast data multiplex and store it for later consumption. In other words, it may soon be possible for viewers to subscribe to content of interest and consume it on-demand, rather than synchronous with the transmission.

Broadcasters will provide a variety of "on-demand" services to their communities, both through their DTV channel and Internet Web servers. News, election returns, sports scores, the local weather forecast, program guides, city directories, restaurant and movie guides...The server that feeds this information to the Web will also feed the DTV data multiplex, periodically updating information stored in the digital media servers of the "viewers."

The traditional assumption that television broadcasting is a one-way medium incapable of delivering interactive services has been rendered meaningless by the shift to digital technology. Consumers may have several back channel options for interacting with television broadcasts—telco, cable and wireless. More important, however, they may not need or want any back channel to consume interactive services delivered as data through the DTV channel. The ability to store broadcast data locally, in an information appliance, makes it possible to deliver interactive applications in much the same way that the Internet currently broadcasts data to servers all over the world.

For example, using the full bandwidth of a 6 MHz DTV channel, a broadcaster can deliver 72 megabytes of data in 30 seconds. This data may include audio, video and graphic objects that are combined in the receiver to create a traditional linear television commercial—it may also include the elements of a Web page to provide an interactive experience for the viewer, such as an electronic brochure. In other words, the digital broadcaster can provide virtually any service that can be delivered by any other data network; and a wired back channel can be used to support transactions, including on-demand data broadcast services.

Perhaps the most important implication, however, is that broadcasters have sufficient bandwidth to deliver high quality audio and video along with these new interactive services. Equally important, they can do this in a totally non-invasive manner. The viewer can choose whether they want to send any information back, essentially building a privacy firewall between the viewer and the service provider. This level of privacy does not exist when a consumer connects to an Internet Web site, as a record of the visit can be recorded by the Web server.

The bottom line is that DTV is likely to evolve into an entirely new medium. As with the transition from radio to television, this medium will require a new business model; the approach described at the beginning of this chapter, a business model that leverages the ability to broadcast data.

MANAGING THE BROADCAST DATA MULTIPLEX

The best way to look at this model is through the management of the data multiplex. There are three general categories of data that may be included in

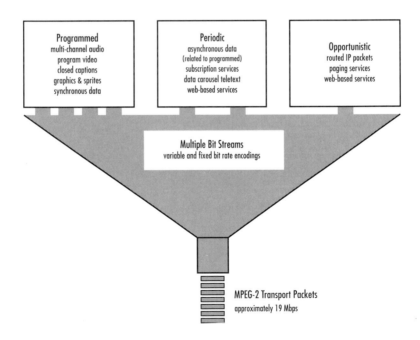

figure 1. The broadcast data multiplex.

the multiplex: programmed, periodic and opportunistic (see figure 1: the broadcast data multiplex).

Programmed data looks the most familiar. These are bits that a broadcaster contracts to deliver at a given point in time—for example, a free and clear program, perhaps simulcast on an NTSC channel, provided to meet the broadcaster's public service commitment. Programmed data is *isochronous* or realtime. These packets must arrive on-time or they are useless.

There are two variations on MPEG-2 encoding of realtime video/audio programs; fixed bit rate and variable bit rate. The choice can have a significant impact on quality of the video that is delivered and the management of the data multiplex.

Entropy coding techniques, such as those used in MPEG-2, produce a variable amount of data, based on the information content of the pictures that are being encoded. With fixed bit rate encoding, as the name implies, the encoder attempts to maintain a constant bit rate. It achieves this by varying the level of quantization, sometimes producing visible compression artifacts when the information content of the pictures is high.

Variable bit-rate coding attempts to maintain a constant level of picture quality by keeping the level of quantization fixed, and letting the bit rate increase with pictures of increased coding complexity. Typically, the decoder is set to operate with an average and peak bit rate in mind.

Encoding video for release using the DVD formats provides a good example. The average bit rate is typically determined by the length of the program or movie being encoded—total capacity divided by total duration determines the average bit rate target. Peak bit rate is established by the peak transfer rate for the DVD disc—rates vary with single and dual layer discs. In digital broadcasting, an example of peak bit rate would be 19 Mbps peaks in HDTV programs encoded for a DTV channel.

In DTV applications, variable bit rate coding offers a potential quality-of-service advantage by delivering consistent picture quality. It also offers a potential business advantage by maximizing the revenue produced by a DTV data multiplex. For example, a broadcaster that carries two programmed services can set the peak bit rates for each so that they do not exceed the 19 Mbps available. When they operate below these peaks—which is most of the time—any data packets left over can be used for periodic and opportunistic services.

Unlike the isochronous nature of video programs, periodic data can be delivered in an *asynchronous* manner—when it can be fit in. A good example of periodic data is the Teletext service that is delivered in the vertical interval of PAL broadcasts in Europe.

Assume a broadcaster chooses to provide advertiser supported news headlines, sports scores, weather maps and forecasts to viewers through a Web site and their DTV channel. When a DTV receiver tunes to the channel, it will receive a program map that indicates all of the services feeding the data multiplex. The receiver can set up a memory buffer to accept periodic data identified in this program map. This data is inserted in the multiplex periodically to update information and serve new customers who are acquiring the channel. Once in memory, this information will be available to viewers on demand (full screen), or it can be displayed continuously on an unused portion of the screen (a window), or as a program overlay.

The rate of update for periodic data becomes a variable, which is factored into the software managing the data multiplex. For example, weather maps may only change every hour and be refreshed every five to ten minutes for new viewers. Sports scores may be updated as they are received for games in progress.

Periodic data can also be used to provide other new revenue streams. For example, a broadcaster could deliver movie guides for local theaters, restaurant guides and printable electronic coupons.

Like programmed data, periodic data can be sold and scheduled, however, due to its asynchronous nature, there is some flexibility in delivery time.

Opportunistic data has similar characteristics to periodic data. The major difference is that it may not be something that can be scheduled, or it may be data with a lower priority and thus may be sold at a lower rate. In either case, it will be delivered on a space-available basis.

A good example of opportunistic data would be a paging service. The message size is small and thus easy to squeeze into the limited residual packets that are left over; and there is some latitude in delivery time. Another good example is the delivery of routed data packets to wireless information appliances, for Internet type services—an appliance of this type may use a back channel to request data packets, or it may simply filter the data carried in a DTV channel, looking for information to which it subscribes.

MAXIMIZING DIGITAL ASSETS: A PRIMER

Lou CasaBianca

This primer explains how to produce more creative content and generate higher profits from strategic management of existing video libraries ("media assets") and digital media-related projects. It proposes the review of a suite of business-process re-engineering models designed to help support the possible leveraging of digital production and workflow data by-products of work-for-hire projects into internal metadata and commercial media assets. Although this section may at first appear to be jargon-heavy, it's important for video professionals to become familiar with these terms.

Although media assets (video and film clips, stock footage, still images, audio content, etc.) can generate increased revenues in their own right, the metadata (data about data; see Metadata And Content later in this section) may in fact prove to be the most valuable element in this digital continuum. The insight from management of this knowledge can be used to increase ROI (return on investment) and margins for your company while also generating intellectual property rights that independent or entrepreneurially minded creative professionals can re-use, sell or license into the commercial, entertainment and/or educational media markets.

For film, video, DVD and Web content creation and production companies and post production facilities owners and managers, this primer can help organize a strategy for increasing the valuation of their business. It can be used to show potential investors and business partners how cataloged media assets and intelligent studio workflow methods accelerate content-production cycle time, increase revenue per employee and increase business valuation above traditional ROI business model annual revenue levels.

For creative and production professionals, this primer lays out an approach to maximize their time spent in creative activities and leverage the content and data sources they've already produced. They can improve the quality of their work through better content creation and production management practices and tools, generating improved efficiencies and content assets to create value in additional revenues and higher profits.

INTRODUCTION

For content-creation companies and video production service providers already involved in—or considering integrating—media asset management systems, this primer articulates possible strategies for maximizing ROI. We advocate systematically cataloging video and digital media files (produced in-house or in work-for-hire client projects) along with capturing and dynamically sharing metadata with the purpose of re-expressing content and leveraging the intrinsic knowledge in related business data in future projects. This means that video production companies, now integrating digital media and Web production capabilities, will begin to recognize the inherent value represented in their production projects and media vaults. Within every project, there are any number of media assets, ranging from company logos and color palettes, to audio and video clips that can be repurposed as creative content.

That same project may have other media assets, ranging from generic video and audio, to computer graphics and photography that can be re-expressed as cross-media content for use on the Web or on DVD projects. Additionally, metadata such as EDLs and compression tables, as well as such unstructured data

DTV IN THE REAL WORLD

UNDERSTANDING DIGITAL

PRE-PRODUCTION

PRODUCTION

AUDIO

GRAPHIC & COMPOSITING

POST PRODUCTION

DELIVERY & DUPLICATION

ENGINEERING & TRANSMISSION

APPENDIX

GLOSSARY

as business proposals, budgets and competitive analysis, support the automation of knowledge-driven apps used in managing enterprise-wide marketing,
brand and sales-automation systems.

In the development of original media for content-creation companies, we
emphasize organizing an environment that allows designers and editors to par-
ticipate as stakeholders in the upside potential from the re-expression of assets
and optimization of workflow strategies in other departments and divisions.

We also underscore the development of strategies designed to support retaining appropriate intellectual property rights for select audio, video and digital
media files, having first negotiated with a client or content provider and later
selling the idea of a license to use these assets to new clients.

COMPETITIVE STRATEGIES

At the center of media asset-driven business strategy—in other words, how
to make more money from content management—rests the systematic re-use
and re-expression of new and pre-existing media. To execute this strategy, the
creative firm will need to invest in technology and set procedures and policies
for media asset management.

Together with technology and set practices, a media asset management system helps the creative firm perform the following tasks:

- Centralize a collection of re-usable media.
- Catalog these media as assets for quick retrieval.
- Coordinate flow of assets through the stages of the production and distribution process.
- Preserve aesthetic or commercial value, using online style guides directing careful re-use.
- Give management ability to control the flow of media in various works in
  progress.
- Prevent unauthorized use of content belonging to the studio or another party, restricting access to authorized personnel.
- Reduce the costs and logistical problems associated with management of
  rights and permissions, licensing, affiliate relations and spin-off merchandising licenses.

Activity-based research from Gistics, Inc. shows that a media-producing firm
or heavy media-using enterprise (e.g., broadcast production company) can realize an eight- to 14-times ROI over its first three years using a media asset management system. For workgroups, a media database can save hundreds of hours
per person over a three-year period, resulting in significant net savings and
increased production cycles. These kinds of returns now make investment in a
media asset management system a fiduciary responsibility. In effect, to ignore

or delay deploying some form of media asset supervision could constitute a breach of management responsibility.

BOTTOM LINE

Re-use and re-expression of content means that creative firms can deliver client work significantly faster at marginal costs. Getting more work done faster produces several key benefits. It enables a creative firm to complete more projects, which adds up when calculating a year's worth of projects. Increases in productivity can translate into additional completed and billed projects—a source of revenue without adding more people.

This means that at the end of the year a creative firm has turned more projects per person than the competition, generally earning more profit for those projects. Getting more work done per person earns higher profit margins, maximizing the output for capital equipment and labor—traditionally the two highest costs of doing business.

CONCLUSION

The strategic application of media asset management systems builds shareholder value, showing investors and potential corporate partners how re-expressible media assets and leveraged metadata can help create competitive advantage in delivering faster cycles, lower costs, license revenues and boost valuation of their companies.

Media asset management systems can help content businesses leverage assets across the enterprise and service providers to transform work-for-hire projects into asset-building processes. Although some clients will insist on retaining and controlling any rights associated with their content, many clients will readily license pre-built media "elements" rather than pay significantly higher prices to commission development of their own content.

For many creative firms and production service bureaus, these systems will quickly become legacy systems, huge "digital" warehouses containing terabytes of data, video and other digital media content. Failure to develop an informed strategy to handle this technology and content migration will eventually force many of these firms into costly re-engineering efforts. This implies that business owners and managers take the time to develop a comprehensive, long-range media asset strategy and invest in a complete solution that will integrate with current systems and scale up in capability into the future.

Most media asset management vendors have moved to systems that use Web browsers to allow users to access "proxies" of high-resolution video, serving as a preview and "offline" creation mechanism. Eventually, editors and producers will edit program content using these proxies on internal intranets, enabling them to view, analyze and develop programs online. Media asset and metadata management will play a pivotal role in how advertising, brand management, broadcast and video service bureau companies find and serve customers.

NEXT STEPS

The rapid emergence of the World Wide Web as an electronic commerce system will magnify the problems associated with inefficient media asset management approaches. Failure to master management of vital brand-related media and knowledge assets will place the enterprise in jeopardy. Media asset management, and the related aspects of digital brand building, will determine success in tomorrow's increasingly content-driven "wired" markets.

ACKNOWLEDGEMENTS

We acknowledge in particular the insight of the founding members of the Media Asset Management Association and the contributions of the co-founders of Gistics, Inc., James L. Byram and Michael Moon. For more information about MAMA, visit www.mamgroup.org or contact Lou CasaBianca at casabianca@mamgroup.org.

METADATA AND CONTENT: A GUIDE FOR VIDEO PROS

Lou CasaBianca and Christine M. Okon

It's not news that this digital age can be a very confusing one when it comes to understanding and utilizing the proliferating varieties of digital audio, video and other forms of "content." It's a situation that's making it harder and more expensive for companies—from TV and movie studios to advertising agencies and broadcasters—to manage and benefit all this "rich media" in terms of cataloging it, organizing it and making it quickly available for future access.

It is, however, essential that companies do exactly that. If so, they can not only extend the value of their media and information assets, but also gain a better understanding of their internal production processes so they can better manage their business relationships with customers and suppliers. The question is how to do this. The answer lies in metadata.

Metadata is "data about the data." It gives structure to the value of knowledge assets, which is vital for any profit-making organization—especially in this age of "repurposing," in which, for example, a movie's footage can be used to produce a "making of" documentary, a TV series, a home video or DVD, a print ad, a T-shirt or a toy; the possibilities are many.

From content creation right on through to distribution, managed metadata provides the continuity that streamlines workflow and creates new benefits. Invented by the same people who brought you the Internet, today's metadata research has its origins in "data mining," which is what the U.S. government called its early research in this area, extracting the value of patterns and trends out of huge quantities of dynamically updated complex digital media types.

Information is, however, only meaningful to the extent that the receiver or subsequent users can relate it to other information—in this case the related media, communications and data sources integrated in the "networked studio." The methodical process of distilling the value out of media and information labors under the constant threat of "information entropy," the loss of its contextual setting, or, in other words, the loss of its metadata.

For our purposes, information entropy occurs in two forms. The first occurs when metadata is either lost or not captured. The second subtler form occurs when metadata becomes separated from its source or loses its own internal consistency and descends into noise. Over time, organizational memory fades or becomes confused ("Was that clip from the original movie or the television series?"). The "half-life" of metadata can be measured in years (e.g., key political events) or sometimes in weeks or days ("Who is that in the photo with Mark McGwire?") and even in minutes or seconds ("Was that last broadcast bulletin about the storm in Florida or the Bahamas?").

Metadata can be implicit, depending on the user's own knowledge and semantic interpretation; it can be explicitly recorded, and even automatically captured. By mid-1999, dynamic capture and analysis of incoming "streaming" or off-air content—filtered by image, sound or keyword—will become the bleeding-edge for next-generation cable and broadcast media-cataloging systems. Why would a cable or broadcast network want to do such a thing? Well, think of multiple feeds being monitored by multiplexed intelligent catalogers that capture clips and browse collections to assemble programs. This technique can support associate producers in assembling programming elements from "live" and archival sources, freeing them up to work on qualitative and logistical issues.

METADATA FORMATS

Media-asset data derives from a combination of a company's experience and on-going consultation with a wide range of users. First and foremost in importance is identifying the essential elements and access paths required for the cataloging of any basic media type-from a still photograph to a television program. Once such elements are identified, asset managers can create sets of data fields for each media type.

The metadata format is the first domain to be defined for an integrated cataloging and management system. This forms the foundation and framework for all other development. Metadata generated or captured at the content-creation

DTV IN THE REAL WORLD
UNDERSTANDING DIGITAL
PRE-PRODUCTION
PRODUCTION
AUDIO
GRAPHIC & COMPOSITING
POST PRODUCTION
DELIVERY & DUPLICATION
ENGINEERING & TRANSMISSION
APPENDIX
GLOSSARY

phase will almost always be more accurate, and can be more easily enhanced and modified at later stages of the workflow process.

Continuing through the production process, metadata can be expanded or added during editing and manipulation. For example, semantic descriptions can be added to automatically captured video time codes or image numbers. The harnessing of metadata to reflect continuity through the workflow process severely challenges most content-logging tool vendors and endusers, who must integrate multi-vendor solutions.

It may also be necessary to import and export information from other databases. To facilitate this, all data fields can be coded so that they can be mapped against both internal standards in production databases and other related "legacy" data, as well as external standards. If this sounds confusing, don't despair; media-asset management may seem jargon-heavy, but it's based on common-sense ways of organizing information. The ability to share data provides increased efficiencies in the cataloging process, while facilitating wider applicability of the content and metadata across the enterprise.

The media-asset management process continues through transmission and distribution, where metadata—such as network protocols, delivery rates or aspect ratios—can be incorporated into applications. For example, a viewer selecting a digital cable excerpt of a television news story can generate new metadata in the form of user preferences to establish a customized broadcast experience. These preferences shape that viewer's customized content, and the demand creation-through-distribution cycle evolves. Customer satisfaction and user feedback also represent a type of metadata that take on new and potentially lucrative potential, when managed by brand managers and adapted to e-commerce.

CHALLENGES

One of the ongoing challenges with managing metadata through the workflow process is the lack of interoperability protocols and inconsistencies with devices (recording, storage and playback systems) used. An overlapping set of metadata elements must be shared by most—if not all—tools. This can include names, descriptions and data types. Maintenance of this shared metadata becomes even more complicated because at various points during the production process, different tools may modify the same metadata element.

In part, this challenge has spawned the formation of several standards efforts. Standardization is not a new story. The arrival of the digital age, however, has created a sense of urgency for organizations and companies to work around the threat of information entropy. The ability to organize data and media as objects now makes it possible to dynamically bind or point to metadata. As a result, a whole new approach to data warehousing and re-expression has opened up. Among the ongoing and emerging standards efforts are the Motion Picture Experts Group's MPEG-7 and the SMPTE.

MPEG-7 (www.mpeg.org) specifies a standardized description of various types of multimedia information. The description associates itself with the content to allow fast and efficient searching for material of interest to users. As ever-increasing amounts of audio-visual information go digital, the need to access the related data requires that it be located first. At the same time, the increasing availability and requirements for timely metadata makes this search even more difficult. Currently, solutions exist that allow searching for textual information.

Currently, since no generally recognized description for identifying still and moving images exists, it's not possible to search across audio-visual content. In select cases, solutions do exist. Some catalogers and multimedia databases allow for searching for pictures using such characteristics as color, texture and information about the shape of objects in the picture. Additionally, similar capabilities exist for audio search, including voice recognition, voice-to-text keyword search and sound-pattern recognition.

Announced by the MPEG in October 1996, "Multimedia Content Description Interface," or MPEG-7, will extend the limited capabilities of proprietary solutions in identifying content that exist today, notably by including more data types. MPEG-7 will specify a standard set of descriptors that can be used to describe various types of multimedia information. It will also standardize ways to define other descriptors as well as structures (description schemes) for the descriptors and their relationships.

To allow fast and efficient searching for material of a user's interest, the combination of descriptors and description schemes will be associated with the content itself. MPEG-7 will also standardize its efforts around DDL (Description Definition Language), as a language to specify description schemes. Audio or video material that has MPEG-7 data associated with it can be indexed and searched according to graphics, 3D models, audio, speech, video and data about how these elements are combined in a multimedia presentation.

The MPEG-7 standard builds on other (standard) representations, such as MPEG-1, -2 and -4. For example, a shape descriptor used in MPEG-4 could be useful in an MPEG-7 context as well. MPEG-7 descriptors do not depend on the ways the described content is coded or stored. MPEG-7 builds on MPEG-4, which provides the means to encode audio-visual material as objects having certain relationships in time (synchronization) and space (on the screen for video). MPEG-7 will allow different granularity in its descriptions, offering the possibility to have multiple levels of differentiation.

THE SMPTE

The Society of Motion Picture and Television Engineers (SMPTE—www.smpte.org) and the European Broadcasting Union (EBU—www.ebu.ch) released their latest proposal in July of 1998 called "Harmonized Standards for the Exchange of Television Program Material as Bit Streams." To attain its objectives, a joint task force comprised of members from both organizations divided its work among six separate sub-groups, with each responsible for a segment of the investigation. These sub-groups work in the following categories: Systems, Compression, Wrappers and File Formats, Metadata, File-Transfer Protocols and Physical Link and Transport Layers for Networks.

WRAPPERS AND METADATA SUMMARY

Leveraging the work that was already underway within the computer industry and within its own organization, SMPTE decided that the metadata requirements could be addressed through the creation of a Metadata Dictionary and a number of formatting standards, all maintained through a registry mechanism. The Sub-Group Request for Technology (RFT), to develop the Wrappers' requirements, generated responses ranging from discussions on specific items—such as Unique Material Identifiers and Frame-Index Tables for use inside Wrappers— to complete solutions for specific applications such as multimedia-presentation delivery. It also included the specifications for data models and container formats in use today in the industry, within multiple products.

This effort addresses the formatting of collections of audio-visual program material and related information for exchange within and between studios and other centers that process or store that information. The goal is to improve interoperability independent of the encoding format for the audio-visual signal through all stages of the production process, from pre-production through distribution and storage. The concept of a wrapper is defined as containing both the "essence" (i.e., audio, video or data—if the "program" is a "data feed") of content as well as the definition and description of its structure, (i.e., its metadata). The task force is advocating the establishment of a single registry of metadata identifiers and definitions.

OMF AND OMM

The Open Media Framework Interchange (OMF—www.avid.com/3rdparty/ omm), promoted by Avid Technology and a group of industry partners, serves as a standard format for the interchange of digital media data among heterogeneous platforms. A full OMF interchange file defines compositions (all the information required to play or re-edit a media presentation), media data (what is played) and a source reference (e.g., videotape, time code). Like other standards efforts, the goal is to link metadata with the media to sustain continuity throughout the entire (and mostly heterogeneous) production process.

Avid and its partners announced the Open Media Management (OMM) initiative at the 1998 National Association of Broadcasters convention. The alliance seeks to make media management more efficient for content creators by linking content-creation tools with digital media-management systems. This metadata integration will help users access and manage shared media assets during the creation process while attempting to provide the flexibility and compatibility that comes with an open environment.

OMM defines an Application Programming Interface (API) that connects Avid systems with leading asset-management software. This will allow users greater availability and faster access to valuable digital assets, improved collaboration and lower management costs, while providing a more open interoperable system. The consortium plans to release the first version of the OMM specification very soon. OMM-compliant applications and asset management systems will follow.

ESSENTIAL ELEMENTS OF METADATA

The specific elements of metadata vary widely among various asset types, but they fall into four general categories:

History Information about how the asset was acquired, processed and used. Dates are essential, and include shooting dates, recording dates, editing dates, transmission dates, repeat dates, review dates and archiving dates.

Ownership Information about copyrights, licenses and other constraints on the asset's use. This can include, for example, publisher details, the terms by which a stock house, say, is providing a given clip. And there may be restrictions on use, such as copyright, territorial and other use-rights-related data.

Technical Information about the format, size and location of the asset. Included in this is what's known as engineering metadata, the physical make-up of the item, e.g. its video standard, recording medium, sampling frequency or compression format. Then there's duration data, including overall interval of segments and details of timings within items. Housekeeping data can include labels, shelf locations, supplier's codes and availability notes. Item numbers, meanwhile, can include both in-house and standard reference numbers, e.g. accession numbers. There is also a trend in which capture devices (digital cameras, scanners, etc.) automatically generate metadata (e.g., time code, digital watermark, exposure, etc.).

Content Information about the content of the asset-titles with notations about subcategories for series, programs, commercials, bumpers and so on. This can include: the type of content, such as its genre (e.g. news, documentary, situation comedy); names, including all contributors, artists, performers, interviewees and production staff; descriptive text, typically a large field for free-text description of the content of the item; and/or subjects, which includes classification numbers, keywords, names and titles as subjects.

SUMMARY

The capture and analysis of metadata within the studio will drive the capabilities of the studio's systems and operation policies. This will require that ana-

DTV IN THE REAL WORLD

UNDERSTANDING DIGITAL

PRE-PRODUCTION

PRODUCTION

AUDIO

GRAPHIC & COMPOSITING

POST PRODUCTION

DELIVERY & DUPLICATION

ENGINEERING & TRANSMISSION

APPENDIX

GLOSSARY

log systems be supplemented or converted to digital infrastructure to store, transfer and track metadata. As the initiatives outlined above reach maturity, they will deliver the ability to extend existing studio infrastructure to intelligent environments, facilitating the management of realtime metadata at the required qualitative and quantitative levels.

Any explicit metadata extends the "beat-the-clock" nature of information entropy. Over time, metadata represents an organization's most valuable information. Future systems will become increasingly sophisticated to the degree that they'll be convenient for non-technical people involved with the content-creation and management process. This will lead to greater capability through the closer involvement of those skilled in the production of the content itself. Changes in these skill sets and systems will permit operations personnel to more effectively manage assets, which will eventually allow them to make decisions automatically. Metadata will prove to be one of the most valuable applications of computers in the studio, with open-ended implications for the content creation and broadcast systems of the future.

ACKNOWLEDGEMENTS

Many thanks to co-author Christine M. Okon, VP of Business Development for Arriba Software, Inc. Particular acknowledgment is made to the work of S. Merrill Weiss, Co-Chairman for the SMPTE and to Horst Schachlbauer, Co-Chairman for the European Broadcasting Union (EBU), in developing the SMPTE Task Force for "Harmonized Standards for the Exchange of Program Material as Bitstreams, Final Report: Analyses and Results" (July 1998).

THE MISSION OF MAMA

The Media Asset Management Association (MAMA) serves as a advanced user-group and independent international industry consortium, created by and for media producers, content publishers, technology providers and value-chain partners to develop open content and metadata exchange protocols for digital media creation and asset management. The Association's mission is to produce user-driven, voluntary, best practice-based protocols and business-to-business communications conventions in the following strategic areas:

- Interoperation of digital content creation and media asset management applications for emerging entertainment, information and technology systems across the Internet, advertising, broadcast, cable, film, interactive and telecommunications industries.
- Intercommunication among metadata file exchange and management protocols over very large database information systems infrastructures, digital content creation studio and broadcast systems, HD television and intelligent high-speed/broad-bandwidth networks.
- Integration of Internet business and knowledge-management systems for

content managers leveraging: advanced search and retrieval, digital water-marking and intellectual property rights management systems.

The MAMA's goal focuses on documenting and publishing open voluntary interoperable media-asset metadata file exchange protocols. The MAM Framework serves as a user base for actual ROI (return on investment) best-practice models.

The membership has defined the development of a shared MAM Lexicon technical/creative language as the focus of the group's initial end-user standardization activities.

Founding user forum members are ABC Network, Capp Studios/Leo Burnett, Digital Roadmaps, Discovery Communications, Inc., The Walt Disney Company, DreamWorks SKG, Gistics, i5Group, Lexichron and Sony Pictures Entertainment.

Founding technology forum members include Apple Computer, Archetype, Bitstream, Bulldog, Cinebase Software, Content Group, Excalibur, IBM, Informix, Islip Media, Magnifi, Oracle, Silicon Graphics, Sun, Virage, WAM!NET and WebWare Corp.

For more information visit the MAMA Web site at www.mamgroup.org.

DTV IN THE REAL WORLD

UNDERSTANDING DIGITAL

PRE-PRODUCTION

PRODUCTION

AUDIO

GRAPHIC & COMPOSITING

POST PRODUCTION

DELIVERY & DUPLICATION

ENGINEERING & TRANSMISSION

APPENDIX

GLOSSARY

A WORLD OF CONTENT.
A UNIVERSE OF POSSIBILITIES.

The future is all about content. Content is a lot about video. And with 40 years of providing the industry's best switchers, digital video platforms, routers and modular products, the Grass Valley Group knows more about video than anybody else.

Especially as it goes digital. Webcasting. Video on demand. D-cinema. Data-enhanced broadcasting. Streaming Internet transmissions. The world is moving from broadcasting to digicasting — to one of Media Without Bounds™.

And wherever digital content moves, Grass Valley Group will be there, with solutions ranging from our Emmy® award-winning Profile® digital video platform line to new technologies for media-asset management and Web publishing. All the hardware, software and new media technologies necessary to take advantage of the universe of opportunities available through digital content.

So open up a world of content, with complete solutions from the Grass Valley Group. Visit www.grassvalleygroup.com for more information. And expand your universe.

GRASS VALLEY GROUP

Media without bounds!™

GLOSSARY OF DIGITAL TELEVISION TERMS

3:2 pull-down: Method used to map the 24 fps of film onto the 30 fps (60 fields) of 525-line TV, so that one film frame occupies three TV fields, the next two, etc. It means the two fields of every other TV frame come from different film frames making operations such as rotoscoping impossible, and requiring care in editing. Some sophisticated equipment can unravel the 3:2 sequence to allow frame-by-frame treatment and subsequently re-compose 3:2. The 3:2 sequence repeats every five TV frames and four film frames, the latter identified as A-D. Only film frame A is fully on a TV frame and so exists at one time code only, making it the editable point of the video sequence.

4fsc: Four times the frequency of SC (subcarrier). The sampling rate of a D2 digital video signal with respect to the subcarrier frequency of an NTSC or PAL analog video signal. The 4fsc frequency is 14.3 MHz in NTSC and 17.7 MHz in PAL.

4:1:1: This is a set of sampling frequencies in the ratio 4:1:1, used to digitize the luminance and color difference components (Y, R-Y, B-Y) of a video signal. The four represents 13.5 MHz, the sampling frequency of Y, and the ones each 3.75 MHz for R-Y and B-Y.

    With the color information sampled at half the rate of the 4:2:2 system, this is generally used as a more economical form of sampling for 525-line picture formats. Both luminance and color difference are still sampled on every line. But the latter has half the horizontal resolution of 4:2:2, while the vertical resolution of the color information is maintained. For 525-line pictures, this means the color is fairly equally resolved in horizontal and vertical directions.

4:2:0: A sampling system used to digitize the luminance and color difference components (Y, R-Y, B-Y) of a video signal. The four represents the 13.5 MHz sampling frequency of Y, while the R-Y and B-Y are sampled at 6.75 MHz—effectively between every other line only (one line is sampled at 4:0:0, luminance only, and the next at 4:2:2).

    This is generally used as a more economical system than 4:2:2 sampling for 625-line formats so that the color signals have a reasonably even resolution in the vertical and horizontal directions for that format.

4:2:2: A commonly used term for a component digital video format.

    A ratio of sampling frequencies used to digitize the luminance and color difference components (Y, R-Y, B-Y) of a video signal. It is generally used as shorthand for ITU-R 601. The term 4:2:2 describes that for every four samples of Y, there are two samples each of R-Y and B-Y, giving more chrominance bandwidth in relation to luminance compared to 4:1:1 sampling.

    ITU-R 601, 4:2:2 is the standard for digital studio equipment and the terms "4:2:2" and "601" are commonly (but technically incorrectly) used synonymously. The sampling frequency of Y is 13.5 MHz and that of R-Y and B-Y is each 6.75 MHz providing a maximum color bandwidth of 3.37 MHz—enough for high-quality chromakeying. The format specifies eight bits of resolution.

    The details of the format are specified in the ITU-R BT.601-2 standard document. *See also: ITU-R BT.601-2.*

4:2:2:4: Same as 4:2:2, but with the addition of a key channel that is sampled four times for every four samples of the luminance channel.

4:4:4: Similar to 4:2:2, except that for every four luminance samples, the color channels are also sampled four times.

4:4:4:4: Similar to 4:2:2:4, except that for every four luminance samples, the color and key channels are also sampled four times.

48sF: 48 segmented frames. The process of taking 24-frame progressive images and deconstructing them to produce 48 interlaced frames each with half of the number of lines of resolution to allow some HDTV processors to pass the signal and for viewing on an interlaced monitor without flicker.

5.1: A type of surround sound. Six discrete audio channels are used: Left, Center, Right, Left Rear (or side) Surround, Right Rear (or side) Surround, and a subwoofer (considered the ".1" as it is limited in bandwidth).
    See also: Dolby Digital.

601: *See: ITU-R BT.601-2.*

8-VSB: **Eight** discrete amplitude level **v**estigial **s**ide-**b**and broadcast transmission technology, used in the ATSC digital television transmission standard. *See also: ATSC, VSB and the Engineering & Transmission chapter.*

AC-3: *See: Dolby Digital.*

ADC (A-D, A/D, A-to-D): Analog to Digital Conversion. Also referred to as digitization or quantization. The conversion of an analog signal into the digital data representation of that signal—normally for subsequent use in a digital machine. For TV, samples of audio and video are taken, the accuracy of the process depending on both the sampling frequency and the resolution of the analog amplitude information—how many bits are used to describe the analog levels. For TV pictures eight or 10-bits are normally used; for sound, 16 or 20-bits are common, and 24-bits are being introduced. The ITU-R 601 standard defines the sampling of video components based on 13.5 MHz, and AES/EBU defines sampling of 44.1 and 48 kHz for audio.
    For pictures, the samples are called pixels, each containing data for brightness and color.
    See also: Binary, Bit.

AES: Audio Engineering Society that promotes standards in the professional audio industry. International Headquarters—60 East 42nd Street, Room 2520, New York, New York 10165-2520. Tel: 212-661-8528. Fax: 212-682-0477. Email: HQ@aes.org. Internet: www.aes.org.

AES/EBU: Informal name for a digital audio standard established jointly by the AES (Audio Engineering Society) and EBU (European Broadcasting Union) organizations. The sampling frequencies for this standard vary depending on the format being used; the sampling frequency for D1 and D2 audio tracks is 48 kHz.

AIF (Audio Interchange File): An audio file format developed by Apple Computer to store high quality sampled sound and musical instrument information. The AIF files are a popular format for transferring between the Macintosh and the PC.
    See also: AU, WAV.

Algorithm: A formula or set of steps used to simplify, modify, or predict data. Complex algorithms are used to selectively reduce the high digital audio and video data rates. These algorithms utilize physiologists' knowledge of hearing and eyesight. For example, we can resolve fine detail in a still scene, but our eye cannot resolve the same detail in a moving scene. Using knowledge of these limitations, algorithms are formulated to selectively reduce the data rate without affecting the viewing experience.
    See also: Compression, MPEG.

Aliasing: Defects or distortion in a television picture. In analog video, aliasing is typically caused by interference between two frequencies such as the luminance and chrominance frequencies or the chrominance and field scanning frequencies. It appears as moiré or herringbone patterns, straight lines that become wavy, or rainbow colors. In digital video, aliasing is caused by insufficient sampling or poor filtering of the digital video. Defects are typically seen as jagged edges on diagonal lines and twinkling or brightening (beating) in picture detail.

Alpha channel: A relative transparency value. Alpha values facilitate the layering of media object on top of each other. In a four digit digital sampling structure (4:2:2:4) the alpha channel is represented by the last digit.

Analog: 1. An adjective describing any signal that varies continuously as opposed to a digital signal, which contains discrete levels. 2. A system or device that operates primarily on analog signals.

Anti-aliasing: The smoothing and removing of aliasing effects by filtering and other techniques. Most, but not all, DVEs and character generators contain anti-aliasing facilities.

Archive: Off-line storage of video/audio onto backup tapes, floppy disks, optical disks, etc.

Artifacts: Undesirable elements or defects in a video picture. These may occur naturally in the video process and must be eliminated in order to achieve a high-quality picture. Most common in analog are cross color and cross luminance. Most common in digital are macroblocks, which resemble pixelation of the video image.

ASCII: American Standard Code for Information Interchange. A standard code for transmitting data, consisting of 128 letters, numerals, symbols, and special codes each of which is represented by a unique binary number.

ASIC: Application specific integrated circuit. An integrated circuit designed for special rather than general applications.

Aspect ratio: The ratio of television picture width to height. In NTSC and PAL video, the present standard is 4:3. In widescreen video, it is typically 16:9, however, 14:9 has been used as a transition.

Asynchronous: Lacking synchronization. In video, a signal is asynchronous when its timing differs from that of the system reference signal. A foreign video signal is asynchronous before it is treated by a local frame synchronizer.

ATM: Asynchronous Transfer Mode. A data transmission scheme using self-routing packets of 53 bytes, 48 of which are available for user data. Typically 25, 155, and 622 Mbps—the latter of which could be used to carry non-compressed ITU-R 601 video as a data file.

ATSC: Advanced Television Systems Committee. Formed to establish technical standards for advanced television systems, including digital high definition television (HDTV). 1750 K Street NW, Suite 800, Washington, DC 20006. Tel: 202-828-3130. Fax: 202-828-3131. Email: atsc@atsc.org. Internet: www.atsc.org.

vertical size value	horizontal size value	aspect ratio information	frame rate code	progressive sequence
(HD) 1,080	1,920	1,3	1,2,4,5	1
(see note)			4,5	0
(HD) 720	1,280	1,3	1,2,4,5,7,8	1
			1,2,4,5,7,8	1
(SD) 480	704	2,3	4,5	0
			1,2,4,5,7,8	1
(SD) 480	640	1,2	4,5	0

Legend for MPEG-2 coded values in Table 3		
aspect ratio information:	1=square samples 2=4:3 display aspect ratio 3=16:9 display aspect ratio	
frame rate code:	1=23.976 Hz 2=24 Hz 4=29.97Hz 5=30 Hz 7=59.94 Hz 8=60 Hz	
progressive sequence:	0=interlace scan 1=progressive scan	

ATSC Formats are 18 voluntary video formats, known as Table 3.

The U.S. digital television transmission standard using MPEG-2 compression and the audio surround-sound compressed with Dolby Digital (AC-3). So that a wide variety of source material, including that from computers, can be best accommodated, two line standards are included—each operating at 24, 30, and 60 Hz.

The Consumer Electronics Manufacturers Association (CEMA) has said that all receivers will be capable of operating with all of the formats.

All pixels are square and pixel sampling rates vary, but all are around 75 MHz. There is a Transport Layer that packages video, audio and auxiliary data and allows their mix to be dynamically varied—opening the door to new services and forms of programming (e.g., many channels of stereo audio, distribution of computer software, or very high resolution images). The data is compressed to 19.39 Mbits per second and delivered using a 6 MHz bandwidth channel. HD and SD assignments are per ATSC announcement on February 20, 1998.

Note that 1,088 lines are actually coded in order to satisfy the MPEG-2 requirement that the coded vertical size be a multiple of 16 (progressive scan) or 32 (interlaced scan).

See also: HD0, HD1, HD2, MPEG-2, HDTV.

Attached: A physical channel of a digital picture manipulator is attached to a logical channel of a controller if the physical channel is successfully acquired by the controller. A physical channel may be attached to only one logical channel of one controller at a time.

ATV: Advanced television. Digital television, including standard, enhanced and high-definition versions.

AU (also SND): Interchangeable audio file formats used in the Sun Sparcstation, Nest and Silicon Graphics (SGI) computers. Essentially a raw audio data format proceeded by an identifying header. The .au file is cross-platform compatible.
See also: AIF, WAV.

Autotiming: Capability of some digital video equipment to automatically adjust input video timing to match a reference video input. Eliminates the need for manual timing adjustments.

AVI: Audio video interleaving. The Microsoft Video for Windows file format for combining video and audio into a single block in time such as a 1/30th second video frame. In this file format, blocks of audio data are woven into a stream of video frames. ASF is intended to supersede AVI.

AVO: Audiovisual object. In MPEG-4, audiovisual objects (also AV objects) are the individual media objects of a scene—such as video objects, images, and 3D objects. AVOs have a time dimension and a local coordinate system for manipulating the AVO are positioned in a scene by transforming the object's local coordinate system into a common, global scene coordinate system.

Axis: Relating to digital picture manipulation, the X axis is a horizontal line across the center of the screen, the Y axis is a vertical line, and the Z axis is in the third dimension, perpendicular to the X and Y axes, and indicates depth and distance.

B frames: Bi-directional predictive frames used in the MPEG-2 signal. These are composed by assessing the difference between the previous and the next frames in a television picture sequence. As they contain only predictive information, they do not make up a complete picture and so have the advantage of taking up much less data than the I frames. However, to see that original picture requires a whole sequence of MPEG-2 frames to be decoded.

See also: I frames, P frames, MPEG.

Back channel: A means of communication from users to content providers. At the same time that content providers are transmitting interactive television (analog or digital) to users, users can connect through a back channel to a Web site—for example, for the original content provider or an advertiser. The back channel can be used to provide feedback, purchase goods and services, and so on. A simple type of back channel is an Internet connection using a modem.

Bandwidth: 1. The complete range of frequencies over which a circuit or electronic system can function with minimal signal loss, typically less than 3 dB. 2. The information-carrying capability of a particular television channel. In PAL systems, the bandwidth limits the maximum visible frequency to 5.5 MHz, in NTSC, 4.2 MHz. The ITU-R 601 luminance channel sampling frequency of 13.5 MHz was chosen to permit faithful digital representation of the PAL and NTSC luminance bandwidths without aliasing. In transmission, the United States analog and digital television channel bandwidth is 6 MHz.

Baseband: A signaling technique in which the signal is transmitted in its original form and not changed by modulation. Local Area Networks as a whole, fall into two categories: baseband and broadband. Baseband networks are simpler and cheaper; the entire bandwidth of the LAN cable is used to transmit a single digital signal. In broadband networks, the capacity of the cable is divided into channels, which can transmit many simultaneous signals. Broadband networks may transmit a mixture of digital and analog signals, as will be the case in hybrid fiber/coax interactive cable television networks.

Baud: A unit of signaling speed equal to the number of signal events per second. Baud is equivalent to bits per second in cases where each signal event represents exactly one bit. Often the term baud rate is used informally to mean baud, referring to the specified maximum rate of data transmission along an interconnection. Typically, the baud settings of two devices must match if the devices are to communicate with one another.

BCD: Binary coded decimal. A coding system in which each decimal digit from 0 to 9 is represented by four binary (0 or 1) digits.

Bel: A measure of voltage, current, or power gain. One bel is defined as a tenfold increase in power. If an amplifier increases a signal's power by 10 times, its power gain is 1 bel or 10 decibels (dB). If power is increased by 100 times, the power gain is 2 bels or 20 decibels. 3 dB is considered a doubling.

BER: Bit error rate.

Betacam: An analog component VTR system using a 1/2-inch tape cassettes. This was developed by Sony and is marketed by them and several other manufacturers. Although recording the Y, R-Y and B-Y component signals onto tape many machines are operated with coded (PAL or NTSC) video in and out. The system has continued to be developed over the years to offer models for the industrial and professional markets as well as full luminance bandwidth (Betacam SP), PCM audio and SDI connections. Digital versions exist as the high-end Digital Betacam and Betacam SX for ENG and similar applications.

Betacam SX: A digital tape recording format developed by Sony which uses a constrained version of MPEG-2 compression at the 4:2:2 profile, Main Level (422P@ML) using 1/2-inch tape cassettes.

DTV IN THE REAL WORLD
UNDERSTANDING DIGITAL
PRE-PRODUCTION
PRODUCTION
AUDIO
GRAPHIC & COMPOSITING
POST PRODUCTION
DELIVERY & DUPLICATION
ENGINEERING & TRANSMISSION
APPENDIX
GLOSSARY

BIFS: Binary format for scenes. In MPEG-4, a set of elements called nodes that describe the layout of a multimedia layout BIFS-Update streams update the scene in time, BIFS-Anim streams animate the stream in time. BIFS are organized in a tree-lined hierarchical scene graph node structure derived from VRML.

Binary: A base-2 numbering system using the digits 0 and 1 (as opposed to 10 digits [0 - 9] in the decimal system). In computer systems, the binary digits are represented by two different voltages or currents, one corresponding to 0 and the other corresponding to 1. All computer programs are executed in binary form.

Binary representation requires a greater number of digits than the base 10 decimal system more commonly used. For example, the base 10 number 254 is 11111110 in binary.

The result of a binary multiplication contains the sum of digits of the original numbers. So:

10101111 x 11010100 = 1001000011101100
(In decimal 175 x 212 = 37,100)
(From right to left, the digits represent 1, 2, 4, 8, 16, 32, 64, 128, 256, 512, 1024, 2048, 4096, 8192, 16384, 32768)

Each digit is known as a bit. This example multiplies two 8-bit numbers to produce a 16-bit result—a very common process in digital television equipment.

See also: Bit, Byte, Digital.

BISDN: Broadband integrated services digital network. *See: ISDN.*

Bit: Binary digit. The smallest unit of data in a digital system. A bit is a single one or zero. A group of bits, such as 8-bits or 16-bits, compose a byte. The number of bits in a byte depends upon the processing system being used. Typical byte sizes are 8, 16, and 32.

Bit bucket: Any device capable of storing digital data—whether it be video, audio or other types of data.

Bit budget: The total amount of bits available on the media being used. In DVD, the bit budget of a single sided/single layer DVD5 disk is actually 4.7 GB.

Bit depth: The number of levels that a pixel might have, such as 256 with an 8-bit depth or 1,024 with a 10-bit depth.

Bitmap: 2-D array of pixels representing video and graphics.

Bit parallel: Transmission of digital video a byte at a time down a multi-conductor cable where each pair of wires carries a single bit. This standard is covered under SMPTE 125M, EBU 3267-E, and ITU-R BT.656 (CCIR 656).

Bit rate reduction: *See: Compression.*

Bit serial: Transmission of digital video a bit at a time down a single conductor such as coaxial cable. May also be sent through fiber optics. This standard is covered under ITU-R BT.656 (CCIR 656).

Bit slippage: 1. Occurs when word framing is lost in a serial signal so that the relative value of a bit is incorrect. This is generally reset at the next serial signal (TRS-ID for composite and EAV/SAV for component). 2. The erroneous reading of a serial bit stream when the recovered clock phase drifts enough to miss a bit. 3. A phenomenon that occurs in parallel digital data buses when one or more bits get out of time in relation to the rest. The result is erroneous data. Differing cable lengths is the most common cause.

Bit stream: A continuous series of bits transmitted on a line.

Block: Rectangular area of picture, usually 8 x 8 pixels in size, which are individually subjected to DCT coding as part of a digital picture compression process.

Artifact of compression generally showing momentarily as misplaced rectangular areas of picture with distinct boundaries. This is one of the major defects of digital compression, its visibility generally depending on the amount of compression used, the quality of the original signal, and the quality of the coder. The visible blocks may be 8 x 8 DCT blocks or "misplaced blocks"—16 x 16 pixel macroblocks, due to the failure of motion prediction/estimation in encoder or other motion vector system, such as a standards converter.

See also: DCT, JPEG, Macroblock, MPEG-2.

Boot up: To start up. Most computers contain a system operating program that they read out of memory and operate from after power up or restart. The process of reading and running that program is called boot up.

BPSK: Biphase shift keying. BPSK is a digital frequency modulation technique used for sending data over a coaxial cable network. This type of modulation is less efficient— but also less susceptible to noise—than similar modulation techniques, such as QPSK and 64QAM.

Broadband: 1. A response that is the same over a wide range of frequencies. 2. Capable of handling frequencies greater than those required for high-grade voice communications (higher than 3 to 4 kilohertz).

Broadcast FTP Protocol (BFTP): A one-way IP multicast based resource transfer protocol, the unidirectional Broadcast File Transfer Protocol (BFTP) is a simple, robust, one-way resource transfer protocol that is designed to efficiently deliver data in a one-way broadcast-only environment. This transfer protocol is appropriate for IP multicast over television vertical blanking interval (IPVBI), in IP multicast carried in MPEG-2, like with the DVB multiprotocol encapsulation, or in other unidirectional transport systems. It delivers constant bitrate (CBR) services or opportunistic services, depending on the characteristics and features of the transport stream multiplexor or VBI insertion device.

Buffer: 1. A circuit or component that isolates one electrical circuit from another. 2. A digital storage device used to compensate for a difference in the rate of flow of information or the time of occurrence of events when transmitting information from one device to another. 3. In telecommunications, a protective material used in cabling optical fiber to cover and protect the fiber. The buffer material has no optical function.

Buffer overload: *See: Video coder overload.*

Bus: A group of conductors that together constitute a major signal path. A signal path to which a number of inputs may be connected to feed to one or more outputs.

Bus address: A code number sent out to activate a particular device on a shared communications bus.

BWF Broadcast WAV: An audio file format based on Microsoft's WAV. It can carry PCM or MPEG encoded audio and adds the metadata, such as a description, originator, date and coding history, needed for interchange between broadcasters.

See also: WAV.

Byte: A group of data bits that are processed together. Typically, a byte consists of 8, 16, 24 or 32 bits.

1 Byte = 8 bits = 256 discrete values (brightness, color, etc.)
1 kilobyte = 2^{10} bytes = 1,024 bytes: (not 1000 bytes)
1 Megabyte = 2^{20} bytes = 1,048,576 bytes: (not 1 million bytes)
1 Gigabyte = 2^{30} bytes = 1,073,741,824 bytes: (not one billion bytes)
1 Terabyte = 2^{40} bytes = 1,099,511,627,776 bytes: (not one trillion bytes)

A full frame of digital television, sampled according to ITU-R 601, requires just under 1 Mbyte of storage (701 kbytes for 525 lines, 829 kbytes for 625 lines). HDTV frames are 4-to-5 times as large and digital film frames may be that much larger again.

DTV IN THE REAL WORLD

UNDERSTANDING DIGITAL

PRE-PRODUCTION

PRODUCTION

AUDIO

GRAPHICS & COMPOSITING

POST PRODUCTION

DELIVERY & DUPLICATION

ENGINEERING & TRANSMISSION

APPENDIX

Cable modem: A data modem that uses the bandwidth of a given cable system, which promise speeds of up to 80 times faster than an ISDN line or six times faster than a dedicated T1 line (the type of connection most large corporations use). Because cable modems provide Internet access over cable TV networks (which rely primarily on fiber optic or coaxial cable), they are much faster than modems that use phone lines. Bandwidths are typically up to 30 Mbps in the downstream direction.

Cache: Local or temporary storage.

CBR: Constant bit rate. CBR refers to the delivery of multimedia where there is dedicated bandwidth and the data can be delivered at a guaranteed constant bit rate. MPEG-1 and 2 are designed for CBR delivery. Constant bit rate cannot be assured on the Internet or most Intranets. Protocols such as RSVP are being developed and deployed to provide bandwidth guarantees.

CCD: Charge coupled device. A device that stores samples of analog signals. Used in cameras and telecines as an optical scanning mechanism. Advantages include good sensitivity in low light and absence of burn-in and phosphor lag found in CRTs.

CCIR: Comité Consultatif International des Radiocommunications (International Radio Consultative Committee), an international standards committee no longer in operation and replaced by the International Telecommunications Union (ITU).

CCIR-601: *See: ITU-R BT.601-2.*

CCIR-656: *See: ITU-R BT.656.*

CDDI: Copper data distributed interface. A high speed data interface—like FDDI but using copper.
   See also: FDDI.

Channel: 1. A digital effects processing path for video. 2. A particular signal path. 3. A portion of the television broadcast spectrum assigned to a particular broadcasting station.

Channel coding: Data encoding and error correction techniques used to protect the integrity of data that is being transported through a channel. Typically used in channels with high bit error rates such as terrestrial and satellite broadcast and videotape recording.

Checksum: A simple check value of a block of data, calculated by adding all the bytes in a block. It is easily fooled by typical errors in data transmission systems; so that for most applications, a more sophisticated system such as CRC is preferred.
   See also: CRC.

Chromakeying: The process of overlaying one video signal over another, the areas of overlay being defined by a specific range of color, or chrominance, on the foreground signal. For this to work reliably, the chrominance must have sufficient resolution, or bandwidth. PAL or NTSC coding systems restrict chroma bandwidth and so are of very limited use for making a chromakey which, for many years, was restricted to using live, RGB camera feeds. An objective of the ITU-R 601 digital sampling standard was to allow high quality chromakeying in post production. The 4:2:2 sampling system allowed far greater bandwidth for chroma than PAL or NTSC and helped chromakeying, and the whole business of layering, to thrive in post production. High signal quality is still important and anything but very mild compression tends to result in keying errors appearing—especially at DCT block boundaries. Chromakeying techniques have continued to advance and use many refinements, to the point where totally convincing composites can be easily created. You can no longer "see the join" and it may no longer be possible to distinguish between what is real and what is keyed.
   See also: Digital chromakeying.

Chromininance: The color component of a video signal that includes information about hue and saturation.
See also: Luminance.

CIF: Common image format used to trade content worldwide. 1. For computers the size is 352x240 pixels. 2. For digital high definition, ratified by the International Telecommunications Union (ITU) in June 1999, the 1920x1080 digital sampling structure is a world format. All supporting technical parameters relating to scanning, colorimetry, transfer characteristics, etc. are universal. The CIF can be used with a variety of picture capture rates: 60p, 50p, 30p, 25p, 24p, as well as 60i and 50i. The standard is identified as ITU-R BT 709-3.

Cinepak: A high-quality medium bandwidth compression that is not real-time but can play back in software. Its 24-bit format produces high-quality video at 320 x 240 resolution and 15 frames per second at a 150 Kbps data rate. Commonly a CD-ROM solution developed a number of years ago and not a competitor to more modern techniques.

Click and drag: A computer term for the user operation of clicking on an item and dragging it to a new location.

Cliff effect: Refers to the abrupt failure of a system over a few dB or less of increasing impairment. In digital television, when a receiver can no longer receive a viable signal.

Clip: 1. In keying, the trigger point or range of a key source signal at which the key or insert takes place. 2. The control that sets this action. To produce a key signal from a video signal, a clip control on the keyer control panel is used to set a threshold level to which the video signal is compared. 3. In digital picture manipulators, a menu selection that blanks portions of a manipulated image that leave one side of the screen and "wraps" around to enter the other side of the screen. 4. In desktop editing, a pointer to a piece of digitized video or audio that serves as source material for editing.

Clip sheet: A nonlinear editing term for the location of individual audio/video clips (or scenes). Also known as a clip bin.

Clock frequency: The master frequency of periodic pulses that are used to synchronize the operation of equipment.

Clock jitter: Undesirable random changes in clock phase.

Clock phase deviation: *See: Clock skew.*

Clock recovery: The reconstruction of timing information from digital data.

Clock skew: A fixed deviation from proper clock phase that commonly appears in D1 digital video equipment. Some digital distribution amplifiers handle improperly phased clocks by reclocking the output to fall within D1 specifications.

Clone: An exact copy, indistinguishable from the original. As in copying recorded material, for example a copy of a non-compressed recording to another non-compressed recording. If attempting to clone compressed material care must be taken not to decompress it as part of the process or the result will not be a clone.

C/N (also CNR): Carrier-to-noise ratio.

C/N threshold: The C/N at threshold of visibility (TOV) for random noise.
See also: TOV

Codec: Coder-decoder. A device that converts analog video and audio signals into a digital format for transmission over telecommunications facilities and also converts received digital signals back into analog format.

Co-channel interference: The interference from a signal on the same channel.

Coding: Representing each video signal level as a number, usually in binary form.

COFDM: Coded orthogonal frequency division multiplexing. Orthogonal Frequency Division Multiplexing (OFDM) is a modulated multi-carrier transmission technique, which splits the available bandwidth into many narrow sub-band channels (typically 2000-8000). Each carrier is modulated by a low rate data stream. The modulation scheme can vary from a simple QPSK to a more complex 64-QAM (or other) depending on the required binary rate and the expected transmission robustness.

For those familiar with Frequency Division Multiple Access (FDMA), OFDM is similar. However, OFDM uses the spectrum much more efficiently by providing a closer packing of the sub-band channels. To achieve this, all the carriers are made orthogonal to one another. By providing for orthogonality of carriers, each carrier has a whole number of cycles over a given symbol period. By doing this, the occupied bandwidth of each carrier has a null at the center frequency of each of the other carriers in the system. This results in minimal interference between the carriers, allowing then to be spaced as close together as is possible. Each individual carrier of the OFDM signal has a narrow bandwidth (for example 1kHz), and the resulting symbol rate is low. This results in the signal having high immunity to multi-path delay spread, as the delay spread must be very long to cause significant inter-symbol interference (> 500 milliseconds).

Coded Orthogonal Frequency Division Multiplexing (COFDM) has the same principle as OFDM except that Forward Error Correction (FEC) is applied to the signal prior to transmission. This overcomes errors in the transmission as a result of lost carriers from multiple propagation effects including frequency selective fading and channel noise.

COFDM can transmit many streams of data simultaneously, each one occupying only a small portion of the total available bandwidth. This approach can have many advantages with proper implementation: 1. Because the bandwidth occupied by each sequence of symbols is relatively small, its duration in time is bigger. As a result, the immunity against multi-path echoes can be higher. 2. Frequency selective fades are spread over many carriers. Instead of completely destroying a number of adjacent symbols, many symbols are instead distorted only slightly. 3 By dividing available bandwidth in multiple narrow sub-bands, the frequency response over each of the individual sub-band channels is essentially flat even with steep multi-path induced fade. This can mean easier equalization requirements.
See also: DVB and the Engineering & Transmission chapter.

Collision: The result of two devices trying to use a shared transmission medium simultaneously. The interference ruins both signals, requiring both devices to retransmit the data lost due to the collision.

Co-location: In transmission, one or more transmitters located on the same antenna mast.

Color depth: The number of bits used to represent the color of a pixel and thus how many colors can be displayed. Color depth is typically 8-, 16-, or 24-bit. 8-bit would give 256 colors. A high color pixel requires at lest 24-bit color (1.1164 billion colors).

Color space: The color range between specified references. Typically references are quoted in television: RGB, Y, R-Y, B-Y, YIQ, YUV and Hue Saturation and Luminance (HSL). In print, Cyan, Magenta, Yellow and Black (CMYK) are used. Moving pictures between these is possible but requires careful attention to the accuracy of processing involved. Operating across the media—print, film and TV, as well as between computers and TV equipment—will require conversions in color space.

Color space conversion: The translation of color value form one color space to another. Since different media types, like video and computer graphics, use different color spaces, color space is often performed on the fly by graphics hardware.

Combiner: In digital picture manipulators, a device that controls the way in which two or more channels work together. Under software control, it determines the priority of the channels (which picture appears in front and which in back) and the types of transitions that can take place between them.

Component (video): The normal interpretation of a component video signal is one in which the luminance and chrominance remain as separate components, such as analog components in MII and Betacam VTRs, digital components Y, B-Y, R-Y(Y, Cr, Cb) in ITU-R 601. RGB is also a component signal. Component video signals retain maximum luminance and chrominance bandwidth.

Component digital: A digital representation of a component analog signal set, most often Y, B-Y, R-Y. The encoding parameters are specified by ITU-R BT.601-2 (CCIR 601). The parallel interface is specified by ITU-R BT.656 (CCIR 656) and SMPTE 125M.

Component digital post production: A method of post production that records and processes video completely in the component digital domain. Analog sources are converted only once to the component digital format and then remain in that format throughout the post production process.

Composite (video): Luminance and chrominance are combined along with the timing reference "sync" information using one of the coding standards—NTSC, PAL or SECAM—to make composite video. The process, which is an analog form of video compression, restricts the bandwidths (image detail) of components. In the composite result color is literally added to the monochrome (luminance) information using a visually acceptable technique. As our eyes have far more luminance resolving power than for color, the color sharpness (bandwidth) of the coded single is reduced to far below that of the luminance. This provides a good solution for transmission but it becomes difficult, if not impossible, to accurately reverse the process (decode) into pure luminance and chrominance which limits its use in post production.

Composite digital: A digitally encoded video signal, such as NTSC or PAL video, that includes horizontal and vertical synchronizing information.

Compress: A digital picture manipulator effect where the picture is squeezed (made proportionally smaller).

Compressed serial digital interface (CSDI): A way of compressing digital video for use on SDI-based equipment proposed by Panasonic. Now incorporated into Serial digital transport interface.
> See: Serial digital transport interface.

Compression: Reduction of the size of digital data files by removing redundant information (lossless) or removing non-critical data (lossy).
> Pictures are analyzed looking for redundancy and repetition and so discard unnecessary data. The techniques were primarily developed for digital transmission but have been adopted as a means of handling digital video in computers and reducing the storage demands for digital VTRs. Compression can be at either a set rate or a variable rate. Also known as Bit Rate Reduction (BRR)

Compression artifacts: Compacting of a digital signal, particularly when a high compression ratio is used, may result in small errors when the signal is decompressed. These errors are known as "artifacts," or unwanted defects. The artifacts may resemble noise (or edge "busyness") or may cause parts of the picture, particularly fast moving portions, to be displayed with the movement distorted or missing.

Compressionist: One who controls the compression process to produce results better than would be normally expected from an automated system.

Compression ratio: The ratio of the data in the non-compressed digital video signal to the compressed version. Modern compression techniques start with the ITU-R 601 component digital television signal so the amount of data of the non-compressed video is well defined—76 Gbytes/hour for the 525/60 standard and 75 Gbytes/hour for 625/50.

The compression ratio should not be used as the only method to assess the quality of a compressed signal. For a given technique greater compression can be expected to result in worse quality but different techniques give widely differing quality of results for the same compression ratio. The only sure method of judgment is to make a very close inspection of the resulting pictures.

Concatenation: Linking together (of systems). Although the effect on quality resulting from a signal passing through many systems has always been a concern, the use of a series of compressed digital video systems is, as yet, not well known. The matter is complicated by virtually all digital compression systems differing in some way from each other—hence the need to be aware of concatenation. For broadcast, the current NTSC and PAL analog compression systems will, more and more, operate alongside digital MPEG compression systems used for transmission and, possibly, in the studio.

Even the same brand and model of encoder may encode the same signal in a different manner.

See also: Mole technology.

Conditional access: Digital television signals can be scrambled in such a way that they cannot be understood by a conventional decoder. Only when unscrambled by a special system can the original pictures be seen by the viewer. By controlling the operation of the de-scrambling system through the use of a pre-paid access card, or by a transmitted code, the broadcaster can control access to a particular channel or service. Conditional access can be used to control many things from pay-per-view subscription through to target viewing areas. The ATSC specification, at press time, was not complete.

Contouring: Digital video picture defect caused quantizing at too coarse a level.

Contribution quality: The level of quality of a television signal from the network to its affiliates. For digital television this is approximately 45 Mbps.

Core: In fiber optic cable, the core is the light-transmitting material at the center of the fiber.

Co-siting: Relates to SMPTE 125M component digital video, in which the luminance component (Y) is sampled four times for every two samples of the two chrominance components (Cb and Cr). Co-siting refers to delaying transmission of the Cr component to occur at the same time as the second sample of luminance data. This produces a sampling order as follows: Y1/Cb1, Y2/Cr1, Y3/Cr3, Y4/Cb3, and so on. Co-siting reduces required bus width from 30 bits to 20 bits.

Coverage area: Coverage area is the area within an NTSC station's Grade B contour without regard to interference from other television stations which may be present. For an ATV station, coverage area is the area contained within the station's noise-limited contour without regard to interference which may be present.

CRC: Cyclic redundant check. Used in data transfer to check if the data has been corrupted. It is a check value calculated for a data stream by feeding it through a shifter with feedback terms "EXORed" back in. It performs the same function as a checksum but is considerably harder to fool.

A CRC can detect errors but not repair them, unlike an ECC—which is attached to almost any burst of data that might possibly be corrupted. They are used on disks, ITU-R 601 data, Ethernet packets, etc.

CSDI: *See: Compressed serial digital interface.*

D1: A format for component digital video tape recording working to the ITU-R 601, 4:2:2 standard using 8-bit sampling. The tape is 19 mm wide and allows up to 94 minutes to be recorded on a cassette. Being a component recording system it is ideal for studio or post production work with its high chrominance bandwidth allowing excellent chroma keying. Also multiple generations are possible with very little degradation and D1 equipment can integrate without transcoding to most digital effects systems, telecines, graphics devices, disk recorders, etc. Being component there are no color framing requirements. Despite the advantages, D1 equipment is not extensively used in general areas of TV production, at least partly due to its high cost. (Often used incorrectly to indicate component digital video.)

D2: The VTR standard for digital composite (coded) NTSC or PAL signals that uses data conforming to SMPTE 244M. It uses 19 mm tape and records up to 208 minutes on a single cassette. Neither cassettes nor recording formats are compatible with D1. D2 has often been used as a direct replacement for 1-inch analog VTRs. Although offering good stunt modes and multiple generations with low losses, being a coded system means coded characteristics are present. The user must be aware of cross-color, transcoding footprints, low chrominance bandwidths and color framing sequences. Employing an 8-bit format to sample the whole coded signal results in reduced amplitude resolution making D2 more susceptible to contouring artifacts. (Often used incorrectly to indicate composite digital video.)

D3: A composite digital video recording format that uses data conforming to SMPTE 244M. Uses 1/2-inch tape cassettes for recording digitized composite (coded) PAL or NTSC signals sampled at 8 bits. Cassettes are available for 50 to 245 minutes. Since this uses a composite signal the characteristics are generally as for D2 except that the 1/2-inch cassette size has allowed a full family of VTR equipment to be realized in one format, including a camcorder.

D4: A format designation never utilized due to the fact that the number four is considered unlucky (being synonymous with death in some Asian languages).

D5: A VTR format using the same cassette as D3 but recording component signals conforming to the ITU-R BT.601-2 (CCIR 601) recommendations at 10-bit resolution. With internal decoding D5 VTRs can play back D3 tapes and provide component outputs. Being a non-compressed component digital video recorder means D5 enjoys all the performance benefits of D1, making it suitable for high-end post production as well as more general studio use. Besides servicing the current 625 and 525 line TV standards the format also has provision for HDTV recording by use of about 4:1 compression (HD D5).
 See also: HD D5.

D6: A digital tape format which uses a 19mm helical-scan cassette tape to record uncompressed high definition television material at 1.88 GBps (1.2 Gbps). D6 is currently the only high definition recording format defined by a recognized standard. D6 accepts both the European 1250/50 interlaced format and the Japanese 260M version of the 1125/60 interlaced format which uses 1035 active lines. It does not accept the ITU format of 1080 active lines. ANSI/SMPTE 277M and 278M are D6 standards.

D7: DVCPRO. Panasonic's development of native DV component format which records a 18 micron (18x10-6m, eighteen thousandths of a millimeter) track on 6.35 mm (0.25-inch) metal particle tape. DVCPRO uses native DCT-based DV compression at 5:1 from a 4:1:1 8-bit sampled source. It uses 10 tracks per frame for 525/60 sources and 12 tracks per frame for 625/50 sources, both use 4:1:1 sampling. Tape speed is 33.813mm/s. It includes two 16-bit digital audio channels sampled at 48 kHz and an analog cue track. Both Linear (LTC) and Vertical Interval Time Code (VITC) are supported. There is a 4:2:2 (DVCPRO50) and progressive scan 4:2:0 (DVCPRO P) version of the format, as well as a high definition version (DVCPROHD).
 See also: DVCPRO50, DVCPROHD, DVCPRO P.

D8: There is no D8. The Television Recording and Reproduction Technology Committee of SMPTE decided to skip D8 because of the possibility of confusion with similarly named digital audio or data recorders (DA-88).

D9 (Formerly Digital-S): A 1/2-inch digital tape format developed by JVC which uses a high-density metal particle tape running at 57.8mm/s to record a video data rate of 50 Mbps. The tape can be shuttled and search up to 32x speed. Video sampled at 4:2:2 is compressed at 3.3:1 using DCT-based intra-frame compression (DV). Two or four audio channels are recorded at 16-bit, 48 kHz sampling; each is individually editable. The format also includes two cue tracks. Some machines can play back analog S-VHS. D9 HD is the high definition version recording at 100 Mbps.

D9 HD: A high definition digital component format based on D9. Records on 1/2-inch tape with 100 Mbps video.

D16: A recording format for digital film images making use of standard D1 recorders. The scheme was developed specifically to handle Quantel's Domino (Digital Opticals for Movies) pictures and record them over the space that sixteen 625 line digital pictures would occupy. This way three film frames can be recorded or played every two seconds. Playing the recorder allows the film images to be viewed on a standard monitor; running at 16x speed shows full motion direct from the tape.

DA-88: A Tascam-brand eight track digital audio tape machine using the 8 mm video format of Sony. It has become the *de facto* standard for audio post production though there are numerous other formats, ranging from swappable hard drives to analog tape formats and everything in between.

DAC (D-A, D/A, D-to-A): Digital-to-analog converter.
See also: ADC.

Data compression: A technique that provides for the transmission or storage, without noticeable information loss, of fewer data bits than were originally used when the data was created.

Data recorders: Machines designed to record and replay data. They usually include a high degree of error correction to ensure that the output data is absolutely correct and, due to their recording format, the data is not easily editable. This compares with video recorders which will conceal missing or incorrect data by repeating adjacent areas of picture and which are designed to allow direct access to every frame for editing. Where data recorders are used for recording video there has to be an attendant "work-station" to see the pictures or hear the sound, whereas VTRs produce the signals directly. Although many data recorders are based on VTRs' original designs, and vice versa, VTRs are more efficient for pictures and sound while data recorders are most appropriate for data.

dB (decibel): A measure of voltage, current, or power gain equal to 1/10 of a bel. Given by the equations 20 log Vout/Vin, 20 log Iout/Iin, or 10 log Pout/Pin. *See also: Bel.*

DBS: Digital broadcast system. An alternative to cable and analog satellite reception initially utilizing a fixed 18-inch dish focused on one or more geostationary satellites. DBS units are able to receive multiple channels of multiplexed video and audio signals as well as programming information, Email, and related data. DBS typically uses MPEG-2 encoding and COFDM transmission. Also known as digital satellite system.

D-Cinema (also E-Cinema): Digital cinema. Typically the process of using video at 1080/24p instead of film for production, post production and presentation.

DCT: 1. Discrete cosine transform. A widely used method of data compression of digital video pictures basically by resolving blocks of the picture (usually 8 x 8 pixels) into frequencies, amplitudes, and colors. JPEG and DV depend on DCT. 2. Also an Ampex data videotape format using discrete cosine transform.

DD2: Using D2 tape, data recorders have been developed offering (by computer standards) vast storage of data (which may be images). A choice of data transfer rates is available to suit computer interfaces. Like other computer storage media, images are not directly viewable, and editing is difficult.

DDR: Digital disk recorder. *See: Disk recorder.*

DDS: Digital data service.

Demultiplexing: Separating elementary streams or individual channels of data from a single muti-channel stream. For example, video and audio streams must be demultiplexed before they are decoded. This is true for multiplexed digital television transmissions.
> *See also: Multiplex.*

DEMUX: Demultiplexer. *See: Demultiplexing.*

Deserializer: A device that converts serial digital information to parallel digital.

Desktop video: Video editing and production done using standard desktop computing platforms running add-on video hardware and software.

D/I: Drop and insert. A point in the transmission where portions of the digital signal can be dropped out and/or inserted.

Diagnostics: Tests to check the correct operation of hardware and software. As digital systems continue to become more complex, built-in automated testing becomes an essential part of the equipment. Some extra hardware and software has to be added to make the tests operate. Digital systems with such provisions can often be quickly assessed by a trained service engineer, so speeding repair.

Digital: Circuitry in which data carrying signals are restricted to either of two voltage levels, corresponding to logic 1 or 0. A circuit that has two stable states: high or low, on or off.

Digital Betacam: A development of the original analog Betacam VTR which records digitally on a Betacam-style cassette. It uses mild intra-field compression to reduce the ITU-R 601 sampled video data by about 2:1. Some models can replay both digital and analog Betacam cassettes.

Digital chromakeying: Digital chromakeying differs from its analog equivalent in that it can key uniquely from any one of the 16 million colors represented in the component digital domain. It is then possible to key from relatively subdued colors, rather than relying on highly saturated colors that can cause color spill problems on the foreground.

A high-quality digital chromakeyer examines each of the three components of the picture and generates a linear key for each. These are then combined into a composite linear key for the final keying operation. The use of three keys allows much greater subtlety of selection than does a chrominance-only key

Digital components: Component video signals that have been digitized.

Digital disk recorder (DDR): A video recording device that uses a hard disk drive or optical disk drive mechanism. Disk recorders offer nearly instantaneous access to recorded material.

Digital effects: Special effects created using a digital video effects (DVE) unit.

Digital parallel distribution amplifier: A distribution amplifier designed to amplify and fan-out parallel digital signals.

Digital-S: *See: D9.*

Digital word: The number of bits treated as a single entity by the system.

Digitizing time: Time taken to record footage into a disk-based editing system, usually from a tape-based analog system, but also from newer digital tape formats without direct digital connections.

DTV IN THE REAL WORLD

UNDERSTANDING DIGITAL

PRE-PRODUCTION

PRODUCTION

AUDIO

GRAPHIC & COMPOSITING

POST PRODUCTION

DELIVERY & DUPLICATION

ENGINEERING & TRANSMISSION

APPENDIX

GLOSSARY

Distribution quality: The level of quality of a television signal from the station to its viewers. For digital television this is approximately 19.39 Mbps.

Dither: A form of smart conversion from a higher bit depth to a lower bit depth, used in the conversion of audio and graphic files. In the conversion from 24-bit color to 8-bit color (millions of colors reduced to 256), the process attempts to improve on the quality of on-screen graphics with reduced color palettes by adding patterns of different colored pixels to simulate the original color. The technique is also known as "error diffusion," and is applied to audio bit rate reduction and graphic resolution.

DNG: Digital news gathering. Electronic news gathering (ENG) using digital equipment and/or transmission.

Dolby Digital (formerly Dolby AC-3): The approved 5.1 channel (surround-sound) audio standard for ATSC digital television, using approximately 13:1 compression

Six discrete audio channels are used: Left, Center, Right, Left Rear (or side) Surround, Right Rear (or side) Surround, and a subwoofer (considered the ".1" as it is limited in bandwidth). The bit rate can range from 56 kbps to 640 kbps, typically 64 kbps mono, 192 kbps two-channel, 320 kbps 35mm Cinema 5.1, 384 kbps Laserdisc/DVD 5.1 and ATSC, 448 kbps 5.1.

When moving from analog recording to a digital recording medium, the digital audio coding used yields an amount of data often too immense to store or transmit economically, especially when multiple channels are required. As a result, new forms of digital audio coding—often known as "perceptual coding"—have been developed to allow the use of lower data rates with a minimum of perceived degradation of sound quality.

Dolby's third generation audio coding algorithm (originally called AC-3) is such a coder.

This coder has been designed to take maximum advantage of human auditory masking in that it divides the audio spectrum of each channel into narrow frequency bands of different sizes, optimized with respect to the frequency selectivity of human hearing. This makes it possible to sharply filter coding noise so that it is forced to stay very close in frequency to the frequency components of the audio signal being coded. By reducing or eliminating coding noise wherever there are no audio signals to mask it, the sound quality of the original signal can be subjectively preserved. In this key respect, a coding system like Dolby Digital is essentially a form of very selective and powerful noise reduction.

Dolby E: A new coding system designed specifically for use with video available from Dolby Laboratories. The audio framing is matched to the video framing, which allows synchronous and seamless switching or editing of audio and video without the introduction of gaps or A/V sync slips. All of the common video frame rates, including 30/29.97, 25, and 24/23.976, can be supported with matched Dolby E audio frame sizes. The Dolby E coding technology is intended to provide approximately 4:1 reduction in bit rate. The reduction ratio is intentionally limited so that the quality of the audio may be kept very high even after a number of encode-decode generations. The fact that operations such as editing and switching can be performed seamlessly in the coded domain allows many coding generations to be avoided, further increasing quality.

A primary carrier for the Dolby E data will be the AES/EBU signal. The Dolby E coding will allow the two PCM audio channels to be replaced with eight encoded audio channels. A VTR PCM track pair will become capable of carrying eight independent audio channels, plus the accompanying metadata. The system is also intended to be applied on servers and satellite links. A time delay when encoding or decoding Dolby E is unavoidable. In order to facilitate the provision of a compensating video delay, the audio encoding and decoding delay have been fixed at exactly one frame. When applied with video recording formats which incorporate frame based video encoding, it can be relatively easy to provide for equal video and audio coding delays. When applied with uncoded video, it may be necessary to provide a compensating one frame video delay.

Dolby Surround (Dolby Stereo, & Dolby 4:2:4): Matrix Analog coding of four audio channels—Left, Center, Right, Surround (LCRS), into two channels referred to as Right-total and Left-total (Rt, Lt). On playback, a Dolby Surround Pro Logic decoder converts the two channels to LCRS and, optionally, a subwoofer channel. The Pro Logic circuits are used to steer the audio and increase channel separation. The Dolby Surround system, originally developed for the cinema, is a method of getting more audio channels but suffers from poor channel separation, a mono limited bandwidth surround channel and other limitations. A Dolby Surround track can be carried by analog audio or linear PCM, Dolby Digital and MPEG compression systems.

Down converting: The process which changes the number of pixels and/or frame rate and/or scanning format used to represent an image by removing pixels. Down converting is done from high definition to standard definition.
See also: Side converting, up converting.

DQPSK: Differential quadrature phase shift keying. DQPSK is a digital modulation technique commonly used with cellular systems. Motorola's CyberSurfr cable modem uses DQPSK to carry data upstream from the subscriber's computer to the Internet on a narrower frequency band than standard QPSK. Narrower bands allow more upstream channels, so the CyberSurfr has additional noise-free channels to choose from when it's installed.

DRAM: Dynamic RAM (Random Access Memory). High density, cost-effective memory chips (integrated circuits). Their importance is such that the Japanese call them the "rice of electronics." DRAMs are used extensively in computers and generally in digital circuit design, but also for building framestores and animation stores. Being solid state, there are no moving parts and they offer the densest available method for accessing or storing data. Each bit is stored on a single transistor, and the chip must be powered and clocked to retain data.

DS0: Digital signal level zero, 64 kbps.

DS1: A telephone company format for transmitting information digitally. DS1 has a capacity of 24 voice circuits at a transmission speed of 1.544 megabits per second.
See also: T1.

DS3: A terrestrial and satellite format for transmitting information digitally. DS3 has a capacity of 672 voice circuits at a transmission speed of 44.736 Mbps (commonly referred to as 45 Mbps). DS3 is used for digital television distribution using mezzanine level compression—typically MPEG-2 in nature, decompressed at the local station to full bandwidth signals (such as HDTV) and then re-compressed to the ATSC's 19.39 Mbps transmission standard.

DSL: Digital subscriber line. The ability to use a standard telephone line to transport data. *x*DSL is the generic term for each of two varieties: ADSL (asynchronous), where the upstream and downstream data rates are different, and SDSL (synchronous), where the upstream and downstream data rates are the same.

DSS: Digital satellite system.Due to trademark issues, the abbreviation is no longer used. See DBS.

DTT: Digital terrestrial television. The term used in Europe to describe the broadcast of digital television services using terrestrial frequencies.

DTV Team, The: Originally Compaq, Microsoft and Intel, later joined by Lucent Technologies. The DTV Team promotes the computer industry's views on digital tele-

DTV IN THE REAL WORLD

UNDERSTANDING DIGITAL

PRE-PRODUCTION

PRODUCTION

AUDIO

GRAPHIC & COMPOSITING

POST PRODUCTION

DELIVERY & DUPLICATION

ENGINEERING & TRANSMISSION

APPENDIX

vision—namely, that DTV should not have interlace scanning formats but progressive scanning formats only. (Intel, however, now supports all the ATSC Table 3 formats, including those that are interlace, such as 1080i.) Internet: www.dtv.org.

DV: This digital VCR format is a cooperation between Hitachi, JVC, Sony, Matsushita, Mitsubishi, Philips, Sanyo, Sharp, Thomson and Toshiba. It uses 6.35 mm (0.25-inch) wide tape in a range of products to record 525/60 or 625/50 video for the consumer (DV) and professional markets (Panasonic's DVCPRO, Sony's DVCAM and Digital-8). All models use digital intra-field DCT-based "DV" compression (about 5:1) to record 8-bit component digital video based on 13.5 MHz luminance sampling. The consumer versions, DVCAM, and Digital-8 sample video at 4:1:1 (525/60) or 4:2:0 (625/50) video (DVCPRO is 4:1:1 in both 525/60 and 625/25) and provide two 16-bit/48 or 44.1 kHz, or four 12-bit/32 kHz audio channels onto a 4 hour 30 minutes standard cassette or smaller 1 hour "mini" cassette. The video recording rate is 25 Mbps.

DVB: Digital video broadcasting. The group, with over 200 members in 25 countries, which developed the preferred scheme for digital broadcasting in Europe. The DVB Group has put together a satellite system—DVB-S—that can be used with any transponder, current or planned, a matching cable system—DVB-C, and a digital terrestrial system—DVB-T. Internet: www.dvb.org.
See also: DVB-T.

DVB-T: The DVB-T is a transmission scheme for terrestrial digital television. Its specification was approved by ETSI in February 1997 and DVB-T services began in 1998. As with the other DVB standards, MPEG-2 sound and picture coding form the basis of DVB-T. It uses a transmission scheme based on Coded Orthogonal Frequency Division Multiplexing (COFDM), which spreads the signals over a large number of carriers to enable it to operate effectively in very strong multipath environments. The multipath immunity of this approach means that DVB-T can operate an overlapping network of transmitting stations with a single frequency. In the areas of overlap, the weaker of the two received signals is rejected.
See also: COFDM, DVB.

DVCAM: Sony's development of native DV which records a 15 micron (15x10-6m, fifteen thousandths of a millimeter) track on a metal evaporated (ME) tape. DVCAM uses DV compression of a 4:1:1 signal for 525/60 (NTSC) sources and 4:2:0 for 625/50 (PAL). Audio is recorded in one of two forms—four 12-bit channels sampled at 32 kHz, or two 16-bit channels sampled at 48 kHz.

DVCPRO: *See: D7.*

DVCPRO50: This variant of DV uses a video data rate of 50 Mbps—double that of other DV systems—and is aimed at the higher quality end of the market. Sampling is 4:2:2 to give enhanced chroma resolution, useful in post production processes (such as chromakeying). Four 16-bit audio tracks are provided. The format is similar to Digital-S (D9).

DVCPRO HD: This variant of DV uses a video data rate of 100 Mbps--four times that of other DV systems--and is aimed at the high definition EFP end of the market. Eight audio channels are supported. The format is similar to D9 HD.

DVCPRO P: This variant of DV uses a video data rate of 50 Mbps—double that of other DV systems— to produce a 480 progressive picture. Sampling is 4:2:0.

DVD: Digital versatile disk: A high density development of the compact disk. It is the same size as a CD but stores from 4.38 GB (seven times CD capacity) on a single sided, single layer disk. DVDs can also be double sided or dual layer-storing even more data. The capacities commonly available at present:

DVD-5: 4.7 GB (1 side, 1 layer)
DVD-9: 8.5 GB (1 side, 2 layers)
DVD-10: 9.4 GB (2 sides, 1 layer each)
DVD-18: 17.0 GB (2 sides, 2 layers)
DVD-R: 4.7 GB (1 side, 1 layer) (write once)
DVD-RAM: 2.6 GB (per side, 1 layer) (rewritable)
*DVD-RAM: 4.7 GB (per side, 1 layer) (rewritable)
*Expected in 2000.

DVE: Digital video effects. A registered trademark of Nippon Electric Company. Refers to video equipment that performs digital effects such as compression and transformation.

DVTR: Digital videotape recorder.

Dynamic Rounding: The intelligent truncation of digital signals. Some image processing requires that two signals are multiplied, for example in digital mixing, producing a 16-bit result from two original 8-bit numbers (see: Byte). This has to be truncated, or rounded, back to 8-bits. Simply dropping the lower bits can result in visible contouring artifacts especially when handling pure computer generated pictures.

Dynamic Rounding is a mathematical technique for truncating the word length of pixels—usually to their normal 8-bits. This effectively removes the visible artifacts and is non-cumulative on any number of passes. Other attempts at a solution have involved increasing the number of bits, usually to 10, making the LSBs (least significant bit) smaller but only masking the problem for a few generations.

Dynamic Rounding is a licensable technique, available from Quantel and is used in a growing number of digital products both from Quantel and other manufacturers.

EAV: End of active video in component digital systems.

EBU: European Broadcasting Union. An organization of European broadcasters that, among other activities, produces technical statements and recommendations for the 625/50 line television system. CP 67, CH-1218 Grand-Saconnex GE, Switzerland. Tel: 011-41-22-717-2221. Fax: 011-41-22-717-2481. Email: ebu@ebu.ch. Internet: www.ebu.ch.

ECC: Error Check and Correct. A block of check data, usually appended to a data packet in a communications channel or to a data block on a disk, which allows the receiving or reading system both to detect small errors in the data stream (caused by line noise or disk defects) and, provided they are not too long, to correct them.

E-Cinema (also D-Cinema): Electronic cinema. Typically the process of using video at 1080/24p instead of film for production, post production and presentation.

EDH: Error detection and handling for recognizing inaccuracies in the serial digital signal. It may be incorporated into serial digital equipment and employ a simple LED error indicator.

Electronic Programming Guide (EPG): An application that provides an on-screen listing of all programming and content that an interactive television service subscriber or digital television viewer has available to them.
See also: PSIP.

Embedded audio: Digital audio that is multiplexed and carried within an SDI connection—so simplifying cabling and routing. The standard (ANSI/SMPTE 272M-1994) allows up to four groups each of four mono audio channels. Generally VTRs only support Group 1 but other equipment may use more, for example Quantel's Clipbox server connection to an edit seat uses groups 1-3 (12 channels). 48 kHz synchronous audio sampling is pretty well universal in TV but the standard also includes 44.1 and 32 kHz

DTV IN THE REAL WORLD

UNDERSTANDING DIGITAL

PRE-PRODUCTION

PRODUCTION

AUDIO

GRAPHIC & COMPOSITING

POST PRODUCTION

DELIVERY & DUPLICATION

ENGINEERING & TRANSMISSION

APPENDIX

GLOSSARY

synchronous and asynchronous sampling. Synchronous means that the audio sampling clock is genlocked to the associated video (8,008 samples per five frames in 525/60, 1,920 samples per frame in 625/50). Up to 24-bit samples are allowed but mostly only up to 20 are currently used. 48 kHz sampling means an average of just over three samples per line, so three samples per channel are sent on most lines and four occasionally—the pattern is not specified in the standard. Four channels are packed into an Ancillary Data Packet and sent once per line (hence a total of 4 x 3 = 12 or 4 x 4 = 16 audio samples per packet per line).

Enhancements: Producers add these to interactive and digital television, as well as other digital content to enhance program material. Examples are supplementary text and graphics that add more depth and richness, or links to reach a Web site, as is done using TV Crossover Links. In analog, the vertical blanking interval (VBI) is used to broadcast enhancements, while in digital, the enhancements are part of the ATSC MPEG-2 stream. Enhancements can be created using industry-standard tools and technologies, like HTML and the ECMA Internet Scripting.

Encryption: The process of coding data so that a specific code or key is required to restore the original data. In broadcast, this is used to make transmissions secure from unauthorized reception as is often found on satellite or cable systems.

Error concealment: In digital video recording systems, a technique used when error correction fails. Erroneous data is replaced by data synthesized from surrounding pixels.

Error correction: In digital video recording systems, a scheme that adds overhead to the data to permit a certain level of errors to be detected and corrected.

Error detection: Checking for errors in data transmission. A calculation is made on the data being sent and the results are sent along with it. The receiver then performs the same calculation and compares its results with those sent. If an error is detected the affected data can be deleted and retransmitted, the error can be corrected or concealed, or it can simply be reported.

Error detection and handling: *See: EDH.*

Essence: The actual program (audio, video and/or data) without metadata.
    See also: Metadata.

Ethernet (IEEE 802.3): A type of high-speed network for interconnecting computing devices. Ethernet can be either 10 or 100 Mbps (Fast Ethernet). Ethernet is a trademark of Xerox Corporation, Inc.

Extended Studio PAL: A 625-line video standard that allows processing of component video quality digital signals by composite PAL equipment. The signal can be distributed and recorded in a composite digital form using D2 or D3 VTRs.

FDDI: Fiber Distributed Data Interface. Standards for a 100 Mbps local area network, based upon fiber optic or wired media configured as dual counter rotating token rings. This configuration provides a high level of fault tolerance by creating multiple connection paths between nodes—connections can be established even if a ring is broken.

Fiber bundle: A group of parallel optical fibers contained within a common jacket. A bundle may contain from just a few to several hundred fibers.

Fiber Channel: *See: Fibre Channel.*

Fiber optics: Thin glass filaments within a jacket that optically transmits images or signals in the form of light around corners and over distances with extremely low losses.

Fibre Channel (also Fiber Channel): A high speed data link planned to run up to 2 Gbps on a fiber optic cable. A number of manufacturers are developing products to utilize the

Fiber Channel—Arbitrated Loop (FC-AL) serial storage interface at 1 Gbps so that storage devices such as hard disks can be connected. Supports signaling rates from 132.8 Mbps to 1,062.5 Mbps, over a mixture of physical media including optical fiber, video coax, miniature coax, and shielded twisted pair wiring. The standard supports data transmission and framing protocols for the most popular channel and network standards including SCSI, HIPPI, Ethernet, Internet Protocol, and ATM.

Field: In an interlaced-scanning format, a frame consists of a field of even scan lines or a field of odd scan lines captured or displayed at different times. In a progressive-scanning format, a field is the same as a frame.
>   *See also: Frame*

FireWire: Apple Computer's trademark for IEEE 1394.
>   *See: IEEE 1394.*

Fixed data rate compression: Techniques designed to produce a data stream with a constant data rate. Such techniques may vary the quality of quantization to match the allocated bandwidth.

Format conversion: The process of both encoding/decoding and resampling digital rates to change a digital signal from one format to another.

Fractual compression: A technique for compressing images that uses fractals. It can produce high quality and high compression ratios. The drawback to fractal compression is that it is computationally expensive, so therefore takes a long time.

Fragmentation: The scattering of data over a disk caused by successive recording and deletion operations. Generally this will eventually result in slow data recall—a situation that is not acceptable for video recording or replay. The slowing is caused by the increased time needed to randomly access data. With such stores, defragmentation routines arrange the data (by copying from one part of the disk to another) so that it is accessible in the required order for replay. Clearly any change in replay, be it a transmission running order or the revision of an edit, could require further de-fragmentation. True random access disk stores, able to play frames in any order at video rate, never need de-fragmentation.

Frame: A frame is one complete image in a sequence of images. In video, the frame captures and displays all pixels and lines of an image. In a progressive-scanning format, there is no decomposition into fields. In an interlaced-scanning format, the frame consists of odd and even line fields, captured or displayed at different times, which in combination contain all pixels and lines of an image. The frame rate of a progressive scan format is twice that of an interlace scan format.

Frame buffer: Memory used to store a complete frame of video.

Frame synchronizer: A digital buffer that, by storage, comparison of sync information to a reference, and timed release of video signals, can continuously adjust the signal for any timing errors.

Freeze: In digital picture manipulators, the ability to stop or hold a frame of video so that the picture is frozen like a snapshot.

Freeze frame: The storing of a single frame of video.

Generation (loss): The signal degradation caused by successive recordings. Freshly recorded material is first generation, one re-recording, or copy, makes the second, etc. This is of major concern in analog linear editing but much less so using a digital suite. Non-compressed component DVTRs should provide at least twenty generations before any artifacts become noticeable, but the very best multi-generation results are possible with disk-based systems. Generations are effectively limitless. Besides the limitations of recording, the action of processors such as decoders and coders will make a significant contribution to generation loss. The decode/recode cycle of NTSC and PAL is well

DTV IN THE REAL WORLD

UNDERSTANDING DIGITAL

PRE-PRODUCTION

PRODUCTION

AUDIO

GRAPHIC & COMPOSITING

POST PRODUCTION

DELIVERY & DUPLICATION

ENGINEERING & TRANSMISSION

APPENDIX

GLOSSARY

known for its limitations but equal caution is needed for digital video compression systems, especially those using MPEG, and the color space conversions that typically occur between computers handling RGB and video equipment using Y, Cr, Cb.

See also: Color space, concatenation, error concealment, error correction, error detection.

GIF (pronounced *jif*): Graphics interchange format. A computer graphics file format developed by CompuServe for use in compressing graphic images, now commonly used on the Internet. GIF compression is lossless, supports transparency, but allows a maximum of only 256 colors. Images that will gain the most from GIF compression are those which have large areas (especially horizontal area) with no changes in color.

GoP: *See: Group of pictures.*

Grand Alliance: The United States grouping, formed in May 1993, to produce "the best of the best" initially proposed HDTV systems. The participants are: AT&T, General Instrument Corporation, Massachusetts Institute of Technology, Philips Consumer Electronics, David Sarnoff Research Center, Thomson Consumer Electronics and Zenith Electronics Corporation.

The format proposed is known as the ATSC format.

See also: ATSC.

Group of pictures: In an MPEG signal the GoP is a group of frames between successive I frames, the others being P and/or B frames. In the widest used application, television transmission, the GoP is typically 12 frames but this can vary—a new sequence starting with an I frame may be generated if there is a big change at the input, such as a cut. If desired, SMPTE time code data can be added to this layer for the first picture in a GoP.

H.263: A standard for variable low bit rate coding of video. H.263 is better than MPEG-1/MPEG-2 for low resolutions and low bit rates. H.263 is less flexible than MPEG, but therefore requires much less overhead.

HD-0: A set of formats based partially on the ATSC Table 3, suggested by The DTV Team as the initial stage of the digital television rollout. Pixel values represent full aperture for ITU-R 601.

total lines per frame	horizontal size value	vertical size value	aspect ratio information	frame rate code
750	1,280	720	1.33 to 2.4 (4:3 to ASC widescreen)	24p, 25p
625	720	576	1.33 to 2.4 (4:3 to 16:9)	24p, 25i, 25p,48p,50p
525	720	486	1.33 to 1.77 (4:3 to 16:9)	23.97p,24p,29.97i, 29.97p, 30p, 59.94p, 60p
525	640	480	1.33 (4:3)	23.97p,25i, 25p, 29.97i, 29.97p, 30p, 50p, 59.94p, 60p

The DTV Team's HD0 Compression Format Constraints

HD-1: A set of formats partially based on the ATSC Table 3, suggested by The DTV Team as the second stage of the digital television rollout, expected to be formalized in the year 2000. Pixel values represent full aperture for ITU-R 601. (Items in bold have been added to HD-0.)

total lines per frame	horizontal size value	vertical size value	aspect ratio information	frame rate code
1,125	**1,920**	**1,080**	**1.33 to 2.4** (4:3 to ASC widescreen)	**24p, 25p**
750	1,280	720	1.33 to 2.4 (4:3 to ASC widescreen)	24p.25p, **48p, 50p, 60p**
625	720	576	1.33 to 1.77 (4:3 to 16:9)	24p, 25i, 25p, 48p, 50p
525	640	480	1.33 (4:3)	23.97p,24p,25i, 25p 29.97i, 29.97p, 30p, 50p, 59.94p, 60p

The DTV Team's HD1 Compression Format Constraints

HD-2: A set of formats partially based on the ATSC Table 3, suggested by The DTV Team as the third stage of the digital television rollout contingent on some extreme advances in video compression over the next five years. Pixel values represent full aperture for

total lines per frame	horizontal size value	vertical size value	aspect ratio information	frame rate code
TBD	**TBD**	**TBD**	**1.33 to 2.4** (4:3 to ASC widescreen)	**TBD**
1,125	1,920	1,080	1.33 to 2.4 (4:3 to ASC widescreen)	24p.25p, **48p, 50p, 60p**
750	1280	720	1.33 to 1.77 (4:3 to ASC widescreen)	24p, 25p, 48p, 50p60p
625	720	576	1.33 to 1.77 (4:3 to 16:9)	24p, 25i, 25p 48p,50p
525	720	486	1.33 to 1.77	23.97p, 24p, 29.97i, 29.97p, 30p, 59.94p, 60p
525	640	480	1.33 (4:3)	23.97p, 24p, 25i, 25p, 29.97i, 29.97p, 30p, 50p, 59.94p, 60p

ITU-R 601. (Items in bold have been added to HD-1.)

The DTV Team's HD2 Compression Format Constraints

HD D5: A compressed recording system developed by Panasonic which uses compression at about 4:1 to record HD material on standard D5 cassettes. HD D5 supports the 1080 and the 1035 interlaced line standards at both 60 Hz and 59.94 Hz field rates, all 720 progressive line standards and the 1080 progressive line standard at 24, 25 and 30 frame rates. Four uncompressed audio channels sampled at 40 kHz, 20 bits per sample, are also supported.

HDCAM: Sometimes called HD Betacam—is a means of recording compressed high-definition video on a tape format (1/2-inch) which uses the same cassette shell as Digital Betacam, although with a different tape formulation. The technology is aimed specifically at the USA and Japanese 1125/60 markets and supports both 1080 and 1035 active line standards. Quantization from 10 bits to 8 bits and DCT intra-frame compression are used to reduce the data rate. Four uncompressed audio channels sampled at 48 kHz, 20 bits per sample, are also supported.

HDTV: High definition television. The 1,125-, 1,080- and 1,035-line interlace and 720 and 1,080-line progressive formats in a 16:9 aspect ratio. Officially a format is high definition if it has at least twice the horizontal and vertical resolution of the standard signal being used. There is a debate as to whether 480-line progressive is also high definition. It is the opinion of the editors that 480-line progressive is not an HDTV format, but does provide better resolution than 480-line interlace, making it an enhanced definition format.

HFC: Hybrid fiber coax. A type of network that contains both fiber-optic cables and copper coaxial cables. The fiber-optic cables carry TV signals from the head-end office to the neighborhood; the signals are then converted to electrical signals and then go to coaxial cables.

HIPPI: High performance parallel interface. A parallel data channel used in mainframe computers that supports data transfer rates of 100 Mbps.

Huffman coding: This compresses data by assigning short codes to frequently-occurring sequences and longer ones to those less frequent. Assignments are held in a Huffman Table. The more likely a sequence is to occur the shorter will be the code that replaces it. It is widely used in video compression systems where it often contributes a 2:1 reduction in data.

I frames: One of the three types of frames that are used in MPEG-2 coded signals. These contain data to construct a whole picture as they are composed of information from only one frame (intraframe). The original information is compressed using DCT.
    See also: B frames, P frames, MPEG.

Icon: In desktop computing and editing, a graphic symbol that represents a file, a tool, or a function.

IEEE 1394 (FireWire): A low-cost digital interface originated by Apple Computer as a desktop LAN and developed by the IEEE 1394 working group. Can transport data at 100, 200, or 400 Mbps. One of the solutions to connect digital television devices together at 200 Mbps.
    Serial Bus Management provides overall configuration control of the serial bus in the form of optimizing arbitration timing, guarantee of adequate electrical power for all devices on the bus, assignment of which IEEE 1394 device is the cycle master, assignment of isochronous channel ID, and notification of errors.
    There are two types of IEEE 1394 data transfer: asynchronous and isochronous. Asynchronous transport is the traditional computer memory-mapped, load and store interface. Data requests are sent to a specific address and an acknowledgment is returned.
    In addition to an architecture that scales with silicon technology, IEEE 1394 features a unique isochronous data channel interface. Isochronous data channels provide guaranteed data transport at a pre-determined rate. This is especially important for time-critical multimedia data where just-in-time delivery eliminates the need for costly buffering.

i.LINK: Sony's trademark for IEEE 1394.
    See: IEEE 1394.

Illegal colors: Colors that force a color system to go outside its normal bounds. Usually these are the result of electronically painted images rather than direct camera outputs. For example, removing the luminance from a high intensity blue or adding luminance to a strong yellow in a paint system may well send a subsequent NTSC or PAL coded signal too high or low—producing at least inferior results and maybe causing technical problems. Out of gamut detectors can be used to warn of possible problems.

Interactive television: A combination of television with interactive content and enhancements. Interactive television provides better, richer entertainment and information, blending traditional TV-watching with the interactivity of a personal computer. Programming can include richer graphics, one-click access to Web sites through TV Crossover Links, electronic mail and chats, and online commerce through a back channel.
See also: Back channel.

Interframe coding: Data reduction based on coding the differences between a prediction of the data and the actual data. Motion compensated prediction is typically used, based on reference frames in the past and the future.

Interlaced: Short for interlaced scanning. Also called line interlace. A system of video scanning whereby the odd- and even-numbered lines of a picture are transmitted consecutively as two separate interleaved fields. Interlace is a form of compression.

Interpolation (spatial): When re-positioning or re-sizing a digital image inevitably more, less or different pixels are required from those in the original image. Simply replicating or removing pixels causes unwanted artifacts. For far better results the new pixels have to be interpolated—calculated by making suitably weighted averages of adjacent pixels—to produce a more transparent result. The quality of the results will depend on the techniques used and the number of pixels (points—hence 16-point interpolation), or area of original picture, used to calculate the result.

Interpolation (temporal): Interpolation between the same point in space on successive frames. It can be used to provide motion smoothing and is extensively used in standards converters to reduce the judder caused by the 50/60 Hz field rate difference. The technique can also be adapted to create frame averaging for special effects.

Intraframe Coding: Video coding within a frame of a video signal.
See also: I frames.

I/O: Input/output. Typically refers to sending information or data signals to and from devices.

IP: *See: TCP/IP.*

ISDB: Integrated services digital broadcasting. Japan's transmission specification for digital broadcasting. ISDB uses a new transmission scheme called BST-OFDM that ensures the flexible use of transmission capacity and service expandability in addition to the benefits of OFDM. Since OFDM uses a large number of carriers that are digitally modulated. It provides sufficient transmission quality under multipath interference. The basic approach of BST-OFDM is that a transmitting signal consists of the required number of narrow band OFDM blocks called BST-segments, each with a bandwidth of 100 kHz.

ISDN: Integrated services digital network. Allows data to be transmitted at high speed over the public telephone network. ISDN operates from the Basic Rate of 64 kbits/sec to the Primary Rate of 2 Mbps (usually called ISDN-30 as it comprises 30 Basic Rate channels). Most of the Western world currently has the capability to install ISDN-2 with 128 kbps and very rapid growth is predicted for ISDN generally. In the television and film industries, audio facilities are already using it. The cost of a call is usually similar to using a normal telephone.

Nominally ISDN operates internationally, but there are variations in standards, service and ISDN adapter technologies. Some operators in the USA use a similar system, Switch 56 (56 kbits/sec and upwards), although the availability of ISDN is becoming wider.

ITU: International Telecommunications Union. An international broadcast standards committee that replaced the CCIR. Place des Nations, CH-1211 Geneva 20, Switzerland. Tel: 011-41-22-730-5111. Fax: 011-41-22-733-7256. Email: itumail@itu.int. Internet: www.itu.int.

ITU-R 601: *See: ITU-R BT.601-2.*

ITU-R BT.601-2: Formerly known as CCIR 601. This international standard defines the encoding parameters of digital television for studios. It is the international standard for digitizing component television video in both 525 and 625 line systems and is derived from the SMPTE RP125. ITU-R 601 deals with both color difference (Y, R-Y, B-Y) and RGB video, and defines sampling systems, RGB/Y, R-Y, B-Y matrix values and filter characteristics. It does not actually define the electro-mechanical interface—see ITU-R BT.656. ITU-R 601 is normally taken to refer to color difference component digital video (rather than RGB), for which it defines 4:2:2 sampling at 13.5 MHz with 720 luminance samples per active line and 8 or 10-bit digitizing. Some headroom is allowed with black at level 16 (not 0) and white at level 235 (not 255)—to minimize clipping of noise and overshoots. Using 8-bit digitizing approximately 16 million unique colors are possible: 28 each for Y (luminance), Cr and Cb (the digitized color difference signals) = 224 = 16,777,216 possible combinations. The sampling frequency of 13.5 MHz was chosen to provide a politically acceptable common sampling standard between 525/60 and 625/50 systems, being a multiple of 2.25 MHz, the lowest common frequency to provide a static sampling pattern for both.

ITU-R BT.656: Formerly known as CCIR 656. The physical parallel and serial interconnect scheme for ITU-R BT.601-2 (CCIR 601). ITU-R BT.656 defines the parallel connector pinouts as well as the blanking, sync, and multiplexing schemes used in both parallel and serial interfaces. Reflects definitions in EBU Tech 3267 (for 625-line signals) and in SMPTE 125M (parallel 525) and SMPTE 259M (serial 525).

ITU-R BT.709-3: Ratified by the International Telecommunications Union (ITU) in June 1999, the 1920x1080 digital sampling structure is a world format. All supporting technical parameters relating to scanning, colorimetry, transfer characteristics, etc. are universal. The CIF can be used with a variety of picture capture rates: 60p, 50p, 30p, 25p, 24p, as well as 60i and 50i.
See also: CIF.

ITU-R BS.775 An international recommendation for multichannel stereophonic sound systems with and without accompanying picture. This recommendation gives speaker placements for various types of sound systems.

Java: A general purpose programming language developed by Sun Microsystems and best known for its widespread use on the World Wide Web. Unlike other software, programs written in Java can run on any platform type (including set-top boxes), as long as they contain a Java Virtual Machine. Internet: java.sun.com.
See also: Windows CE.

Jitter: An undesirable random signal variation with respect to time.

JPEG: Joint Photographic Experts Group. ISO/ITU-T. JPEG is a standard for the data compression of still pictures (intrafield). In particular its work has been involved with pictures coded to the ITU-R 601 standard. JPEG uses DCT and offers data compression of between two and 100 times and three levels of processing are defined: the baseline, extended and "lossless" encoding. *See also: Motion-JPEG.*

Keyframe: A set of parameters defining a point in a transition, such as a DVE effect. For example, a keyframe may define a picture size, position and rotation. Any digital effect must have a minimum of two keyframes, start and finish, although more complex moves will use more—maybe as many as 100. Increasingly, more parameters are becoming "keyframeable," meaning they can be programmed to transition between two, or more, states. Examples are color correction to made a steady change of color, and keyer settings, perhaps to made an object slowly appear or disappear.

Latency: The factor of data access time due to disk rotation. The faster a disk spins the quicker it will be at the position where the required data can start to be read. As disk diameters have decreased so rotational speeds have tended to increase but there is still much variation. Modern 31/2-inch drives typically have spindle speeds of between 3,600 and 7,200 revolutions per minute, so one revolution is completed in 16 or 8 milliseconds (ms) respectively. This is represented in the disk specification as average latency of 8 or 4 ms.

Layered embedded encoding: The process of compressing data in layers such that successive layers provide more information and thus higher quality reconstruction of the original. That is, a single stream of data can supply a range of compression and thus, in the case of video, a scalable range of video resolution and picture quality. This is particularly useful for a muticast where a single stream is sent out and people are connecting over varying bandwidths. The low bandwidth connection can take just the lower layers while the high-bandwidth connection can take all of the layers for the highest quality.

Letterbox: Image of a widescreen picture on a standard 4:3 aspect ratio television screen, typically with black bars above and below. Used to maintain the original aspect ratio of the source material.
>   *See also: Side panels and pillarbox.*

Live-streaming: Streaming media that is broadcast to many people at a set time.
>   *See also: On-demand streaming.*

Lossless compression: Reducing the bandwidth required for transmission of a given data rate without loss of any data.

Lossy compression: Reducing the total data rate by discarding data that is not critical. Both the video and audio for DTV transmission will use lossy compression.
>   *See also: Algorithm.*

LSB: Least significant bit. The bit that has the least value in a binary number or data byte. In written form, this would be the bit on the right.
>   For example: **Binary 1101 = Decimal 13**
>   In this example the right-most binary digit, 1, is the least significant bit—here representing 1. If the LSB in this example were corrupt, the decimal would not be 13 but 12. *See also: MSB.*

Luminance: The component of a video signal that includes information about its brightness.
>   *See also: Chrominance.*

Macroblock: In the typical 4:2:0 picture representation used by MPEG-2, a macroblock consists of four eight by eight blocks of luminance data (arranged in a 16 by 16 sample array) and two eight by eight blocks of color difference data which correspond to the area covered by the 16 by 16 section luminance component of the picture. The macroblock is the basic unit used for motion compensated prediction.
>   *See also: Block, Slice.*

MAMA: The Media Asset Management Association. MAMA serves as a advanced usergroup and independent international industry consortium, created by and for media producers, content publishers, technology providers, and value-chain partners to develop open content and metadata exchange protocols for digital media creation and asset management. Internet: www.mamgroup.org.

Mbone: **M**ulticast back**bone**. A virtual network consisting of portions of the Internet in which multicasting has been enabled. The Mbone originated from IEFT in which live audio and video were transmitted around the world. The Mbone is a network of hosts connected to the Internet communicating through IP multicast protocols, multicast-enabled routers, and the point-to-point tunnels that interconnect them.

Megabyte (Mbyte): One million bytes (actually 1,048,576); one thousand kilobytes.

DTV IN THE REAL WORLD

UNDERSTANDING DIGITAL

PRE-PRODUCTION

PRODUCTION

AUDIO

GRAPHIC & COMPOSITING

POST PRODUCTION

DELIVERY & DUPLICATION

ENGINEERING & TRANSMISSION

APPENDIX

GLOSSARY

Metadata (side information): Informational data about the data itself. Typically information about the audio and video data included in the signal's data stream. *See also: Essence.*

Mezzanine compression: Contribution level quality encoded high definition television signals. Typically split into two levels: High Level at approximately 140 Mbps and Low Level at approximately 39 Mbps (for high definition within the studio, 270Mbps is being considered). These levels of compression are necessary for signal routing and are easily re-encoded without additional compression artifacts (concatenation) to allow for picture manipulation after decoding. DS3 at 44.736 will be used in both terrestrial and satellite program distribution.

Modem: Modulator/demodulator. A device that transforms a typical two-level computer signal into a form suitable for transmission over a telephone line. Also does the reverse—transforms an encoded signal on a telephone line into a two-level computer signal.

Mole Technology: A seamless MPEG-2 concatenation technology developed by the ATLANTIC project (BBC [U.K.], Centro Studi e Laboratori telecomunicazione [Italy], Ecole Nationale Superieure des Telecommunications [France], Ecole Polytechnique Fédérale de Lausanne [Switzerland], Electrocraft [U.K.], Fraunhofer-Institut für Integrierte Schaltungen [Germany], Instituto de Engenharia de Sistemas e Computadores [Portugal], Snell & Wilcox [U.K.]) in which an MPEG-2 bit stream enters a Mole-equipped decoder, and the decoder not only decodes the video, but the information on how that video was first encoded (motion vectors and coding mode decisions). This "side information" or "metadata" in an information bus is synchronized to the video and sent to the Mole-equipped encoder. The encoder looks at the metadata and knows exactly how to encode the video. The video is encoded in exactly the same way (so theoretically it has only been encoded once) and maintains quality.

If an opaque bug is inserted in the picture, the encoder only has to decide how the bug should be encoded (and then both the bug and the video have been theoretically encoded only once).

Problems arise with transparent or translucent bugs, because the video underneath the bug must be encoded, and therefore that video will have to be encoded twice, while the surrounding video and the bug itself have only been encoded once theoretically.

What Mole can not do is make the encoding any better. Therefore the highest quality of initial encoding is suggested.

Montreux International Television Symposium & Technical Exhibition (TV Montreux): A bi-annual international conference for the television broadcast industry. Internet: www.montreux.ch/symposia/TV/home.html.

Moore's Law: A prediction for the rate of development of modern electronics. This has been expressed in a number of ways but in general states that the density of information storable in silicon roughly doubles every year. Or, the performance of silicon will double every eighteen months, with proportional decreases in cost. For more than two decades this prediction has held true. Moore's law initially talked about silicon but it could be applied to disk drives: the capacity of disk drives doubles every two years. That has been true since 1980, and will continue well beyond 2000. Named after Gordon E. Moore, physicist, co-founder and chairman emeritus of Intel Corporation.

Motion compensation: The use of motion vectors to improve the efficiency of the prediction of pixel values. The prediction uses motion vectors to provide offsets into past and/or future reference frames containing previously decoded pixels that are used to form the prediction and the error difference signal.

Motion estimation: An image compression technique that achieves compression by describing only the motion differences between adjacent frames, thus eliminating the need to convey redundant static picture information from frame to frame. Used in the MPEG standards.

Motion-JPEG: Using JPEG compressed images as individual frames for motion. For example, 30 Motion-JPEG frames viewed in one second will approximate 30-frame per second video.

MOV: The file extension used by MooV format video files on Windows. These MOV files are generated with Apple Computer's QuickTime and played on Windows systems via QuickTime for Windows.

MPEG: Compression standards for moving images conceived by the Motion Pictures Expert Group, an international group of industry experts set up to standardize compressed moving pictures and audio. MPEG-2 is the basis for ATSC digital television transmission.

Its work follows on from that of JPEG to add interfield compression, the extra compression potentially available through similarities between successive frames of moving pictures. Four MPEG standards were originally planned, but the accommodation of HDTV within MPEG-2 has meant that MPEG-3 is now redundant. MPEG-4 is intended for unrelated applications, however, can be used to display ATSC formats on a PC. The main interest for the television industry is in MPEG-1 and MPEG-2. A group of picture blocks, usually four, which are analyzed during MPEG coding to give an estimate of the movement between frames. This generates the motion vectors that are then used to place the macroblocks in decoded pictures.
See also: B frames, GoP, I frames, P frames.

MPEG-1: A group of picture blocks, usually four, which are analyzed during MPEG coding to give an estimate of the movement between frames. This generates the motion vectors that are then used to place the macroblocks in decoded pictures. This was designed to work at 1.2 Mbps, the data rate of CD-ROM, so that video could be played from CDs. However the quality is not sufficient for TV broadcast.

MPEG-2: This has been designed to cover a wide range of requirements from "VHS quality" all the way to HDTV through a series of algorithm "profiles" and image resolution "levels." With data rates of between 1.2 and 15 Mbps, there is intense interest in the use of MPEG-2 for the digital transmission of television—including HDTV—applications for which the system was conceived. Coding the video is very complex, especially as it is required to keep the decoding at the reception end as simple and inexpensive as possible. MPEG-2 is the compression used by the ATSC and DVB standards.

MPEG can offer better quality pictures at high compression ratios than pure JPEG compression, but with the complexity of decoding and especially coding and the 12-long group of pictures (GoP), it is not an ideal compression system for editing. If any P or B frames are used then even a cut will require the re-use of complex, and not perfect, MPEG coding. However, MPEG Splicers are beginning to appear to alleviate this difficulty.

Of the six profiles and four levels creating a grid of 24 possible combinations, 12 have already been implemented. The variations these define are so wide that it would not be practical to build a universal coder or decoder. Interest is now focused on the Main profile, Main level, sometimes written as MP@ML, which covers broadcast television formats up to 720 pixels x 576 lines at 30 frames per second. These figures are quoted as maximums so 720 x 486 at 30 frames are included, as are 720 x 576 at 25 frames. As the coding is intended for transmission the economy of 4:2:0 sampling is used.

A recent addition to MPEG-2 is the studio profile. Designed for studio work its sampling is 4:2:2. The studio profile is written as 422P@ML. To improve the picture quality, higher bit rates are used. The first applications for this appear to be in electronic news gathering (ENG), and with some video servers.

See also: B frames, Compression, GoP, I frames, JPEG, P frames.

MPEG-4: The third standard developed by MPEG. Started in July 1993 MPEG-4 has benefited from the huge R&D investments made by participating companies and provides a harmonised range of responses to the diverse needs of the digital audio-visual industry, including compatibility with other major standards such as H.263 and VRML.

MPEG 4:2:2: Also referred to as Studio MPEG, Professional MPEG and 442P@ML. Sony's Betacam SX is based on MPEG 4:2:2. *See: MPEG-2.*

MPEG-7: A standardized description of various types of multimedia information. This description will be associated with the content itself, to allow fast and efficient searching for material that is of interest to the user. MPEG-7 is formally called "Multimedia Content Description Interface." The standard does not comprise the (automatic) extraction of descriptions/features. Nor does it specify the search engine (or any other program) that can make use of the description. It is not a new compression standard, but an attempt to manage motion imaging and multimedia technology.

MPEG-21: The Motion Picture Experts Group's attempt to get a handle on the overall topic of content delivery. By defining a Multimedia Framework from the viewpoint of the consumer, they hope to understand how various components relate to each other and where gaps in the infrastructure might benefit from new standards. A technical report on the MPEG-21 framework is scheduled for mid-2000.

MPEG IMX: Sony's trademark for a family of devices, such as DVTRs, that are I frame-only 50 Mbps MPEG-2 streams using Betacam style cassettes. Plays Digital Betacam, Betacam SX, Betacam SP, Betacam, and, MPEG IMX, outputting 50 Mbps MPEG I-frame on SDTI-CP regardless of the tape being played. It can also handle other (lower) input and output data rates, but the recordings are 50 Mbps I-frame in any case.

See also: SDTI-CP.

MPEG splicing: The ability to cut into an MPEG bit stream for switching and editing, regardless of type of frames (I, B, P).

MSB: Most significant bit. The bit that has the most value in a binary number or data byte. In written form, this would be the bit on the left.

For example: **Binary 1110 = Decimal 14**

In this example, the left-most binary digit, 1, is the most significant bit—here representing 8. If the MSB in this example were corrupt, the decimal would not be 14 but 6.

See also: LSB.

Multicast: 1. Data flow from single source to mutiple destinations; a multicast may be distinguished from a broadcast in that number of destinations may be limited. 2. A term often used incorrectly to describe digital television program multiplexing.

Multimedia content description interface: *See: MPEG-7.*

Multipath interference: The signal variation caused when two RF signals take multiple paths from transmitter to receiver. In analog television, this creates ghosting. In digital television, this can cause the receiver not to output a signal as it can not differentiate between signals.

Multipoint: A term used by network designers to describe network links that have many possible endpoints.

Multiplex: 1. To transmit two or more signals at the same time or on the same carrier frequency. 2. To combine two or more electrical signals into a single, composite signal, such as ATSC multicasting.

Multiplexer: Device for combining two or more electrical signals into a single, composite signal.

Mux: *See: Multiplex.*

Netshow: Microsoft NetShow is a service that runs on Windows NT servers, delivering the high-quality streaming multimedia to users on corporate intranets and the Internet. It consists of server and tools components for delivering audio, video, illustrated audio, and other multimedia types over the network. NetShow provides the foundation for building rich, interactive mutimedia applications for commerce, distance learning, news and entertainment delivery, and corporate communications.

Nonlinear: A term used for editing and the storage of audio, video and data. Information (footage) is available anywhere on the media (computer disk or laser disc) almost immediately without having to locate the desired information in a time linear format.

Nonlinear editing: Nonlinear distinguishes editing operation from the "linear" methods used with tape. Nonlinear refers to not having to edit material in the sequence of the final program and does not involve copying to make edits. It allows any part of the edit to be accessed and modified without having to re-edit or re-copy the material that is already edited and follows that point. Nonlinear editing is also non-destructive—the video is not changed but the list of how that video is played back is modified during editing.

NTSC: National television system committee. The organization that developed the analog television standard currently in use in the U.S., Canada, and Japan. Now generally used to refer to that standard. The NTSC standard combines blue, red, and green signals modulated as an AM signal with an FM signal for audio.
     See also: PAL and SECAM.

NVOD: Near video on demand. Rapid access to program material on demand achieved by providing the same program on a number of channels with staggered start times. Many of the hundreds of TV channels soon to be on offer will be made up of NVOD services. These are delivered by a disk-based transmission server.

Nyquist frequency (Nyquist rate): The lowest sampling frequency that can be used for analog-to-digital conversion of a signal without resulting in significant aliasing. Normally, this frequency is twice the rate of the highest frequency contained in the signal being sampled.

Off-line (editing): A decision-making process using low-cost equipment usually to produce an EDL or a rough cut which can then be conformed or referred to in a high quality on-line suite—so reducing decision-making time in the more expensive on-line environment. While most off-line suites enable shot selection and the defining of transitions such as cuts and dissolves, very few allow settings for the DVEs, color correctors, keyers and layering that are increasingly a part of the on-line editing process.

On-demand streaming: Streaming media content that is transmitted to the client upon request.
     See also: Live streaming.

On-line (editing): Production of the complete, final edit performed at full program quality—the buck stops here! Being higher quality than off-line, time costs more but the difference is reducing. Preparation in an off-line suite will help save time and money in the on-line. To produce the finished edit on-line has to include a wide range of tools,

DTV IN THE REAL WORLD

UNDERSTANDING DIGITAL

PRE-PRODUCTION

PRODUCTION

AUDIO

GRAPHIC & COMPOSITING

POST PRODUCTION

DELIVERY & DUPLICATION

ENGINEERING & TRANSMISSION

APPENDIX

GLOSSARY

offer flexibility to try ideas and accommodate late changes, and to work fast to maintain the creative flow and to handle pressured situations.

OC3: Optical Carrier Level 3. A 155 Mbps ATM SONET signal stream that can carry three DS3 signals.

Open Cable: A project aimed at obtaining a new generation of set-top boxes that are interoperable. These new devices will enable a new range of interactive services to be provided to cable customers.

Operating system: The base program that manages a computer and gives control of the functions designed for general purpose usage—not for specific applications. Common examples are MS-DOS and Windows for PCs, Mac OS8 for Apple Macintosh, and UNIX (and its variations IRIX and Linux). For actual use, for example, as a word processor, specific applications software is run on top of the operating system.

Optical disks: Disks using optical techniques for recording and replay of material. These offer large storage capacities on a small area, the most common being the 5-1/4-inch compact disk, being removable and having rather slower data rates than fixed magnetic disks—but faster than floppies. Write Once, Read Many or "WORM" optical disks first appeared with 2 GB capacity on each side of a 12-inch platter—useful for archiving images. In 1989 the read/write magneto-optical (MO) disk was introduced which can be re-written around a million times. With its modest size, just 5-1/4-inches in diameter, the ISO standard cartridge can store 325 MB per side—offering low priced removable storage for over 700 TV pictures per disk. A variant on the technology is the phase change disk but this is not compatible with the ISO standard.

An uprated MO disk system introduced in 1994 has a capacity of 650 MB per side, 1.3 GB per disk. In 1996 a second doubling of capacity was introduced offering 2.6 GB on a removable disk. Besides the obvious advantages for storing TV pictures this is particularly useful where large format images are used, in print and in film for example.

The NEC DiskCam system uses optical disks for storage.

Oversampling: Sampling data at a higher rate than normal to obtain more accurate results or to make it easier to sample.

P frames: One of the three types of frames used in the coded MPEG-2 signal. These contain only predictive information (not a whole picture) generated by looking at the difference between the present frame and the previous one. They contain much less data than the I frames and so help towards the low data rates that can be achieved with the MPEG signal. To see the original picture corresponding to a P frame a whole MPEG-2 GoP has to be decoded.
See also: B frames, I frames and MPEG.

PAL: Phase alternate line. The television broadcast standard throughout Europe (except in France and Eastern Europe, where SECAM is the standard). This standard broadcasts 625 lines of resolution, nearly 20 percent more than the U.S. standard, NTSC, of 525.
See also: NTSC and SECAM.

Palette: In 8-bit images or displays, only 256 different can be displayed at any one time. This collection of 256 colors is called the palette. In 8-bit environments, all screen elements must be painted with the colors contained in the palette. The 256-color combination is not fixed—palettes can and do change frequently. But at any one time, only 256 colors can be used to describe all the objects on the screen or image.

Pan and Scan: The technique used to crop a widescreen picture to conventional 4:3 television ratio, while panning the original image to follow the on-screen action.

Pan and Scanner: One who pans and scans, typically during a live event originating in a widescreen format (16:9) but simulcast in 4:3.

Parallel: One transmission path for each bit.

Parallel cable: A multi-conductor cable carrying simultaneous transmission of digital data bits. Analogous to the rows of a marching band passing a review point.

Parallel data: Transmission of data bits in groups along a collection of wires (called a bus). Analogous to the rows of a marching band passing a review point. A typical parallel bus may accommodate transmission of one 8-, 16-, or 32-bit byte at a time.

Parallel digital: A digital video interface which uses twisted pair wiring and 25-pin D connectors to convey the bits of a digital video signal in parallel. There are various component and composite parallel digital video formats.

Parity: A method of verifying the accuracy of transmitted or recorded data. An extra bit appended to an array of data as an accuracy check during transmission. Parity may be even or odd. For odd parity, if the number of 1's in the array is even, a 1 is added in the parity bit to make the total odd. For even parity, if the number of 1's in the array is odd, a 1 is added in the parity bit to make the total even. The receiving computer checks the parity bit and indicates a data error if the number of 1s does not add up to the proper even or odd total.

PCM: Pulse code modulation. A method by which sound is digitally recorded and reproduced. Sounds are reproduced by modulating (changing) the playback rate and amplitude of the sampled (stored) digital pulses (waves). This enables the PCM sound to be reproduced with a varying pitch and amplitude.

Picture: A source image or reconstructed data for a single frame or two interlaced fields. A picture consists of three rectangular matrices of eight-bit numbers representing the luminance and two color difference signals.

PID: Packet identifier. The identifier for transport packets in MPEG-2 Transport Streams.

Pillarbox: Describes a frame that the image fails to fill horizontally (a 4:3 image on a 16:9 screen), in the same way that a letterbox describes a frame that the image fails to fill vertically (a 16:9 image on a 4:3 screen)
See also: Letterbox and side panels.

Pixel: A shortened version of "Picture cell" or "Picture element." The name given to one sample of picture information. Pixel can refer to an individual sample of R, G, B luminance or chrominance, or sometimes to a collection of such samples if they are co-sited and together produce one picture element.

Plant native format: A physical plant's highest video resolution.

Point-to-multipoint: An arrangement, either permanent or temporary, in which the same data flows or is transferred from a single origin to multiple destinations; the arrival of the data at all the destinations is expected to occur at the same time or nominally the same time.

Pre-read: *See: Read before write.*

Progressive: Short for progressive scanning. A system of video scanning whereby lines of a picture are transmitted consecutively, such as in the computer world.

Protocol: Set of syntax rules defining exchange of data including items such as timing, format, sequencing, error checking, etc.

PSIP: Program and system information protocol. A part of the ATSC digital television specification that enables a DTV receiver to identify program information from the station and use it to create easy-to-recognize electronic program guides for the viewer at home. The PSIP generator insert data related to channel selection and electronic program guides into the ATSC MPEG transport stream.

See also: Electronic Program Guide.

QAM: Quadrature amplitude modulation. A downstream digital modulation technique that conforms to the International Telecommunications Union (ITU) standard ITU-T J. 83 Annex B which calls for 64 and 256 quadrature amplitude modulation (QAM) with concatenated trellis coded modulation, plus enhancements such as variable interleaving depth for low latency in delay sensitive applications such as data and voice. Using 64 QAM, a cable channel that today carries one analog video channel could carry 27 Mbps of information, or enough for multiple video programs. Using 256 QAM, the standard 6 MHz cable channel would carry 40 Mbps.

See also: The Engineering & Transmission chapter.

QPSK: Quadrature phase shift keying. QPSK is a digital frequency modulation technique used for sending data over coaxial cable networks. Since it's both easy to implement and fairly resistant to noise, QPSK is used primarily for sending data from the cable subscriber upstream to the Internet.

Quantization: The process of sampling an analog waveform to convert its voltage levels into digital data.

Quantizing: The process of converting the voltage level of a signal into digital data before or after the signal has been sampled.

Quantizing error: Inaccuracies in the digital representation of an analog signal. These errors occur because of limitations in the resolution of the digitizing process.

Quantizing noise: The noise (deviation of a signal from its original or correct value) which results from the quantization process. In serial digital video, a granular type of noise that occurs only in the presence of a signal.

QuickTime: Apple Computer's system-level software architecture supporting time-based media, giving a seamless integration of video, sound, and animation. For Macintosh and Windows computers.

RAID: Redundant array of independent disks. A grouping of standard disk drives together with a RAID controller to create storage that acts as one disk to provide performance beyond that available from individual drives. Primarily designed for operation with computers RAIDs can offer very high capacities, fast data transfer rates and much-increased security of data. The latter is achieved through disk redundancy so that disk errors or failures can be detected and corrected.

A series of RAID configurations is defined by levels and, being designed by computer people, they start counting from zero. Different levels are suited to different applications.

Level 0: No redundancy—benefits only of speed and capacity—generated by combining a number of disks. Also known as "striping."

Level 1 Complete mirror system—two sets of disks both reading and writing the same data. This has the benefits of level 0 plus the security of full redundancy—but at twice the cost. Some performance advantage can be gained in read because only one copy need be read, so two reads can occur simultaneously.

Level 2: An array of nine disks. Each byte is recorded with one bit on each of eight disks and a parity bit recorded to the ninth. This level is rarely, if ever, used.

Level 3: An array of $n+1$ disks recording 512 byte sectors on each of the n disks to create n x 512 "super sectors" + 1 x 512 parity sector on the additional disk which is used to check the data.

The minimum unit of transfer is a whole superblock. This is most suitable for systems in which large amounts of sequential data are transferred—such as for audio and video. For these it is the most efficient RAID level since it is never necessary to read/modify/write the parity block. It is less suitable for database types of access in which small amounts of data need to be transferred at random.

Level 4: The same as Level 3 but individual blocks can be transferred. When data is written it is necessary to read the old data and parity blocks before writing the new data as well as the updated parity block, which reduces performance.

Level 5: The same as Level 4, but the role of parity the disk is rotated for each block. In level 4 the parity disk receives excessive load for writes and no load for reads. In Level 5 the load is balanced across the disks.

Soft RAID: A RAID system implemented by low level software in the host system instead of a dedicated RAID controller. While saving on hardware, operation consumes some of the host's power.

RAM: Random access memory. A temporary, volatile memory into which data can be written or from which data can be read by specifying an address.

Rate conversion: 1. The process of converting from one digital sample rate to another. The digital sample rate for the component digital video format is 13.5 MHz. For the composite digital video format, it is either 14.3 MHz for NTSC or 17.7 MHz for PAL. 2. Often used incorrectly to indicate both resampling of digital rates and encoding/decoding.

Read before write: A feature of some videotape recorders that plays back the video or audio signal off of tape before it reaches the record heads, sends the signal to an external device for modification, and then applies the modified signal to the record heads so that it can be re-recorded onto the tape in its original position.

RealAudio: Popular software for streaming audio and video over the Internet. made by RealNetworks of Seattle, Washington.

Realtime: Computation or processing done in the present to control physical events occurring in the present. For example, when a digital effects system operator moves a joystick and the video images on the monitor appear to move simultaneously, the computations required to make the images move are said to have occurred in realtime. *See also: Rendering.*

RealVideo: Popular software for streaming audio and video over the Internet. made by RealNetworks of Seattle, Washington.

Rec. 601: *See: ITU-R BT.601-2.*

Reclocking: The process of clocking digital data with a regenerated clock.

Rendering: The process of non-realtime drawing of a picture relying on computer processing speed for graphics and compositing.

Resolution: 1. Detail. In digital video and audio, the number of bits (four, eight, 10, 12, etc.) determines the resolution of the digital signal. Four bits yields a resolution of one in 16. Eight bits yields a resolution of one in 256. Ten bits yields a resolution of one in 1,024. Eight bits is the minimum acceptable for broadcast television. 2. A measure of the finest detail that can be seen, or resolved, in a reproduced image. While influenced by the number of pixels in an image (for high definition approximately 2,000 x 1,000, broadcast NTSC TV 720 x 487, broadcast PAL TV 720 x 576), note that the pixel numbers do not define ultimate resolution but merely the resolution of that part of the equipment. The quality of lenses, display tubes, film process and film scanners, etc., used to produce the image on the screen must all be taken into account. This is why a live broadcast of the Super Bowl looks better than a broadcast recorded and played off of VHS, while all are NTSC or PAL.

Resolution independent: Term used to describe the notion of equipment that can operate at more than one resolution. Dedicated TV equipment is designed to operate at a single resolution although some modern equipment, especially that using the ITU-R 601 standard, can switch between the specific formats and aspect ratios of 525/60 and 625/50.

By their nature, computers can handle files of any size, so when applied to imaging, they are termed resolution independent. As the images get bigger so the amount of processing, storage and data transfer demanded increases—in proportion to the resulting file size. So, for a given platform, the speed of operation slows. Other considerations when changing image resolution may be reformatting disks, checking if the RAM is sufficient to handle the required size of file, allowing extra time for RAM/disk caching and how to show the picture on an appropriate display.

Return loss: A measure of the ratio of signal power transmitted into a system to the power reflected or returned. It can be thought of as an echo that is reflected back by impedance changes in the system. Any variation in impedance from the source results in some returned signal. Real-life cabling systems do not have perfect impedance structure and matching, and therefore have a measurable return loss. Twisted pairs are not completely uniform in impedance. Changes in twist, distance between conductors, cabling handling, cable structure, length of link, patch cord variation, varying copper diameter, dielectric composition and thickness variations, and other factors all contribute to slight variations in cable impedance. In addition, not all connecting hardware components in a link may have equal impedance. At every connection point there is the potential for a change in impedance. Each change in the impedance of the link causes part of the signal to be reflected back to the source. Return loss is a measure of all the reflected energy caused by variations in impedance of a link relative to a source impedance of 100 ohms. Each impedance change contributes to signal loss (attenuation) and directly causes return loss.

RGB: The abbreviation for the red, green and blue signals, the primary colors of light (and television). Cameras and telecines have red, blue and green receptors, the TV screen has red, green and blue phosphors illuminated by red, green and blue guns. Much of the picture monitoring in a production center is in RGB. RGB is digitized with 4:4:4 sampling which occupies 50 percent more data than 4:2:2.

Ringing: An oscillatory transient on a signal occurring as a result of bandwidth restrictions and/or phase distortions. A type of ringing causes ghosting in the video picture.

RLE: Run length encoding. A compression scheme. A run of pixels or bytes of the same color or value are coded as a single value recording the color or byte value and the number duplications in the run.

ROM: Read only memory. A memory device that is programmed only once with a permanent program or data that cannot be erased.

RP-125: A SMPTE parallel component digital video recommended practice. Now SMPTE 125M.
See: SMPTE 125M.

RS-232: A standard, single-ended (unbalanced) interconnection scheme for serial data communications.

RS-422: A medium range (typically up to 300 m/1000 ft or more) balanced serial data transmission standard. Data is sent using an ECL signal on two twisted pairs for bi-directional operation. Full specification includes 9-way D-type connectors and optional additional signal lines.

RS-422 is widely used for control links around production and post areas for a range of equipment.

Run-length coding: A system for compressing data. The principle is to store a pixel value along with a message detailing the number of adjacent pixels with that same value.

This gives a very efficient way of storing large areas of flat color and text but is not so efficient with pictures from a camera, where the random nature of the information, including noise, may actually mean that more data is produced than was needed for the original picture.

Sampling: Process by which an analog signal is measured, often millions of times per second for video, in order to convert the analog signal to digital. The official sampling standard for standard definition television is ITU-R 601.

For TV pictures eight or 10 bits are normally used; for sound, 16 or 20-bits are common, and 24-bits are being introduced. The ITU-R 601 standard defines the sampling of video components based on 13.5 MHz, and AES/EBU defines sampling of 44.1 and 48 kHz for audio.

Sampling frequency: The number of discrete sample measurements made in a given period of time. Often expressed in megahertz for video.

SAV: Start of active video. A synchronizing signal used in component digital video.

Scalable coding: The ability to encode a visual sequence so as to enable the decoding of the digital data stream at various spatial and/or temporal resolutions. Scalable compression techniques typically filter the image into separate bands of spatial and/or temporal data. Appropriate data reduction techniques are then applied to each band to match the response characteristics of human vision.

Scalable video: Refers to video compression that can handle a range of bandwidths, scaling smoothly over them.

Scrambling: 1. To transpose or invert digital data according to a prearranged scheme in order to break up the low-frequency patterns associated with serial digital signals. 2. The digital signal is shuffled to produce a better spectral distribution.
See also: Encryption.

SCSI: Small computer systems interface. A very widely used high data rate general purpose parallel interface. A maximum of eight devices can be connected to one bus, for example a controller, and up to seven disks or devices of different sorts—Winchester disks, optical disks, tape drives, etc.—and may be shared between several computers.

SCSI specifies a cabling standard (50-way), a protocol for sending and receiving commands and their format. It is intended as a device-independent interface so the host computer needs no details about the peripherals it controls. But with two versions (single ended and balanced), two types of connectors and numerous variations in the level of implementation of the interface, SCSI devices cannot "plug and play" on a computer with which they have not been tested. Also, with total bus cabling for the popular single ended configuration limited to 18 feet (6 meters), all devices must be close.

SCSI is popular and has continued development over a number of years resulting in the following range of maximum transfer rates:
Standard SCSI: 5 Mbps (max.)
Fast SCSI: 10 Mbps (max.)
Ultra SCSI: 20 Mbps (max.)
For each of these there is the 8-bit normal "narrow" bus (1 byte per transfer) or the 16-bit Wide bus (2 bytes per transfer), so Wide Ultra SCSI could transfer data at a maximum rate of 40 Mbps. Note that these are peak rates. Continuous rates will be considerably less. Also, achieving this will depend on the performance of the connected device.

Differential SCSI: An electrical signal configuration where information is sent simultaneously through sets of wires in a cable. Information is interpreted by the difference in voltage between the wires. Differential interfaces permit cable lengths up to 75 feet (25 meters).

Single-Ended SCSI: An electrical signal configuration where information is sent through one wire in a cable. Information is interpreted by the change in the voltage of the signal. Single-ended interfaces permit cable lengths up to 18 feet (6 meters).

SDDI: *See: Serial digital data interface.*

SDI: *See: Serial digital interface.*

SDTI: *See: Serial digital transport interface.*

SDTI-CP: Serial digital transport interface-content package. Sony's way of formatting MPEG IMX (50 Mbps, I frame MPEG-2 streams) for transport on a serial digital transport interface.
See also: Serial digital transport interface.

SECAM: Sequential couleur avec mémoire. The television broadcast standard in France, the Middle East, and most of Eastern Europe, SECAM provides for sequential color transmission and storage in the receiver. The signals used to transmit the color are not transmitted simultaneously but sequentially line for line. SECAM processes 625 lines, a maximum of 833 pixels per line and 50 Hz picture frequency. SECAM is used as a transmission standard and not a production standard (PAL is typically used).

Sequence: A coded video sequence that commences with a sequence header and is followed by one or more groups of pictures and is ended by a sequence end code.

Serial: One bit at a time, along a single transmission path.

Serial digital: Digital information that is transmitted in serial form. Often used informally to refer to serial digital television signals.

Serial digital data interface (SDDI): A way of compressing digital video for use on SDI-based equipment proposed by Sony. Now incorporated into Serial digital transport interface.
See: Serial digital transport interface.

Serial digital interface (SDI): The standard based on a 270 Mbps transfer rate. This is a 10-bit, scrambled, polarity independent interface, with common scrambling for both component ITU-R 601 and composite digital video and four channels of (embedded) digital audio. Most new broadcast digital equipment includes SDI which greatly simplifies its installation and signal distribution. It uses the standard 75 ohm BNC connector and coax cable as is commonly used for analog video, and can transmit the signal over 600 feet (200 meters) depending on cable type.

Serial digital transport interface (SDTI): SMPTE 305M. Allows faster-than-realtime transfers between various servers and between acquisition tapes, disk-based editing systems and servers, with both 270 Mb and 360 Mb are supported. With typical realtime compressed video transfer rates in the 18 Mbps to 25 Mbps to 50 Mbps range, SDTI's 200+ Mbps payload can accommodate transfers up to four times normal speed.
The SMPTE 305M standard describes the assembly and disassembly of a stream of 10-bit data words that conform to SDI rules. Payload data words can be up to 9 bits. The 10th bit is a complement of the 9th to prevent illegal SDI values from occurring. The basic payload is inserted between SAV and EAV although an appendix permits additional data in the SDI ancillary data space as well. A header immediately after EAV provides a series of flags and data IDs to indicate what's coming as well as line counts and CRCs to check data continuity.

Serial interface: A digital communications interface in which data is transmitted and received sequentially along a single wire or pair of wires. Common serial interface standards are RS-232 and RS-422.

Serializer: A device that converts parallel digital information to serial.

Serial storage architecture (SSA): A high speed data interface developed by IBM and used to connect numbers of storage devices (disks) with systems. Three technology generations are planned: 20 Mbps and 40 Mbps are now available, and 100 Mbps is expected to follow.

Serial video processing: A video mixing architecture where a series of video multipliers, each combining two video signals, is cascaded or arranged in a serial fashion. The output of one multiplier feeds the input of the next, and so on, permitting effects to be built up, one on top of the other.

Server (file): A storage system that provides data files to all connected users of a local network. Typically the file server is a computer with large disk storage which is able to record or send files as requested by the other connected (client) computers—the file server often appearing as another disk on their systems.

　　The data files are typically around a few kilobytes in size and are expected to be delivered within moments of request

Server (video): A storage system that provides audio and video storage for a network of clients. While there are some analog systems based on optical disks, most used in professional and broadcast applications are based on digital disk storage.

　　Aside from those used for video on demand (VOD), video servers are applied in three areas of television operation: transmission, post production and news. Compared to general purpose file servers, video severs must handle far more data, files are larger and must be continuously delivered.

　　There is no general specification for video servers and so the performance between models varies greatly according to storage capacity, number of channels, compression ratio and degree of access to store material—the latter having a profound influence.

　　Store sizes are very large, typically up to 500 Gigabytes or more. Operation depends entirely on connected devices, edit suites, automation systems, secondary servers, etc., so the effectiveness of the necessary remote control and video networking is vital to success.

Set-top box (STB): These receivers (named because they typically sit on top of a television set) convert and display broadcasts from one frequency or type—analog cable, digital cable, or digital television) to a standard frequency (typically channel 3 or 4) for display on a standard analog television set.

Side converting: The process which changes the number of pixels and/or frame rate and/or scanning format used to represent an image by interpolating existing pixels to create new ones at closer spacing or by removing pixels. Side converting is done from standard resolution to standard resolution and high definition to high definition.
　　See also: Down converting, up converting.

Side panels: Image of a standard 4:3 picture on a widescreen 16:9 aspect ratio television screen, typically with black bars on the side. Used to maintain the original aspect ratio of the source material.
　　See also: Letterbox, pillarbox.

SIGGRAPH: The Association of Computing Machinery (ACM)'s Special Interest Group on Computer Graphics (SIGGRAPH). Internet: www.siggraph.org.

Signaling rate: The bandwidth of a digital transmission system expressed in terms of the maximum number of bits that can be transported over a given period of time. The signaling rate is typically much higher than the average data transfer rate for the system due to software overhead for network control, packet overhead, etc.

Simple profile: MPEG image streams using only I and P frames is less efficient than coding with B frames. This profile, however, requires less buffer memory for decoding.

Simulcast: To broadcast the same program over two different transmission systems. Currently, some AM and FM stations simulcast the same program for part of the day, and some radio stations simulcast the audio from televised music events.

Although not initially required by the FCC, it is believed that most television stations will simulcast their DTV and NTSC signal. Simulcasting will be required towards the end of the DTV transition period to protect the public interest.

Slice: A series of macroblocks. A slice is the basic synchronizing unit for reconstruction of the image data and typically consists of all the blocks in one horizontal picture interval—typically 16 lines of the picture.

SMPTE: 1. Society of Motion Picture and Television Engineers. A professional organization that sets standards for American television. 595 W. Hartsdale Ave., White Plains, NY, 10607-1824. Tel: 914-761-1100. Fax: 914-761-3115. Email: smpte@smpte.org Internet: www.smpte.org. 2. An informal name for a color difference video format that uses a variation of the Y, R-Y, and B-Y signal set.

SMPTE 125M (formerly RP-125): The SMPTE standard for a bit parallel digital interface for 55-line interlace component video signals. SMPTE 125M defines the parameters required to generate and distribute component video signals on a parallel interface.

SMPTE 244M: The SMPTE standard for a bit parallel digital interface for composite video signals. SMPTE 244M defines the parameters required to generate and distribute composite video on a parallel interface.

SMPTE 259M: The SMPTE standard for standard definition serial digital component and composite interfaces.

SMPTE 272M: The SMPTE standard for formatting AES/EBU audio and auxiliary data into digital video ancillary data space.

SMPTE 292M: The SMPTE standard for bit-serial digital interface for high-definition television systems.

SMPTE 293M: The SMPTE standard defining the data representation of the 720x483 progressive signal at 59.94 Hz.

SMPTE 294M: The SMPTE standard defining the serial interfaces for both 4:2:2P (progressive) on two-SMPTE 259M links and 4:2:0P (progressive) on a single SMPTE 259M link (at 360Mbps).

SMPTE 299M: The SMPTE standard for 24-bit digital audio format for HDTV bit-serial interface. Allows eight embedded AES/EBU audio channel pairs.

SMPTE 305M: The SMPTE standard for Serial Digital Transport Interface (SDTI).

SMPTE 310M: The SMPTE standard for synchronous serial interface (SSI) for MPEG-2 digital transport streams; used as the "standard" for the output from the ATSC systems multiplexer and the input to DTV transmitters.

Soft RAID: A RAID system implemented by low level software in the host system instead of a dedicated RAID controller. While saving on hardware, operation consumes some of the host's power.
See also: RAID.

Sonet: **S**ynchronous **o**ptical **net**work. A set of standards for the digital transmission of information over fiber optics. Based on increments of 51 Mbps. It was developed to cost effectively support broadband services and multi-vendor internetworking.

Spatial resolution: The number of pixels horizontally and vertically in a digital image.

Sprites: In MPEG-4, static background scenes. Sprites can have dimensions much larger than what will be seen in any single frame. A coordinate system is provided to position objects in relation to each other and the sprites. MPEG- 4's scene description capabilities are built on concepts used previously by the Internet community's Virtual Reality Modeling Language (VRML).

SRAM: Static RAM. This type of memory chip in general behaves like dynamic RAM (DRAM) except that static RAMs retain data in a six-transistor cell needing only power to operate (DRAMs require clocks as well). Because of this, current available capacity is 4 Mbits—lower than DRAM—and costs are higher, but speed is also greater.

SSA: *See: Serial Storage Architecture.*

Statistical multiplexing: Increases the overall efficiency of a multi-channel digital television transmission multiplex by varying the bit-rate of each of its channels to take only that share of the total multiplex bit-rate it needs at any one time. The share apportioned to each channel is predicted statistically with reference to its current and recent-past demands.
> *See also: Multiplex.*

Storage capacity: Using the ITU-R 601 4:2:2 digital coding standard, each picture occupies a large amount of storage space—especially when related to computer storage devices such as DRAM and disks. So much so that the numbers can become confusing unless a few benchmark statistics are remembered. Fortunately, the units of mega, giga, tera and penta make it easy to express the very large numbers involved. The capacities can all be worked out directly from the 601 standard. Bearing in mind that sync words and blanking can be regenerated and added at the output, only the active picture area need be stored.
> **For the 525 line TV standard the line data is:** 720(Y) + 360(Cr) + 360(Cb) = 1,440 pixels/line
> 487 active lines/picture there are 1,440 x 487 = 701,280 pixels/picture
> (sampling at 8-bits, a picture takes 701.3 kbytes)
> 1 sec takes 701.3 x 30 = 21,039 kbytes, or 21 Mbytes
> **For the 625 line TV standard the active picture is:** 720(Y) + 360(Cr) + 360(Cb) = 1,440 pixels/line
> With 576 active lines/picture there are 1,440 x 576 = 829,440 pixels/picture
> (sampling at 8-bits, a picture takes 830 kbytes)
> 1 second takes 830 x 25 = 20,750 kbytes, or 21 Mbytes
> So both 525 and 625 line systems require approximately the same amount of storage for a given time:
> 1 minute takes 21 x 60 = 1,260 Mbytes, or 1.26 Gbytes
> 1 hour takes 1.26 x 60 = 76 Gbytes
> **Useful numbers (referred to non-compressed video):**
> 1 Gbyte will hold 47 seconds.
> 1 hour takes 76 Gbytes.

Stream: 1. To transmit multimedia files that begin playing upon arrival of the first packets, without needing to wait for all the data to arrive. 2. To send data in such a way as to simulate real-time delivery of multimedia.

Streaming media: Multimedia content—such as video, audio, text, or animation—that is displayed by a client a client as it is received from the Internet, broadcast network, or local storage.

Sub-pixel: A spatial resolution smaller than that of pixels. Although digital images are composed of pixels it can be very useful to resolve image detail to smaller than pixel

DTV IN THE REAL WORLD

UNDERSTANDING DIGITAL

PRE-PRODUCTION

PRODUCTION

AUDIO

GRAPHIC & COMPOSITING

POST PRODUCTION

DELIVERY & DUPLICATION

ENGINEERING & TRANSMISSION

APPENDIX

GLOSSARY

size, i.e., sub-pixel. For example, the data for generating a smooth curve on television needs to be created to a finer accuracy than the pixel grid itself, otherwise the curve will look jagged. Again, when tracking an object in a scene or executing a DVE move, the size and position of the manipulated picture must be calculated, and the picture resolved, to a far finer accuracy than the pixels, otherwise the move will appear jerky.
See also: Pixel.

Sweetening: Electronically improving the quality of an audio or video signal, such as by adding sound effects, laugh tracks, and captions.

Synchronous: A transmission procedure by which the bit and character stream are slaved to accurately synchronized clocks, both at the receiving and sending end.

T1: In telecommunications, the paired cable used to transport DS1 service.

Table 3 Compression Format Constraints: *See: ATSC.*

TCP/IP: Transmission control protocol/internet protocol. An Internet protocol suite developed by the U.S. Department of Defense in the 1970s. TCP governs the exchange of sequential data. IP routes outgoing and recognizes incoming messages.

TDM: Time division multiplex. The management of multiple signals on one channel by alternately sending portions of each signal and assigning each portion to particular blocks of time.

Tearing: A lateral displacement of the video lines due to sync instability. Visually it appears as though parts of the images have been torn away.

Temporal aliasing: A defect in a video picture that occurs when the image being sampled moves too fast for the sampling rate. A common example occurs when the rapidly rotating spokes of a wagon's wheels appear to rotate backwards because of video scanning that moves more slowly than the spokes.

Temporal resolution: The ability of the display to reproduce adequate detail to allow the visual system to distinguish the separate parts or components of an object that is moving through the display.

Time code: 1. Vertical interval time code (VITC). This is SMPTE time code that is recorded as video signals in the vertical interval of the active picture. It has the advantage of being readable by a VTR in still or jog. Multiple lines of VITC can be added to the signal allowing the encoding of more information than can be stored in normal LTC. 2. Linear time code (LTC). Time code recorded on a linear analog track (typically an audio channel) on a videotape. Also called longitudinal time code. Time code can be drop frame (59.94 Hz) that matches actual elapsed time by dropping occasional frames or non-drop frame (60 Hz) that runs continuously although it does not exactly match actual elapsed time.

Timeline: In nonlinear editing, the area in which audio and video clips are applied, typically giving duration in frames and seconds. Also seen in animation and composition software.

TOV: Threshold of visibility. The impairment level (or D/U in dB) beyond which a source of impairment or interference may introduce visible deficiencies in more sensitive program material. For all tests, TOV was determined by expert observers.

Transcode: The process of converting a file or program from one formator resolution to another.

Truncation: Removal of the lower significant bits on a digital word—as could be necessary when sending a 16-bit word on an 8-bit bus. If not carefully handled it can lead to unpleasant artifacts on video signals.
See also: Dynamic Rounding.

TV Crossover Links: A type of enhancement which notifies users that there is enhanced or Web content associated with a program or an advertisement. A TV Crossover Link appears as a small icon in the corner of the TV screen at a point in time determined by content producers. Clicking the link displays a panel, giving the viewer an option to go to the content enhancement (Web site) or continue watching TV. If the viewer chooses to go to the Web site, the receiver connects to the site, while the current program or advertisement remains on-screen. Pressing the View button on the remote control or keyboard returns to TV viewing. The term is a trademark of the Microsoft Corporation.

Up converting (up-rezing): The process which increases the number of pixels and/or frame rate and/or scanning format used to represent an image by interpolating existing pixels to create new ones at closer spacing. Despite its name the process does not increase the resolution of the image. Up converting is done from standard definition to high definition.
    See also: Down converting, side converting.

Vaporware: Software or hardware that is promised or talked about but is not yet completed—and may never be released.

Variable bit rate reduction: *See: Compression.*

Video coder overload (also buffer overload): Video coder overload is tested using rapid scene cuts, at most only a few frames apart, to stress digital compression systems by presenting them with a video signal that contains little or no temporal redundancy (frame-to-frame correlation).

Video for Windows: Microsoft's system-level Windows software architecture that is similar to Apple Computer's QuickTime.

Video-on-demand (VOD): When video can be requested at any time and is available at the discretion of the end-user, it is then video-on-demand.

VRML: Virtual reality modeling language. An ISO standard for 3-D multimedia and shared virtual worlds on the Internet.

VSB: Vestigial side band. VSB is a digital frequency modulation technique used to send data over a coaxial cable network. Used by Hybrid Networks for upstream digital transmissions, VSB is faster than the more commonly used QPSK, but it's also more susceptible to noise.

VSWR: Voltage standing wave ratio. The ratio of the maximum value of a standing wave to its minimum value and is related to the return loss by the equation: $RL = 20\log [(VSWR + 1)/(VSWR-1)]$ Thus a VSWR of 1.5:1 corresponds to a return loss of $20\log(5) = 13.97dB$.

WAV (pronounced *wave*): The Windows-compatible audio file format. The WAV file can be recorded at 11 kHz, 22 kHz, and 44 kHz, and in 8- or 16-bit mono and stereo.
    See also: AIF, AU.

Wavelet-based compression: An asymmetrical image compression technique that is scalable and can provide high quality. The drawback is that it becomes more computationally expensive as the picture resolution and frame rates go up. The encode and decode are asymmetrical in that one side is a lot more expensive computationally than the other. The ImMix Cube and TurboCube used wavelet-based compression.

WebTV: WebTV Networks, Inc. is a leading manufacturer of set-top boxes used for viewing interactive television and regular television. These receivers let users access the Internet, including use of electronic mail and online chats. WebTV set-top boxes like the WebTV Plus Receiver connect to a standard television and a phone line. The

WebTV Plus Receiver supports TV Crossover Links and WebPIP. WebPIP lets users simultaneously view Web pages and TV programming on the same screen, without a special picture-in-picture TV. WebTV is a trademark and service of the Microsoft Corporation.

Widescreen: Term given to picture displays that have a wider aspect ratio than normal. For example, TV's normal aspect ratio is 4:3 and widescreen is 16:9. Although this is the aspect ratio used by HDTV, widescreen is also used with normal definition systems.

Window: 1. Video containing information or allowing information entry, keyed into the video monitor output for viewing on the monitor CRT. A window dub is a copy of a videotape with time code numbers keyed into the picture. 2. A video test signal consisting of a pulse and bar. When viewed on a monitor, the window signal produces a large white square in the center of the picture. 3. A graphical user interface that presents icons and tools for manipulating a software application. Most applications have multiple windows that serve different purposes.

Window shades: *See also: Pillar box, side panels.*

Windows CE: Microsoft Windows CE is a 32-bit real-time embedded operating system (RTOS) designed from the ground up to empower the development of a new range of emerging computing appliances, including set-top boxes, digital versatile disc (DVD) drives, entertainment consoles, smart phones, highly portable and personal computing devices like handheld computers, and home appliances. Windows CE is modular, allowing use of a minimum set of software components needed to support receiver requirements. This uses less memory and improves operating system performance. Windows CE provides a subset of the Win32 application program interface (API) set, which provides an effective amount of application source-code level portability and compatibility and user interface consistency with other Microsoft Windows operating systems and Windows applications.
    See also: Java.

Windows Media Player: Delivers the most popular streaming and local audio and video formats, including ASF, WAV, AVI, MPEG, Quick-Time, and more. Windows Media Player can play anything from low-bandwidth audio to full-screen video.

WORM: Write Once/Read Many—describes storage devices on which data, once written, cannot be erased or re-written. Being optical, WORMs offer very high recording densities and are removable, making them very useful for archiving.

WYSIWYG: What you see is what you get—usually, but not always. Referring to the accuracy of a screen display to show how the final result will look. For example a word processor screen showing the final layout and typeface that will appear from the printer.

YUV: A color model used chiefly for video signals in which colors are specified according to their luminance—the Y component—and their hue saturation—the U and V components.

*The editors would like to thank
the Harris Corporation, the Microsoft
Corporation, NVISION, Quantel and Tektronix
for their cooperation in compiling this glossary.
Some portions of this glossary were reprinted with permission of the above companies.*

ABOUT THE CONTRIBUTORS

Jeff Alred shot the 1998 ESPN Summer X Games in high definition using Sony HDCAM equipment-the first time he ever used high definition equipment. Mr. Alred was one of the associate producers of ESPN's Outside the Lines: Inside the Kentucky Derby which won an Emmy Award in 1997 for Sports in the Outstanding Live Event Turnaround category.

Mark Bell has been a part of emerging technologies in television for more 20 years. From Emerson College's transfer to color television in the 1970s to participation in Avid's Camcutter development focus group, he has acquired a diverse grasp of the industry's operational and technological developments. Mr. Bell has top-market expertise in studio, master control, and tape room operations, news/production/documentary photography and sound work, ENG, SNG and event transmission, and a great record on equipment maintenance. He started contributing to TELEVISION BROADCAST magazine in 1994 and was named a faculty member of the well-regarded National Press Photographers Association News Video Workshop in 1995. He also wrote "Look Up and Live," an ENG safety article distributed to more than 12,000 readers by the NPPA. In addition, Mr. Bell maintains "Repair!" a specialty equipment repair shop, and operates "Technically Write!" a technical writing firm, from which he publishes the *ENG Safety Newsletter*.

Craig Birkmaier is a technologist with more than 30 years of experience in the video industry. His company, PCUBE Labs (www.pcube.com)-based in Gainesville, FL-is a technology consultancy focused on the convergence of the three most powerful technologies of the 20th century: video, computing, and telecommunications. PCUBE Labs works in cooperation with Two Head Film and Video (www.two-head.com) to test, develop, and review new products. PCUBE Labs specializes in the observation, improvement, and-if necessary-invention of human interface technologies linking content producers and their tools. He is also a contributing editor to TELEVISION BROADCAST and VIDEOGRAPHY magazines.

Lou CasaBianca serves as Chairman/CEO of the i5Group, which supports broadcast and cable network, diversified content publishers, music and motion picture studios Mr. CasaBianca has created magazines and written books on new media and directed film, video, and interactive programs for broadcast, corporate, and entertainment applications. He produced and/or executive produced Island Records recording and world tour projects featuring Al DiMeola, Klaus Schulze, Michael Shrieve, Steve Winwood, and Stomu Yamashta. He has produced/directed more than 100 broadcast and multimedia projects for Fortune 1000 companies. His current business focus centers on serving as Chief Content Officer and Editor-in-Chief of ContentWorld Ventures, Inc. (CWV) and *Content Magazine*, a joint venture with Syllabus Press, Inc. He founded and serves as chairman of the Media Asset Management Association (MAMA), a non-profit educational organization with a mandate to support the development of open standards to enable MAM WWW and broadcast applications.

Matt Charles has worked in professional audio magazine publishing for the last 10 years and has been producing, recording and performing music for the last 14 years.

Colette Connor is Editor of VIDEOGRAPHY magazine. She regularly contributes feature articles on shooting made-for-TV documentaries and video productions, as well as writing news and other features profiling equipment manufacturers and post production facilities. Previously, Ms. Connor was Associate Producer on network reality-based specials for Paul Klein's PKO Television Ltd. Prior to that, she was a marketing and public relations executive for satellite and cable communications, and, earlier, feature films. Her editorial background includes writing and editing monthly newsstand publications, and business and political reporting for community newspapers.

Randall Paris Dark is Founder, President and CEO of HD VISION, Inc. He has more than 150 HD productions to his credit, in a career which began more than ten years ago with *Chasing Rainbows*, the world's first mini-series imaged in high definition. Before founding HD VISION, he spent three years as Vice President and Producer for Captain New York, where he was responsible for the production of a number of HD projects that were nominated for awards. More recently, Randall has produced and directed several productions for HD VISION that have garnished nominations at the International Electronic Cinema Festival and also produced and directed a production which earned HD VISION two Telly Awards. Over the past four years Mr. Dark and HD VISION. have been involved in numerous high-profile productions such as: Woodstock II, Super Bowl XXX, Victor, Victoria! on Broadway, the 1996 Summer Olympic Games, and Christmas at the White House.

Gary Eskow is producer of more than 200 commercial sound tracks and a winner of multiple industry awards.

Robert R. Gerhart has been working in the video production field for more than 10 years, having started out as the owner of a small commercial/industrial production facility in southern New Jersey. Now the President of Visual Alchemy, Inc. (www.visual-alchemy.com) located in Sarasota, FL, Mr. Gerhart has turned his focus to post production, editing, 3D animation and special effects. He holds a Master of Fine Arts degree in Video Production from Summit University of Louisiana. His strong technical and artistic background has also earned him a position as a contributing editor for TELEVISION BROADCAST magazine, writing the monthly feature "Hands-On Post." Utilizing his studio facility for testing, he reviews desktop-platform editing, compositing and animation packages.

Robert M. Goodman is an Emmy-nominated director and award-winning writer with over 18 years of experience in film and video production. He specializes in writing and directing documentaries, results-oriented marketing programs and infomercials that sell. Mr. Goodman is currently completing a nonfiction feature called *Gifts in the Mail* that celebrates the 100-year history of American picture postcards. He's a contributing editor for VIDEOGRAPHY magazine, a contributing writer for the *Independent Film & Video Monthly*, and one of the authors of the *American Society of Cinematographer's Guide to Digital Video*.

Michael Grotticelli is Editor of TELEVISION BROADCAST magazine. Prior to that, he was News Editor of *TV Technology* magazine from 1996-98. He has covered the video production industry for more than ten years, both as a publicist, reporter and Managing Editor of VIDEOGRAPHY magazine.

Ross Kauffman is the DTV Group Consultant for Hearst-Argyle Television, Inc.

Terence Keegan is news editor for *Medialine*, a trade magazine for the recorded media industry.

Mike Keller serves as Director of Engineering at WCVB-TV, the ABC affiliate in Boston.

Ken Kerschbaumer is Associate Editor at *Broadcasting and Cable* magazine. Prior to joining *Broadcasting and Cable* he was editor of *Digital Television* magazine, and also has worked for TELEVISION BROADCAST, GOVERNMENT VIDEO and TVBEUROPE while working for Miller Freeman PSN.

Steve "Woody" La Cerra is Senior Editor of EQ magazine. He is also the Chief Tech at End Result Recording in New York and a freelance audio engineer/producer. He has worked with Blue Oyster Cult, Twisted Sister, Dagger and Reason, and his debut solo CD is available on North America Music. Check out his Web site at www.highstrung-pro.com/lacerra.

Steve Lampen is Technology Specialist for Belden Electronics Division in San Francisco. Steve holds a FCC Lifetime General License and is an SBE Certified Radio Broadcast Engineer. On the data side he is a BICSI Registered Communication Distribution Designer. He has worked extensively in the sound, recording, film , and broadcast communities. His book, *Wire, Cable, and Fiber Optics for Video and Audio Engineers*, is published by McGraw-Hill, and his "Wired for Sound" column appears monthly in *Radio World* magazine.

Jon Leland is an award-winning video producer, Web site designer, consultant and keynote speaker. He was the founding director of creative services at USA Network and is currently the president and creative director of the San Rafael, CA electronic media design company, Communication Bridges http://www.combridges.com. Mr. Leland is also the publisher and editorial director of the Media Mall Web site http://www.mediamall.com.

Sheldon Liebman has been involved in computer graphics and video since receiving his MBA from Rensselaer Polytechnic Institute (Troy, NY) in 1981. Mr. Liebman began work as a graphics programmer and quickly shifted into the areas of sales and marketing, where he is still active. During his career, he has been part of a number of pioneering companies. As Vice President of Marketing for Lyon Lamb Video Animation Systems, he developed the specification for the company's second-generation frame-by-frame VTR controller, the MiniVAS. He was also one of the founders of Digital Arts, an early pioneer in PC-based 3D animation. In 1991, Mr. Liebman formed L&S Marketing, Inc. to provide marketing, public relations and writing services to the computer and video industries. Through this company, He has become a regular contributor to VIDEOGRAPHY and GOVERNMENT VIDEO magazines, as well as a consultant to a number of small manufacturers. He currently resides in Albuquerque, New Mexico, with his wife and two sons.

George Maier has spent more than thirty years involved in transmission system technology. He majored in EE studies at Northeastern University, and has worked for a number of well known transmission equipment companies, including Western Electric (now Lucent Technologoes), M/A-COM's Communications Equipment Group (now Advanced Broadband), Harris Corporation Broadcast Division, Northern Telecom, Telco Systems, ADC Telecommunication and Artel Video Systems. In November 1997, Mr. Maier started Orion Broadcast Solutions as a consulting firm, specializing in technical assistance and market development in the video transmission area. He is a regular contributor to TELEVISION BROADCAST magazine and may be reached at gmaier@ultranet.com.

Renville H. McMann, Jr. began his career serving on FM broadcasting pioneer Edwin H. Armstrong's staff during the 1930s. He later joined the NBC Research Laboratory, where he served as liaison engineer with RCA Laboratories on the first successful color VTR. He joined CBS Laboratories in 1955, where he co-invented the first home video-cassette system with Dr. Peter Goldmark, who he succeeded as President of CBS Laboratories in 1971. While at CBS, Mr. McMann also served as the principal inventor and major participant in the development of the Starlight TV camera for transmitting color pictures from inside the human body, an encoded signal color-correction device, the digital noise reducer, and the CBS Minicam Mark VI, the first handheld color TV camera system. The holder of 36 patents, Mr. McMann served as President of Thomson-CSF Laboratories from 1975 until his appointment in 1982 as VP of Advanced Television, CBS Technology Center. He has chaired the HDTV committee of the Advanced Television Systems Committee, and has been involved in other ATV organizations.

Brian McKernan is the Editorial Director of Miller Freeman PSN's Video Division, which includes VIDEOGRAPHY, TELEVISION BROADCAST, GOVERNMENT VIDEO, and videography.com. He is also the U.S. Editorial Director of TELEVISION BROADCAST EUROPE and the Executive Editor (U.S.) for Content Creation Europe. Mr. McKernan was the Editor-in-Chief of VIDEOGRAPHY for 11 years, prior to which he served as Television Editor at *Broadcast Management/Engineering* and Assistant Editor at *Omni* magazine. Mr. McKernan's other publishing credits include: editing and packaging the book *The Age of Videography: Twenty Years That Changed the Way We See Ourselves* (Miller Freeman PSN, 1996); contributing a chapter to *HDTV: The Policies,*

Politics, and Economics of Tomorrow's Television (Union Square Press, 1990); and editing *Producer to Producer: Insider Tips for Success in Media* (Michael Wiese Productions, 1997).

Ron Merrell is Executive Editor of TELEVISION BROADCAST, where he specializes in RF issues, and the Executive Editor of GOVERNMENT VIDEO. He spent four years in the Air Force as a communications and electronics troubleshooter. Later he worked at McDonnell Aircraft as an electronics/communications inspector on the Voodoo line. He was granted a Wall Street Scholarship to attend the University of Missouri School of Journalism, where he earned his master's degree. Mr. Merrell was a professor of journalism and communications at Wisconsin State University and lectured at several midwest universities. He also worked for Intertec Publishing as their first Editorial Director, where he edited an wrote for *Broadcast Engineering* for 12 years, and where he started Video Systems magazine.

William C. Miller is Manager of Production Technology in ABC-TV's Broadcast Operations and Engineering division. He earned a B.A. from Columbia University in 1973. He has been active in standards work for many years, both with ATSC and SMPTE. Mr. Miller is a Fellow of SMPTE, and for the last four years has been the Society's Engineering Vice President. He is a member of NATAS, and was awarded an Emmy by them for his contributions to ABC's coverage of the 1988 Winter Olympics. He has written a number of papers and articles about broadcast technology, and is an occasional contributor to TELEVISION BROADCAST.

Christine M. Okon is an expert in emerging digital content trends and applications as well as digital media and Internet development and production. She is currently the Director of Business Development for Arriba Soft Corporation and has published articles on digital media content creation, development and management in Advanced Imaging, MacUser, InfoWorld, Electronic Publishing and other trade journals. Ms. Okon holds a Master of Arts in Linguistics and Literature and a Bachelor of Arts in English and German, both from Northern Illinois University.

Bobby Owsinski is a 20-year veteran of the music business. He has worked in many creative facets of the music business including producer, guitar and keyboard player, recording engineer, songwriter, and arranger. He has hundreds of records and live events to his credit with artists such as ex-Rolling Stone Mick Taylor, Bobby Caldwell, Lou Rawls, Chick Corea, The Byrds, and Blues legends Willie Dixon, Joe Houston and Gerry Groom. He has produced acts for Polygram, Mercury, Warner Bros., RCA, Chrysalis, and Manhattan/EMI. He has also produced, engineered, and performed the music for several movies, including *Lovesick*, *The Hunger*, and *Mortal Kombat II*, and television shows, including *Into The Night With Rick Dees*, *Roller Games*, and *Baywatch Nights*. He has also been active as an educator, serving as a professor at Berklee College of Music, Trebas Recording Institute, and most recently, Nova Institute where he created their highly successful Multimedia Production course.

Glen Pensinger has been active as an operating and maintenance engineer in commercial and educational television for more than 35 years, including positions with KTVU Oakland, KGO-TV San Francisco, and the ABC Television Network. Mr. Pensinger is currently a Television Engineer for San Jose State University in California with responsibility for the design, installation, and maintenance of their television facilities which include distance learning systems, wideband video and data distribution, studio, field and post production systems. He is a Fellow of SMPTE and has served the Society as Western Regional Governor, San Francisco Section Chair, and General Arrangements Chair for the 17th, 19th and 29th Television and Advanced Imaging Conferences. He is also a Society of Broadcast Engineers Certified Senior Broadcast Engineer as well as a member of AES and IEEE.

Mark J. Pescatore has been part of the TELEVISION BROADCAST magazine team since 1994, and is currently a contributing editor. He also serves as Educational Television Field Editor for GOVERNMENT VIDEO magazine. He has been a television station program manager and has taught college courses in mass communication and television production. Mr. Pescatore has a Master of Arts in Telecommunication and Film from The University of Alabama, a Bachelor of Arts in Communication from Florida Atlantic University, and an Associate of Arts in Mass Communication from Broward Community College. He is currently pursuing his Ph.D. in Journalism and Mass Communication at The University of North Carolina at Chapel Hill. He is the co-editor of the second edition of *The Guide To Digital Television* published by Miller Freeman PSN in 1999.

Mark Schubin Engineer, writer, historian, teacher, forensic analyst, consultant, expert witness, researcher, and judge. Mr. Schubin is a Fellow of the Society of Motion Picture and Television Engineers, a multiple Emmy award winner, and a recipient of many other honors. His clients range >from Children's Television Workshop to IBM to the Metropolitan Opera to Hong Kong's STAR-TV. He also serves as Technical Editor for Videography magazine and a contributor to Television Broadcast magazine.

Michael Silbergleid is president of The SilverKnight Group, a consulting, marketing and public relations firm specializing in high technology. Silbergleid was most recently Editor-In-Chief of TELEVISION BROADCAST magazine from March 1998 until June 1999 and had been the editor September 1994. Prior to joining the magazine, he was Manager of Educational Television and Telecommunication Engineering for the Huntsville City School System in Alabama and has been a producer, director, video editor, chief engineer and facilities designer. Mr. Silbergleid has a Master of Arts degree in Telecommunication and Film Management from The University of Alabama and two Bachelor of Arts degrees, in Dramatic Arts And Dance and Speech Communications, both from the State University of New York at Geneseo. He is the editor of the first edition and co-editor of the second edition of *The Guide To Digital Television* published by Miller Freeman PSN in 1998 and 1999, respectively.

David Sparano received a Bachelor of Science degree from Siena College and a Master of Science degree from Rensselaer Polytechinc Institute. He is currently a senior applications engineer with Harris Corporation Broadcast Division in Quincy, Illinois. Mr. Sparano is fluent in four languages and has presented seminars on DTV throughout North and South America.

Nigel Spratling has worked in the television industry for more than 20 years, during which time he held senior positions with Philips Electronics in Europe and AVS Broadcast in the UK and the US. He joined NVISION after resigning as vice president of post production with Snell & Wilcox. He was a co-founder of Vatek, the designers of the AVS Integra digital video switcher and effects system. Mr. Spratling is currently the vice president of marketing for ADC/NVISION.

Jonathan H. Stott studied Engineering and Electrical Sciences at Churchill College, Cambridge University, graduating with Distinction in 1972. He then joined the BBC Research Department (now BBC R&D), where he is a Project Manager in Spectrum Planning Group. Most of his career has been taken up with applying digital techniques to broadcasting. Recently, he was deeply involved with the development and introduction of digital terrestrial television, starting with participation in the European RACE dTTb project. This led to his becoming a member of the Task Force on System Comparison, which, under the leadership of Lis Grete Mˉller from Denmark, drew up the DVB-T specification for modulation and coding of digital terrestrial television. He led the theoretical and simulation work within the BBC R&D team that is at the forefront of digital television developments in Europe. He now leads a BBC R&D team looking at the application of digital techniques to sound broadcasting at frequencies below 30 MHz in collaboration with the DRM consortium.

Mark A. Thalhimer directs the Future of News project for the Radio and Television News Directors Foundation in Washington, D.C., with support from the Robert R. McCormick Tribune Foundation.

Craig Todd currently holds the title of Senior Member of the Technical Staff, and has been with Dolby Laboratories for 20 years. Mr. Todd has been developing multichannel sound for more than 15 years, beginning with his work on the Dolby Surround Sound matrix system. More recently he has worked on the development of technology for digital audio coding and broadcasting. For the last several years, Mr. Todd has concentrated on multichannel digital audio for television. The result of his efforts is the Dolby Digital (AC-3) coding technology, and its acceptance, by the U.S. "Grand Alliance" and the FCC Advisory Committee, for incorporation into the U.S. ATSC broadcast standard. Mr. Todd holds a bachelor's degree in Physics from the California Institute of Technology.

Bob Turner has been a videotape editor since 1976, and is one of the leading independent authorities on digitized video nonlinear editing systems. He considers himself a freelance video editor first and foremost, although lately he's best known for his "Hands-On Reviews" of new communications technologies and nonlinear post production systems in VIDEOGRAPHY magazine. His article "1,001 Questions To Ask Before Purchasing a Nonlinear Edit System" has been published twice by the Society of Motion Picture and Television Engineers, and has also been translated in 12 languages. He now consults with NLE manufacturers and potential purchasers. His book on nonlinear editing tools should be released within the coming year.

John Watkinson holds an honors degree in Electronic Engineering and a master's degree in Sound and Vibration. He is an independent consultant in digital audio, video and data technology and is the author of 17 books, including *The Art of Digital Audio* and *The Art of Digital Video*, acclaimed as the definitive works on the subject. He is a Fellow of the Audio Engineering Society and is listed in Who's Who in the World, in Contemporary Authors and by the American Biographical Institute. He regularly presents papers at conventions of learned societies and has presented training courses on a range of technological subjects for studios, broadcasters and facilities around the world. He has worked for the Digital Equipment Corporation, Ampex Corporation and Sony prior to forming his own consultancy in 1989. He writes regularly in *TV Technology* (Video Watch), *Studio Sound* (Dr. John) and SYSTEMS CONTRACTOR NEWS. He lives in the countryside southwest of London, England.

Tim Wetmore is Editorial Director of the audio division at Miller Freeman PSN and has been a journalist for 17 years after receiving his master's degree in writing from Columbia University. He has also worked in recording studios and had a short (two years), frightening experience as a broadcaster in the mid-1980s.

INDEX

ISBN 0-9670700-1-5